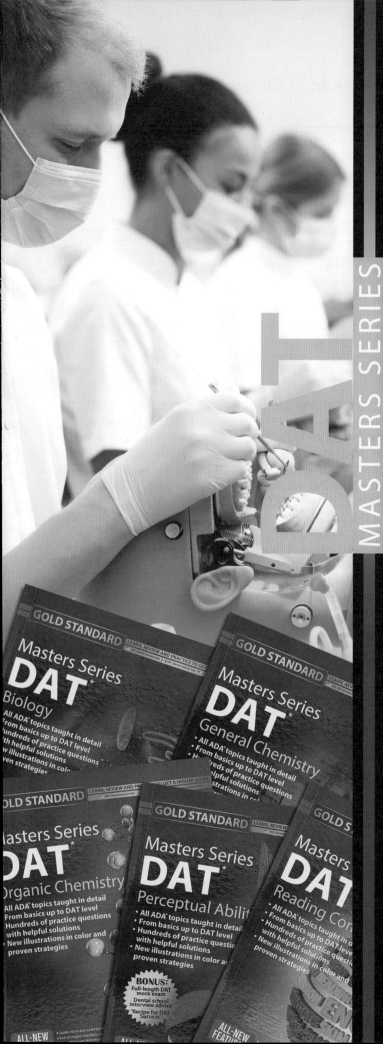

GOLD STANDARD — LEARN, REVIEW AND PRACTICE TO GET A HIGHER SCORE

Masters Series
DAT*
Quantitative Reasoning (QR)

- All ADA* topics taught in detail
- From basics up to DAT level
- Hundreds of practice questions with helpful solutions
- New illustrations in color and proven strategies

ALL-NEW FEATURES!

- Spoiler Alerts and 'Level of Importance' reflecting the latest ADA materials.
- End-of-chapter checklists, updated learning objectives, and extensive cross-referencing
- Many of the new features are elements of the Laith Learning System (LLS™) to help you recall key, relevant facts and concepts

DAT-Prep.com
Book VI of VI from the Gold Standard Set

*DAT is a registered trademark of the American Dental Association (ADA) which is not affiliated with this book.
**OAT is a registered trademark of the Association of Schools and Colleges of Optometry (ASCO) which is not affiliated with this book. The ADA designs the real exam for both the DAT and the OAT.

ADA* Official Topics (syllabus: US DAT and OAT)

"Mathematical Problems: algebra (equations and expressions, inequalities, exponential notation, absolute value, ratios and proportions, and graphical analysis); Data Analysis, Interpretation, and Sufficiency; Quantitative Comparison; and Probability and Statistics • Applied Mathematics (Word) Problems"

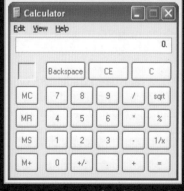

DAT-prep.com: Home of Gold Standard DAT

The Gold Standard Team of authors and editors includes professionals with advanced academic degrees in dentistry, medicine, and the arts, as well as Ivy League dental students with exceptional DAT scores.

© RuveneCo Inc.

*DAT is a registered trademark of the American Dental Association (ADA) which is not affiliated with this book.

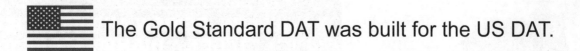

The Gold Standard DAT was built for the US DAT.

 The Gold Standard DAT is identical to OAT prep except PAT, which is replaced by OAT Physics; see our Gold Standard OAT book for Physics review and OAT practice test.

Copyright © 2022 Gold Standard Multimedia Education (Worldwide), DAT Masters Series: Quantitative Reasoning (QR/Math)

ISBN 978-1-927338-50-6

RuveneCo Inc
Gold Standard Multimedia Education
559-334 Cornelia St
Plattsburgh, NY 12901
E-mail: learn@gold-standard.com
Online at www.gold-standard.com

The Dental Admission Test (DAT) consists of 280 multiple-choice questions distributed across quite a diversity of question types in four tests. The DAT is a computer-based test (CBT). This exam requires approximately five hours to complete - including the optional tutorial, break, and post-test survey. The following are the four subtests of the Dental Admission Test:

1. **Survey of the Natural Sciences (NS) – 100 questions; 90 min.**
   - General Biology (BIO): 40 questions
   - General Chemistry (CHM): 30 questions
   - Organic Chemistry (ORG): 30 questions

2. **Perceptual Ability Test (PAT) - 90 questions; 6 subsections; 60 min.**
   - Apertures: 15 questions
   - View Recognition: 15 questions
   - Angle Discrimination: 15 questions
   - Paper Folding: 15 questions
   - Cube Counting: 15 questions
   - 3-D Form Development: 15 questions

3. **Reading Comprehension (RC) – 50 questions; 3 reading passages; 60 min.**

4. **Quantitative Reasoning (QR) – 40 questions; 45 min.**
   - Mathematics Problems: 30 questions
   - Applied Mathematics/Word Problems: 10 questions

> You will get six scores from:
> (1) BIO (2) CHM (3) ORG (4) PAT (5) QR (6) RC.
>
> You will get two additional scores which are summaries:
> (7) Academic Average (AA) = BIO + CHM + ORG + QR + RC
> (8) Total Science (TS) = BIO + CHM + ORG

Common Formula for Acceptance:

GPA + DAT score + Interview = Dental School Admissions*

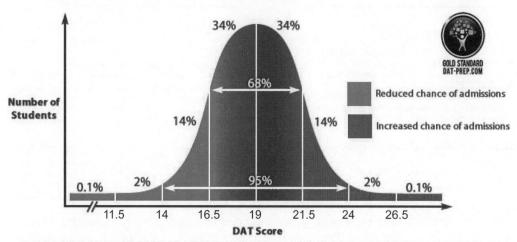

Figure 1: Typical Overall DAT Score Distribution (Approx.); No. of Test Administrations Annually = 13 000 (Approx.)

*Note: In general, Dental School Admissions Committees will only examine the DAT score if the GPA is high enough; they will only admit or interview if the GPA + DAT score is high enough. Some programs also use autobiographical materials and/or references in the admissions process. Different dental schools may emphasize different aspects of your DAT score, for example: PAT, BIO, TS, AA. The average score for any section is approximately 19/30; the average AA for admissions is usually 18-21 depending on the dental school; the AA for admissions to Harvard is around 23-24; the 100th percentile is usually 25 meaning that virtually 100% of the approximately 13,000 students who take the DAT every year have an AA less than 25. Only a handful of students score 25/30. Our two student contributors scored 27/30 (AA).

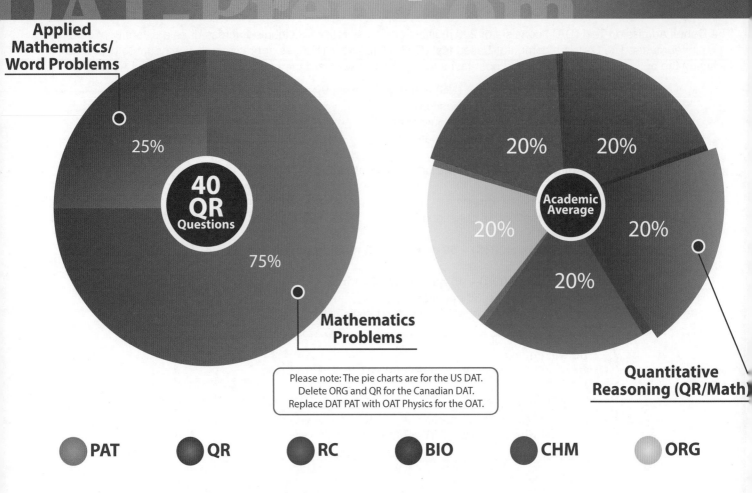

Applied Mathematics/ Word Problems

25%

40 QR Questions

75%

Mathematics Problems

Academic Average

20% 20%

20% 20%

20%

Quantitative Reasoning (QR/Math)

Please note: The pie charts are for the US DAT.
Delete ORG and QR for the Canadian DAT.
Replace DAT PAT with OAT Physics for the OAT.

● **PAT**   ● **QR**   ● **RC**   ● **BIO**   ● **CHM**   ● **ORG**

The DAT is challenging, get organized.
dat-prep.com/dat-study-schedule

1. How to study
- Learn, review and practice using the DAT Masters Series book(s) and/or videos.
- Complete all exercises and multiple-choice practice questions in this book.
- Consolidate: create and study from your personal summaries (= Gold Notes) daily and/or Anki (*free online flashcards including DAT "Feralis" notes*).

2. Once you have completed your studies
- Complete a full-length DAT practice test.
- Analyze mistakes and all answers/explanations.
- Consolidate: Review all your Gold Notes and create more, with or without Anki.

3. Full-length practice tests
- Take multiple DAT practice tests (varied sources).
- ADA practice exams: Currently, the 2007 exam is free but the most recent exam is paid.
- Free full-length Gold Standard (GS) mock exam GS-Free with helpful, detailed worked solutions.
- Consider other GS or third practice tests if needed.

4. How much time do you need to study?
- On average, 3-6 hours per day for 3-6 months; depending on life experiences, 2 weeks may be enough and 8 months could be insufficient.
- Try to study 'full throttle' for 1-2 weeks and then adjust your expectations for the required time.

5. Recommended DAT Communities
- Although Reddit has a DAT forum, by far, the most active DAT forum on the net is by the Student Doctor Network (SDN): forums.studentdoctor.net/forums/dat-discussions.70/
- Of course, if you have any questions about the content in this book, access for free: dat-prep.com/forum

Is there something in the Masters Series that you did not understand? Don't get frustrated, get online:
dat-prep.com/forum

Table of Contents

Note that: H = High-level Importance; M = Medium-level Importance; L = Low-level Importance.

Note that: H = High-level Importance; M = Medium-level Importance; L = Low-level Importance.

Note that: H = High-level Importance; M = Medium-level Importance; L = Low-level Importance.

Tera 10^12 times the base unit
Giga 10^9 times the base unit
Mega 10^6 times the base unit
Micro 10^-6 of the base unit
Nano 10^-9 of the base unit
Pico 10^-12 of the base unit

26
10
24

DAT QUANTITATIVE REASONING (QR)
8 Chapters

01
Fundamentals of the DAT Quantitative Reasoning

0 of 40 DAT QR Questions*

02
Numbers and Operations

6 of 40 DAT QR Questions*

03
Scientific Measurement and Dimensional Analysis

3 of 40 DAT QR Questions*

04
Algebra, Graph Analysis and Quantitative Comparison

12 of 40 DAT QR Questions*

05
Geometry

5 of 40 DAT QR Questions*

06
Trigonometry

0 of 40 DAT QR Questions*

07
Probability and Statistics

4 of 40 DAT QR Questions*

08
Applied Mathematics

10 of 40 DAT QR Questions*

$$\left(-\frac{1}{2}, \frac{\sqrt{3}}{2}\right) \quad (0, 1) \quad \left(\frac{1}{2}, \frac{\sqrt{3}}{2}\right)$$

$$\frac{\sqrt{2}}{2}, \frac{\sqrt{2}}{2}$$

$$\frac{\pi}{2} \quad 90°$$

$$\frac{2\pi}{3} \, 120° \quad 60° \, \frac{\pi}{3}$$

$$\frac{3\pi}{4} \, 135° \quad 45° \, \frac{\pi}{4}$$

$$\frac{5\pi}{6} \, 150° \quad 30° \, \frac{\pi}{6} \quad \sin(\theta)$$

$$\theta \quad 0° \, 0$$

$$\pi \, 180° \quad \cos(\theta) \quad 360° \, 2\pi \quad (1, 0)$$

$$\frac{7\pi}{6} \, 210° \quad 330° \, \frac{11\pi}{6}$$

$$\frac{5\pi}{4} \, 225° \quad 315° \, \frac{7\pi}{4}$$

$$\frac{4\pi}{3} \, 240° \quad 300° \, \frac{5\pi}{3} \quad \left(\frac{\sqrt{3}}{2}, -\frac{1}{2}\right)$$

$$270° \quad \frac{3\pi}{2}$$

$$(0, -1) \quad \left(\frac{1}{2}, -\frac{\sqrt{3}}{2}\right)$$

Slope = rise/run =
$(y_2 - y_1)/(x_2 - x_1)$

DAT-prep.com

averages based on past testing patterns, adjusted for new trends as of the date of publication, in which the question specifically requires content (*assumed knowledge*) found in that specific chapter.

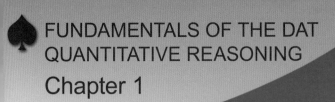
Memorize	Understand	Importance
* Basic Rules and Formulas * Conversions and Numerical Relationships * Shortcuts	* Nature of Questions	**Low level: 0 of 40** DAT Quantitative Reasoning questions are based on content in this chapter (avg. based on past testing patterns). * Note that approx. **70% of the questions in DAT QR are from just 3 of 8 chapters: 2, 4 and 8.**

DAT-Prep.com

Introduction ▐▐▐▐

Beyond the math, the DAT Quantitative Reasoning section stresses proper time management. The more you practice, the more efficient you will become at solving the problems. Knowing what the test covers and building on speed and confidence are thus crucial to your preparation.

DAT QR is far from university-level math! No matrix. No calculus. Real DAT questions range from those that an average high school student would find straightforward up to "specialty" math questions that are not beyond high school, but would be helped by "specialty" training, which is why you have this book. Let's begin!

Multimedia Resources at DAT-Prep.com

Free Online Forum

Special Guest

1.1 General Introduction

The DAT Quantitative Reasoning Test is a section of speed and mathematical logic. It consists of 40 multiple-choice items and has a time limit of 45 minutes. This means that you have only about one minute to read, analyze, and solve each problem. Nonetheless, the most effective way to prepare for this section is to understand the question types and the concepts that each question assesses. With constant practice, you can then decide which time-saving methods will make you efficient in completing all 40 questions on time.

In general, the DAT QR is meant to gauge your knowledge of the following math areas:

- Algebra (equations and expressions, inequalities, exponential notation, absolute value, ratios and proportions, and graphical analysis)

- Numerical Calculations (fractions and decimals, percentages, approximations, and scientific notation)

- Conversions (temperature, time, weight, and distance)

- Probability and Statistics

- Data Analysis, Interpretation, and Sufficiency

- Quantitative Comparison

- Applied Mathematics (Word) Problems

Note that some of the preceding topics only became widespread in 2017. In other words, some QR question types are not included in older ADA practice materials like the 2007 (*free*) or 2009 official practice materials. However, these question types are included in the ADA's online 2022 DAT practice test available through Prometric.

Just in case you missed it, we quoted the ADA's official DAT QR syllabus towards the bottom of the very first page of this book. But, of course, we will continuously highlight key knowledge, concepts and strategies throughout this book.

1.2 Format of the Test

Preparing for the DAT Quantitative Reasoning Test should also entail familiarizing yourself with the actual set-up of this section: One question is presented at a time and a pop-up on-screen calculator is provided with a click of a button.

The calculator is very basic and the only functions that will be available are addition, subtraction, division, multiplication, the positive/negative (+/-) sign, a period or point sign, the square root key, and 1/x key. These can be operated by using the mouse – not the keyboard.

Low-level Importance

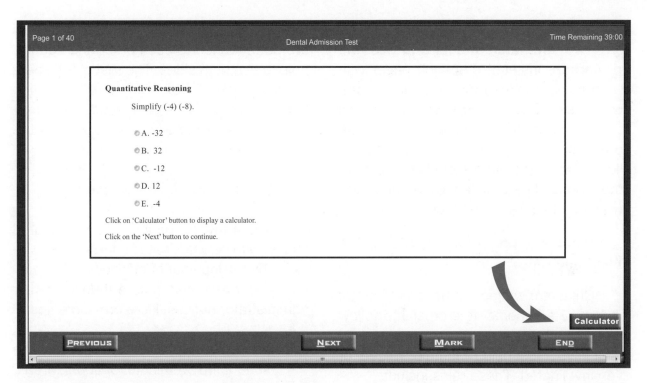

Figure QR.1.1: The Quantitative Reasoning Test Page. The calculator button is provided on every page of the QR section.

Other features of your computer-based test: There is a crossing out tool (STRIKEOUT), which you can use to cross out answer choices you want to eliminate. There is a "MARK" button particularly helpful for time-consuming QR questions: You can click to mark a question (*for yourself*) to indicate that you want to revisit the question if you have extra time (*see* Fig. QR 1.1). There is also a highlighter tool which is very useful for RC.

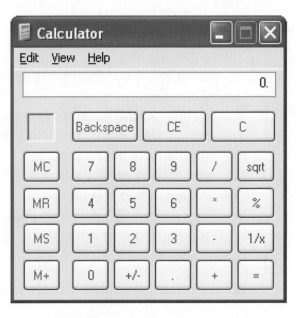

FIGURE QR.1.2: Simulation of the DAT On-screen Calculator.

Low-level Importance

1.3 DAT Laminated Sheets and Markers

Some students are surprised to receive **two laminated sheets and two fine tip markers** instead of scratch paper with a pen or pencil when they take their computer-based DAT at a Prometric center. All of your calculations and notetaking must be done with these materials as you are not allowed to bring other materials to the computer. Some tips and familiarity with your new exam tool can be helpful.

What are the rules regarding the given materials?

Rules are written on the top of both of the laminated sheets. It is crucial to follow these rules! Violating these rules could result in your test being withheld, voided, or even invalidated. These rules include:

1. Do not erase the laminated sheet.
2. Do not write outside the provided grid box.
3. Do not write on the laminated sheet before the test begins.
4. Do not write on the laminated sheet during breaks.
5. You can only use the materials provided.
6. You cannot fold, bend, or distort the laminated sheets in any manner.
7. You cannot write on any surface other than the laminated sheets.
8. You may exchange laminated sheets and markers during the exam by raising your hand.

What do the laminated sheets look like?

You will be provided two laminated

8.5" x 11" sheets. The laminated sheets are not attached to each other and you are able to use both sides. The rest of the sheet includes a grid box. Similar to graphing paper, the grid box is comprised of 1 cm x 1 cm squares. Generally, the top 25% of the sheets are covered in instructions.

What if I run out of space?

You may exchange used laminated sheets with new laminated sheets during the exam by raising your hand. However, it may take a few moments before the test center administrator notices. Here are some tips:

- You can conserve space until the scheduled 30-minute (*optional*) break. During the break, you will be able to exchange your sheets without the stressful distraction.
  - The con is that you need to practice only using the two sheets before and after the break.
- You can trade in one sheet at a time. As you continue taking the test and writing on the second laminated sheet, you can hold up your used sheet.
  - The con is that you can get distracted by raising your hand and attempting to get the attention of the Prometric staff.

What are the markers like?

You are provided with two fine tip markers with black ink. Markers cannot be used on any surface other than the sheets. Usually, Prometric provides Staedtler markers.

TIP: The markers dry up easily! Always cap your marker when not in use so that the risk of drying out or leaking is minimized.

What if my markers dry up?

You may exchange the markers during the exam by raising your hand, but it may take a few moments before the test center administrator notices. Here are some tips:

- Always cap your marker when not in use so that the risk of drying out or leaking is minimized.

- Check that your markers work and are fully capped when receiving them from the Prometric staff.

- You can trade in one marker at a time. As you continue taking the test and writing with your second marker, you can hold up your dried marker.

  - The con is that you can get distracted by raising your hand and attempting to get the attention of the Prometric staff.

Am I allowed to erase?

No! Although it is possible to erase your writing, do NOT lick your finger and erase during the real DAT! If you make a mistake, just cross it out and continue on another line.

How can I get a DAT laminated sheet to practice with?

Easy! You can make one or you can purchase one from Gold Standard!

Make your own noteboard: Although it's not exactly the same, some students just purchase a small whiteboard and fine tip marker, or they laminate graph paper at a photocopy shop.

Gold Standard (GS) DAT's noteboards: They are correctly formatted and include 2 *erasable* fine tip Staedtler markers. Note that the exam uses non-erasable markers but, unlike Prometric, we wanted to be sure that students could reuse the noteboards. The GS DAT noteboard is included in many Masters Series packages or available separately at DAT-prep.com or Amazon.com. Please note: DAT noteboards are quite different from MCAT or GMAT noteboards.

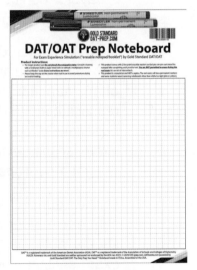

Simulated, Laminated
DAT Noteboard

Low-level Importance

How can I optimize the use of my DAT simulation laminated sheets at home?

Using the given material during practice tests will help you get even more comfortable with the exam! Here are some tips to optimize the use:

1. Practice, practice, practice!

    a. Practice capping the markers!
    b. Practice only writing crucial things and writing small to conserve space!
    c. Practice crossing out mistakes instead of erasing!
    d. Practice cordoning off your DAT QR calculations with lines to avoid confusion when you are rechecking your work.

2. If your marker dries up, try writing on some regular paper and, more often than not, your marker will be resuscitated! (*Of course, you are not allowed to do that during the real exam, so just raise your hand and you will get a new one.*)

3. Unlike during the real DAT, you can erase your erasable laminated sheets at home! After each practice exam section, you may want to take pictures of your work for later practice test assessment before erasing. (*Of course, you are not allowed to do that during the real exam, so you may want to practice crossing out instead of erasing!*)

IMPORTANT:

Don't clean your laminated sheets in a bathtub! Water will seep in between the lamination and make it unusable. Clean it gently with a damp cloth or paper towel. Some students find that the marker stains the lamination over time. That will usually clear up with a multipurpose cleaner like Windex®.

Any suggestions on how to use these materials?

Everyone is different: some students barely use their laminated sheets while others almost fill one or more up. Find a strategy that works best for you!

1. Organize your writing by putting the question number in a circle and drawing lines to separate your work. This organization makes your work more clear, which reduces the risk of error and permits you to review your work at the end of that section, if time allows.

2. Brain dump! **Once your exam section begins**, write down all the pertinent equations, mnemonics, or any other relevant information that you have identified during your DAT QR prep.

Didn't Prometric stop using the DAT noteboards?

Yes, the ADA and Prometric discontinued the use of the noteboards during the height of the global pandemic (2020-2021). The noteboards started to be used again in 2022.

1.4 How to Do Well in the QR Section

Speed and confidence in solving each problem is central in succeeding in this section. Undoubtedly, the best preparation route is to study the basics and practice with as many questions as you can under timed conditions.

Learn and review the required operations for each of the areas specified by the ADA. Thereafter, make sure that you do all of the chapter review questions plus realistic practice tests, i.e., those which reflect the actual exam.

The ADA offers the *DAT Sample Test Items* (*first published in 2007, no updates*) as a free download in pdf format and they offer a paid full-length practice test. Taking these tests will give you a clearer idea of the types of questions presented in the real DAT. However, for a simulation of the computer based test (CBT), the Gold Standard program at DAT-prep. com is a good alternative. If needed, there are many other free and paid third-party DAT practice tests available. Regardless, you should keep three important things in mind with your QR preparation: Practice makes perfect, specific tips apply to specific topics, and logic does work with math.

1.4.1 Practice Makes Perfect

There are two main goals that you should aim to achieve as you proceed with your practice tests.

1. **Be able to instantly recognize and categorize the area of math involved in a question**

By quickly identifying the type of math problem presented, you can mentally prepare yourself for the different strategies used to solve the question. This gives you a clear direction on how to approach a problem, allowing you to be more time-effi-cient. When you do your practice tests, you should thus try to adopt the following techniques in order to hone your proficiency in dealing with quantitative items:

- **Ready Formulas**

If you know your squares, cubes, roots, pi, conversions between units, formulas for the area of a triangle, circle, sphere, cylinder and so forth, you would know which questions you can solve with the least amount of time. By recognizing possible relationships between numbers, you can easily determine the appropriate mathematical formula (and short-cuts!) to use.

One of the typical questions that show up in the DAT simply asks for the equivalent temperature value of Fahrenheit to Celsius. You can solve this almost instantly if you know the appropriate conversion formula!

• Guesstimating

This strategy is most useful if the values in the answer choices are very spread out yet the question is fairly straightforward. Most questions on the DAT QR will usually have one option that is blatantly wrong. You can then guesstimate (estimate by guesswork) or round off the numbers when doing the calculations. For example, if the question asks you to add 2,301 to 1,203, you could guesstimate and round the given numbers to 2,300 + 1,200 = 3,500. This is much easier to do mentally. Guesstimating can be faster than a calculator and can result in a correct response just as often.

If you are unsure of your choice, as mentioned, the DAT allows you to mark an answer so you can come back to it later if you have spare minutes left.

• Working Backwards

If you find yourself stuck on a question, you can work backwards from the answer choices by plugging in an option to see if it makes sense. Starting with the middle value would help you decide quickly whether the answer choice is too small or too large.

For questions that frequently slow you down, make sure that you carefully go through the solutions in the answer key. Identify where you fall short. You might just be missing a shortcut. Repeat with more exercises until you are able to master the required manipulations. Remember that the main point of these numerous practices is for you to learn how to pace yourself so that you finish all the questions the first time through with about ten minutes left to spare. This gives you time to go back to questions you skipped earlier, or to double check your responses.

Moreover, when you practice regularly, you tend to become comfortable with the various strategies. This will also help you identify the areas where you may need further improvement.

2. Become familiar with the tools provided in the actual exam

As already mentioned, the actual DAT provides an on-screen calculator in the QR section. You are not permitted to use anything else except the laminated sheets and marker-pens at the test center.

You should be prepared to deal with possible setbacks. Because the calculator can only be operated by the mouse, this should serve only as a last resort. Using as much mental math as you can is beneficial in order to save time. Likewise, practice writing quickly and neatly on your laminated sheets.

1.4.2 Specific Tips Apply to Specific Topics

The next chapters will discuss each of the essential topics listed in the following table. However, this quick "must-know" list can serve as your constant reminder to keep you confidently on track with your QR preparation.

Math Area	Must Know Topics or Skills	Tips
Numbers and Operations	♠ Converting square roots to their exponential forms ♠ Multiplying and dividing numbers in scientific notation ♠ Converting units of time (hours to seconds), distance (mi to km, in to cm), temperature (°F to °C), weight (lbs to kg)	♠ Be comfortable solving without a calculator. ♠ Be on the lookout for common terms that can be canceled out. ♠ Pay attention to the units given in the problems and the answer choices. ♠ When comparing fractions, convert the denominators to the same value.
Algebra	♠ Solving equations ♠ Solving inequalities and differentiating between "and" or "or"	♠ Understanding the rules in solving algebraic equations is important in solving problems involving angles and triangles.
Geometry	♠ Converting between angles and radians (there are 180 degrees in 1 pi) ♠ 30-60-90 and 45-45-90 triangles ♠ Areas of circle, sphere, triangle, cylinder ♠ Volumes of cylinder, cube, sphere	♠ Remember that squares can be bisected to form two 45-45-90 triangles. ♠ Certain polygons such as hexagons are actually made up of smaller triangles.

Low-level Importance

Geometry (cont'd)	♠ Identity circle ♠ Sum of interior angles in a polygon: (N-2) x 180 ♠ Graph of a line: y = mx + b (know where the line intercepts the y-axis; know how to find a line that is parallel or perpendicular to any given line) ♠ Circumference, arc length, area of a sector ♠ Distance and midpoint between two points on a coordinate plane	♠ In dealing with the identity circle, remember that any angle over 360 is simply the same as (n-360) where *n* is the angle. ♠ A common question type relating to circumference, arc length, and area of a sector requires solving for the distance covered by a revolution of a wheel.
Word Problems	♠ Distance = velocity x time ♠ Average velocity = $\dfrac{\text{total distance}}{\text{total time}}$ (remember you can always rearrange this equation to find what you need) ♠ Combined work problems: 1/time it takes one person to do the job + 1/time it takes for another person to do the same job = 1/total time it takes to do the job ♠ Simple vs. compound interest	♠ A common question type in this area involves two vehicles moving towards each other or starting at the same point. ♠ Remember that compound interest generates more interest than a simple interest given the same period of time.

1.4.3 Logic Works with Math

Do not feel intimidated when you are confronted with a seemingly unfamiliar problem. Reread the question and understand what is given and what is really asked. Sometimes, the answers are obvious and all you need is to simply use some logical reasoning. With word problems, thinking critically when solving is especially important because the answer is usually not just straight plug-and-chug values.

NOTE

In the succeeding pages, we will review each area specified by the ADA for the Quantitative Reasoning section, as well as techniques, for the respective topics. Each chapter comes with a set of exercises that will help reinforce your knowledge and skills.

Low-level Importance

1.5 Ranking the Importance of DAT QR Chapters

Level of Importance

All chapters in this book are ranked according to the level of importance in terms of containing assumed knowledge that is testable on the real DAT. 'Importance' deals with the classic student conundrum: How much effort should I invest in studying this or that chapter? How relevant is it to the DAT? The data is clear. Our calculations are based on ADA practice tests composed of questions which have previously appeared on real, past DATs, but have been retired. Each question is cross referenced for your assessment. You will likely find that, except for trigonometry, the ADA has been quite consistent over the years.

You do not have to accept our judgement as to the number of practice questions which can be solved by content within a chapter: You can just look at the Spoiler Alert at the end of each of the following chapters and decide for yourself. However, the labels representing the *relative importance* are, of course, subjective (i.e. High, Medium, Low).

Naturally, no one outside of the ADA can accurately predict your future exam experience right down to the balance of each individual question. However, there are clear high-probability patterns that can inform the way you study.

What is *DAT-30*?

DAT-30 is low yield. The majority of DAT QR questions are straightforward: only a handful out of 40 questions on the real exam are very challenging for most students. To get those few correct, consistently, requires a lot more work. If you are trying to get a DAT score of 18-21, then you should probably not chase very rare questions: this might mix up your understanding of fundamentals and lead to a lowering of your score. For students aiming for a perfect score, *DAT-30* will explore topics that are considered fair game (i.e. *could* show up on the real exam), but will *not* show up on *most* tests. We will identify *DAT-30* topics or questions when they arise.

Practice Questions

We are using a learning system that applies many different techniques to teach: *Need for Speed*, workbook format, traditional didactic, foundational, hundreds of traditional DAT-style questions, and occasional *DAT-30*.

Let's get started!

Low-level Importance

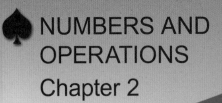

NUMBERS AND OPERATIONS
Chapter 2

Memorize	Understand	Importance
* Properties of Real Numbers * Order of Operations * Rules on Zero * Important Fraction-Decimal Conversions * Properties of Exponents * Common squares and cubes of integers	* Integer, Rational, and Real Numbers * Absolute Value * Basic Operations and Definitions * Fractions, Mixed Numbers, Decimals and Percentages; Scientific Notation * Root and Exponent Manipulations * Ratios and Proportions	**Medium level: 6 of 40** **DAT Quantitative Reasoning questions** are based on content in this chapter (avg. based on past testing patterns). * Note that approx. **70%** of the questions in DAT QR are from just 3 of 8 chapters: 2, 4 and 8.

DAT-Prep.com

Introduction ▌▌▌▌

Whether you notice it or not, nearly every problem you will come across in the DAT Quantitative Reasoning section will require you to perform some basic arithmetic. Becoming extremely familiar with the material and key concepts in this chapter will provide the foundation for your overall success.

To truly understand DAT QR then, for some students, we will need to start with the very basics. If the math is too basic for you, either skim through until it gets to your level, or at least complete the *Need for Speed* exercises at the beginning of chapters and the multiple-choice questions at the end of chapters. As for your entire DAT Masters Series studies, please take very brief notes ('Gold Notes') and study from them frequently according to your DAT study schedule.

Time is of the essence on the DAT, so being able to breeze through the basics is crucial, and if you put in the effort now, you will surely thank yourself later.

Let's get started!

Multimedia Resources at DAT-Prep.com

Free Online Forum

Special Guest

2.0 DAT Has a *Need for Speed*!

Yes, this is the cart before the horse! This new section is intended to help you quickly assess your level of DAT QR (= *basic math*). Answer any or all of the questions. If it has been a really long time since you have completed longhand calculations, do what you can and then begin studying Chapter 2 sequentially. After completing this chapter, return to the table below to ensure that you can complete all entries. Then you can proceed to answer the additional multiple-choice questions at the end of this chapter.

For those of you who are able to answer quickly but get stuck at some point, take note of the section number associated with the problem, and then you can skip forward to that particular section. We used

a pink highlighter throughout the chapter so that you can quickly identify the practice questions from the table in order to check your answers and to find the solutions. We are not teaching you math. We are teaching DAT Math: Skills specifically required to answer DAT QR questions.

Do not use a tangible calculator. Get used to using a mouse with your onscreen computer calculator. Yes, it is cumbersome. For that reason, it would be helpful for you to develop or sharpen your longhand calculations. Consider the strategy of using the calculator, when time permits during the real DAT QR, to double check your longhand calculations. When needed for the exercises below, complete your calculations on a noteboard or with scratch paper.

Section	DAT Quantitative Reasoning *Need for Speed* Exercises	
2.1.2	$\sqrt{2}$ (2 digits is sufficient) =	
	Pi (3 digits is sufficient) = π =	
2.1.3	$|-3| =$	$|-4 \times 8| =$
2.2.1	$(-5) + (-12) + (-44) =$	
	$7 + (-10) =$	$7 - (-10) =$
	$81 \div 9 =$	
	$-20 \div -4 =$	
	$16 \div -2 =$	

Medium-level Importance

2.2.1.1	$(-8) - (-7) =$	$64 / (-8) =$
2.2.3	$2^2 + [(3 + 2) \times 2 - 9] =$	
2.3.2	$\left[1.2 + \left(37 - \sqrt{5}\right) \times 2.331\right] \times 0 =$	
	$0 \div \left[1.2 + \left(37 - \sqrt{5}\right) \times 2.331\right] =$	
2.4.2A	$\dfrac{2}{3} \times \dfrac{4}{5} =$	
2.4.2B	$3 / (4 / 3) =$	$(3 / 4) / 3 =$
2.4.2C	$\dfrac{3}{5} - \dfrac{1}{5} =$	$\dfrac{2}{3} + \dfrac{2}{7} =$
2.4.2D	Circle the higher fraction: $\dfrac{4}{5}$ or $\dfrac{3}{7}$	
	Circle the lowest fraction: $\dfrac{4}{5}$ or $\dfrac{3}{7}$ or $\dfrac{9}{13}$	
2.4.2E *(reduce each expression)*	$\dfrac{20}{28} =$	$\dfrac{5}{9} \times \dfrac{6}{25} =$
2.4.2F *(convert to a fraction)*	$6\dfrac{2}{5} =$	
2.4.3B	$3.33 + 23.6 =$	
	$3.03 \times 1.2 =$	
	$\dfrac{4.4}{1.6} =$	

Medium-level Importance

2.4.3B	Consider the number 5.3618:

- Round to the nearest tenth =

- Round to the nearest hundredth =

Fraction	Decimal	Fraction	Decimal
1/2		1/6	
1/3		1/8	
1/4		1/10	
1/5			

2.4.3C	What is 25% of 40?

What is 350% of 2/5?

What percentage of 50 is 23?

A store sells a pair of pants at a profit of 15%. A reseller buys the pants from the store and resells them at a 20% profit. If a supplier sold the pants to the store for $100, how much would a customer have to pay the reseller?

2.5.1 *(simplify)*	$4^3 =$	$2^x \times 3^x =$
	$a^2 \times a^3 =$	$\dfrac{6^x}{2^x} =$
	$\dfrac{x^5}{x^3} =$	$(x^3)^4 =$

2.5.2 (simplify)	$2.0 \times 10^4 \times 10 \times 10^2 =$	
	$34.5 \times 10^{-5} + 6.7 \times 10^{-4} =$	
2.5.3 (simplify)	$2^4 =$	$8^{\frac{2}{3}} =$
2.5.4 (simplify)	$3^{-2} =$	
	$\left[1.2 + \left(37 - \sqrt{5} \right) \times 2.331 \right]^0 =$	

2.5.6 (squares and cubes of common numbers; fill in the 22 empty cells)

x	1	2	3	4	5	6	7	8
x^2								
x^3						-	-	-

x	9	10	11	12	13	14	15	20
x^2								
x^3	-		-	-	-	-	-	-

2.6.2	Solve for x: $\dfrac{2}{3} = \dfrac{5}{x}$

Medium-level Importance

2.1 Integers, Rational Numbers, and the Number Line

2.1.1 Integers

Integers are whole numbers without any decimal or fractional portions. They can be any number from negative to positive infinity including zero.

> **EXAMPLES**   −2, −1, 0, 1, 2, 3 etc.

2.1.2 Rational Numbers

Rational numbers are numbers that can be written as fractions of integers. "Rational" even contains the word "ratio" in it, so if you like, you can simply remember that these are ratio numbers.

Most problems you will encounter in DAT QR will only require you to deal with rational numbers. Make sure you are extra careful when ratios and fractions (QR 2.4) are involved because they are notorious for causing mistakes.

EXAMPLES

$$\frac{1}{2}$$

$$-5 \left(-5 = \frac{-5}{1} \right)$$

$$1.875 \left(1.875 = \frac{15}{8} \right)$$

> **NOTE**
>
> Every integer is also a rational number, but not every rational number is an integer. You can write them as fractions simply by dividing by 1.

> **NOTE**
>
> If you start with a group of only rational numbers and add, subtract, multiply, and/or divide among them, you will always end up with a rational solution.

Irrational numbers are numbers that cannot be written as fractions of integers. Irrational numbers are normally numbers that have a decimal number that goes on forever with no repeating digits.

EXAMPLES

$$\sqrt{2} = 1.4142135623730950...$$

$$Pi = \pi = 3.14159265358979...$$

$$e = 2.718281828459045...$$

2.1.3 Real Numbers, the Number Line and Absolute Value

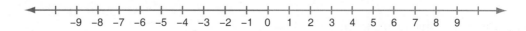

The **number line** is an infinite straight line on which every point corresponds to a real number. As you move up the line to the right, the numbers get larger, and down the line to the left, the numbers get smaller.

Real numbers are all numbers that can be represented on the number line. These include both rational and irrational numbers.

EXAMPLES

$$0, -\frac{1}{3}, \sqrt{2}, \text{ etc.}$$

Absolute value refers to how far a real number is from zero on the number line and it is indicated by a bar "|" placed on either side of a number or expression. Put simply, "absolute value" means to remove any negative sign in front of a number (*if present*), thus the number must be positive (or zero).

EXAMPLES

$|-3| = 3$, and $|8| = 8$, and $|-4\times8| = 32$

We will explore the absolute value in the context of inequalities in QR 4.2.2 B.

2.2 Basic Arithmetic

2.2.1 Basic Operations

An **operation** is a procedure that is applied to numbers. The fundamental operations of arithmetic are addition, subtraction, multiplication, and division.

A **sum** is the number obtained by adding numbers.

EXAMPLE

The sum of 7 and 2 is 9 since $2 + 7 = 9$.

A **difference** is the number obtained by subtracting numbers.

EXAMPLE

In the equation $7 - 2 = 5$, 5 is the difference of 7 and 2.

A **product** is the number obtained by multiplying numbers.

Medium-level Importance

EXAMPLE

The product of 7 and 2 is 14 since $7 \times 2 = 14$.

A **quotient** is the number obtained by dividing numbers.

EXAMPLE

In the equation $8 \div 2 = 4$, 4 is the quotient of 8 and 2.

Unlike a sum or a product, difference and quotient can result in different numbers depending on the order of the numbers in the expression:

$$10 - 2 = 8 \text{ while } 2 - 10 = -8$$
$$20 \div 5 = 4 \text{ while } 5 \div 20 = 0.25$$

The sum and difference of positive numbers are obtained by simple addition and subtraction, respectively. The same is true when adding negative numbers, except that the sum takes on the negative sign.

EXAMPLES

$(-3) + (-9) = -12$

$(-5) + (-12) + (-44) = -61$

On the other hand, when adding two integers with unlike signs, you need to ignore the signs first, and then subtract the smaller number from the larger number. Then follow the sign of the larger number in the result.

EXAMPLES

$(-6) + 5 \Rightarrow 6 - 5 = 1 \Rightarrow -1$

$7 + (-10) \Rightarrow 10 - 7 = 3 \Rightarrow -3$

When subtracting two numbers of unlike signs, start by changing the minus sign into its reciprocal, which is the plus sign. Next reverse the sign of the second number. This will make the signs of the two integers the same. Now follow the rules for adding integers with like signs.

EXAMPLES

$(-6) - 5 = (-6) + (-5) = -11$

$7 - (-10) = 7 + 10 = 17$

Multiplication and division of integers are governed by the same rules: If the numbers have like signs, the product or quotient is positive. If the numbers have unlike signs, the answer is negative.

EXAMPLES

$$5 \times 6 = 30$$
$$-5 \times -3 = 15$$
$$81 \div 9 = 9$$
$$-20 \div -4 = 5$$
$$7 \times -4 = -28$$
$$-9 \times 6 = -54$$
$$-15 \div 3 = -5$$
$$16 \div -2 = -8$$

An **expression** is a grouping of numbers and mathematical operations.

EXAMPLE

2 + (3 × 4) × 5 is a mathematical expression.

An **equation** is a mathematical sentence consisting of two expressions joined by an equals sign. When evaluated properly, the two expressions must be equivalent.

EXAMPLE

$2 \times (1+3) = \dfrac{16}{2}$ is an equation

since the expressions on both sides of the equals sign are equivalent to 8.

> **NOTE**
>
> Whenever you see simple calculations in these chapters, take the time to make sure that you are able to complete the presented calculations quickly and efficiently. We know that you have learnt all of these skills before and that you will have access to a calculator during DAT QR; however, we just want to firmly rebuild your foundation for more complex, speed-driven, math.

2.2.1.1 Summary of Properties of Positive and Negative Integers

Positive + Positive = Positive

$$5 + 4 = 9$$

Negative + Negative = Negative

$$(-6) + (-2) = -8$$

Positive + Negative = Sign of the highest number and then subtract

$$(-5) + 4 = -1$$
$$(-8) + 10 = 2$$

Negative − Positive = Negative

$$(-7) - 10 = -17$$

Positive − Negative = Positive + Positive = Positive

$$6 - (-4) = 6 + 4 = 10$$

Negative − Negative = Negative + Positive = Sign of the highest number and then subtract

$$(-8) - (-7) = (-8) + 7 = -1$$

Negative × Negative = Positive

$$(-2) \times (-5) = 10$$

Positive/Positive = Positive

$$8/2 = 4$$

Negative × Positive = Negative

$$(-9) \times 3 = -27$$

Positive/Negative = Negative

$$64/(-8) = -8$$

2.2.2 Properties of the Real Numbers

Whenever you are working within the real numbers (*standard for DAT QR*), these properties hold true. It isn't necessary to memorize the name of each property, but you must be able to apply them all.

Symmetric Property of Equality: The right and left hand sides of an equation are interchangeable, so if $a = b$, then $b = a$.

Transitive Property of Equality: If $a = b$ and $b = c$, then $a = c$. This means that if you have two numbers both equal to one other number, those two numbers are also equal.

Commutative Property of Addition: When adding numbers, switching the position of the numbers will not change the outcome, so $a + b = b + a$.

Associative Property of Addition: When adding more than two numbers, it doesn't matter what order you do the addition in, so $(a + b) + c = a + (b + c)$.

Commutative Property of Multiplication: When multiplying numbers, switching the position of the numbers will not change the outcome, so $a \times b = b \times a$.

Associative Property of Multiplication: When multiplying more than two numbers, it doesn't matter what order you do the multiplication in, so $(a \times b) \times c = a \times (b \times c)$.

Identity Property of Addition: When zero is added or subtracted to any number, the answer is the number itself, so $10b - 0 = 10b$.

Identity Property of Multiplication: When a number is multiplied or divided by 1, the answer is the number itself, so $6a \times 1 = 6a$.

Distributive Property of Multiplication: When multiplying a factor on a group of numbers that are being added or subtracted, the factor may be distributed by multiplying it by each number in the group, so $a (b - c) = ab - ac$.

> Subtraction and division do not follow associative laws.

2.2.3 Order of Operations

Knowing the order of operations is fundamental to evaluating numerical expressions. If you follow it properly, you will always come up with the correct answer! Here it is in list form, to be followed from the top down:

Parentheses
Exponents (including square roots)
Multiplication
Division
Addition
Subtraction

Medium-level Importance

This forms the simple acronym **PEMDAS**, which is a great way to keep the operations straight. Alternatively, some people find it easier to remember the phrase "**P**lease **E**xcuse **M**y **D**ear **A**unt **S**ally."

If you don't like either of these techniques, feel free to come up with your own, or use BODMAS which is described in the NOTE below. It's important to have this clear because, as simple as it may seem, being able to carry out the order of operations quickly is crucial for common DAT QR question types.

Using PEMDAS, let's evaluate this expression composed only of integers.

$$2^2 + [(3 + 2) \times 2 - 9]$$

First, evaluate the expression contained in the inner set of parentheses.

$$= 2^2 + [(5) \times 2 - 9]$$

You can then choose to strictly follow the PEMDAS order by evaluating the exponent next. Alternatively, you can perform the operations within the square brackets, working your way outward, for a more organized procedure as follows:

First, perform the multiplication.

$$= 2^2 + (10 - 9)$$

Then, perform the subtraction.

$$= 2^2 + 1$$

Now evaluate the exponent.

$$= 4 + 1$$

Finally, evaluate the remaining expression.

$$= 5$$

> **NOTE**
>
> - Multiplication and division have the same rank. It is generally recommended to do them in order from left to right as they appear in the expression, but you can also do them in whatever order that makes most sense to you.
>
> - The same goes for addition and subtraction. Execute them from left to right, or in the order that feels most comfortable.
>
> - When you encounter nested parentheses, evaluate the innermost ones first then work your way outward.

> **NOTE**
>
> Don't like PEMDAS? BODMAS is equally helpful! BODMAS stands for "B"rackets, "O"f or "O"rder, "D"ivision, "M"ultiplication, "A"ddition and "S"ubtraction. As long as you have the order correct, the means to help you remember can be whatever is easiest for you.

Medium-level Importance

2.3 Rules on Zero

2.3.1 Addition and Subtraction with Zero

Zero is a unique number, and it has special properties when it comes to operations.

Zero is known as the **additive identity** of the real numbers since whenever it is added to (or subtracted from) a number, that number does not change.

Let's examine a simple expression.

$$(3 + 2) - 4$$

We can add or subtract zero anywhere within the expression and the value will not change:

$$(3 - 0 + 2) - 4 + 0$$
$$= (3 + 2) - 4$$

The addition or subtraction of the two zeros has no effect whatsoever on the outcome.

2.3.2 Multiplication and Division with Zero

When adding zero in an expression, it is easy to come up with a practical picture of what the operation represents; you begin with a collection of things and add zero more things to them. When multiplying and dividing with zero, however, such a conceptualization is more difficult. The idea of using zero in this manner is far more abstract.

Fortunately, you don't need to wrestle with trying to picture what multiplication or division with zero looks like. You can simply remember these easy rules:

Multiplying by Zero: The result of multiplying any quantity by zero is *always* equal to zero.

Remember that by the commutative property of multiplication, $a \times b = b \times a$, so

if we let $b = 0$, then we have $a \times 0 = 0 \times a$. This means that instead of trying to imagine multiplying a number by zero, you can reverse the thought and consider multiplying zero by a number instead. This second statement is more natural to visualize. You start with nothing, and then no matter how many times you duplicate that nothing, you still end up with nothing.

EXAMPLE

$$3 \times 0 = 0$$
$$123.79 \times 0 = 0$$
$$\left[1.2 + \left(37 - \sqrt{5} \right) \times 2.331 \right] \times 0 = 0$$

In the last example, there is no need to go through the order of operations and evaluate the expression inside the

Medium-level Importance

parentheses. Because you can see immediately that the entire parenthetical expression is being multiplied by zero, you know that the end result will be zero.

Zero Divided by a Number: The result of dividing zero by any quantity is *always* equal to zero. As with multiplication by zero, if you start with nothing and then take a portion of that nothing, you still end up with nothing.

EXAMPLE

$$0 \div 3 = 0$$

$$0 \div 123.79 = 0$$

$$0 \div \left[1.2 + \left(37 - \sqrt{5} \right) \times 2.331 \right] = 0$$

Just like with the multiplication by zero example, you do not need to evaluate the parenthetical expression in order to know that the solution is zero.

Dividing by Zero: Dividing any nonzero quantity by zero results in a solution that is not defined and is therefore undefined.

You should never have to deal with this case on the DAT. If you end up with division by zero in a calculation, you have probably made a mistake.

Similarly, you should never end up with zero divided by zero (an undefined quantity). If you do, you should go back and check your work.

2.4 Fractions, Decimals, and Percentages

2.4.1 Fractions

A **fraction** is the quotient of two numbers. It represents parts of a whole and may be seen as a proportion. The number on top is the *numerator*, and the one on the bottom is the *denominator*. Another way of understanding fractions is to consider one as the number of parts present (*numerator*) and the amount of parts it takes to make up a whole (*denominator*). These values can be divided by each other, and this fraction is the quotient.

EXAMPLE

$$\frac{2}{7}$$

In this fraction, 2 is the numerator and 7, the denominator.

Remember, all rational numbers (including integers) can be written as fractions.

Medium-level Importance

2.4.2 Manipulating Fractions

A. Fraction Multiplication

To multiply fractions, simply multiply the numerators together (this will be the new numerator) and then multiply the denominators together (this will be the new denominator).

EXAMPLE

$$\frac{2}{3} \times \frac{4}{5}$$

Multiply the numerators and denominators separately.

$$= \frac{(2 \times 4)}{(3 \times 5)}$$

$$= \frac{8}{15}$$

B. Fraction Division

A **reciprocal** is the number obtained by switching the numerator with the denominator of a fraction. For example, the reciprocal of $\frac{2}{3}$ is $\frac{3}{2}$.

To divide a number by a fraction, multiply that number by the reciprocal of the fraction. {"*Dividing fractions is easy as pie, flip the second fraction then multiply.*"}

EXAMPLE

$$3 / (4 / 3) = 3 \div \frac{4}{3}$$

Switch the numerator and the denominator in the fraction and multiply. Remem-

ber that 3 is really 3 ÷ 1 so the new denominator would be the product of 1 × 4.

$$= \frac{3}{1} \times \frac{3}{4}$$

$$= \frac{9}{4}$$

Note: 3/(4/3) is not the same as (3/4)/3. Using the rule for fraction division, (3/4)/3 = 3/4 × 1/3 = 3/12 = 1/4. {*We will continue to format fractions in this book using the various ways the ADA formats fractions on exams.*}

C. Fraction Addition and Subtraction

With fractions, addition and subtraction are not so easy. You can only add or subtract fractions from each other if they have the same denominator. If they satisfy this condition, then to add or subtract, you do so with the numerators only and leave the denominator unchanged.

EXAMPLE

$$\frac{1}{5} + \frac{3}{5}$$

Both fractions have the same denominator, so add the numerators.

$$= \frac{1 + 3}{5}$$

$$= \frac{4}{5}$$

EXAMPLE

$$\frac{3}{5} - \frac{1}{5}$$

Both fractions have the same denominator, so subtract the numerators.

$$= \frac{3 - 1}{5}$$

$$= \frac{2}{5}$$

What if the denominators of two fractions you are adding or subtracting are not the same? In this case, you must find the Lowest Common Denominator (LCD), the smallest number that is divisible by both of the original denominators.

Ideally, you would like to find the smallest common denominator because smaller numbers in fractions are always easier to work with. But this is not always easy to do, and usually it isn't worth the extra time it will take to do the necessary calculation. The simplest way to find a common denominator is to multiply each fraction by a new fraction in which the numerator and denominator are both the same as the denominator of the other fraction.

EXAMPLE

$$\frac{2}{3} + \frac{2}{7}$$

Don't be confused by the fact that the numerators are the same. We still need to find a common denominator because the denominators are different.

$$= \left(\frac{2}{3} \times \frac{7}{7} \right) + \left(\frac{2}{7} \times \frac{3}{3} \right)$$

$$= \frac{14}{21} + \frac{6}{21}$$

Now that we have the same denominator, we can add the numerators.

$$= \frac{20}{21}$$

This method of finding common denominators utilizes the fact that any number multiplied by 1 is still the same number. The new fractions we introduce are always made of equivalent numerators and denominators, which make the fraction equal to 1, so the values of the original fractions do not change.

D. Comparing Fractions

Another method with which you should be familiar when manipulating fractions is comparing their values (i.e., which of the given fractions is greater than or lesser than the other) when they have different denominators. We will show you three ways to do this.

When you are confronted with only two fractions, finding their common denominator makes the task of evaluating the values easier.

1. Similar to the preceding discussion on adding or subtracting fractions that have different denominators, the fastest way to come up with a common denominator is to multiply both the numerator and denominator of each fraction by the other's denominator.

Let's say you are given the two fractions:

$$\frac{4}{5} \text{ and } \frac{3}{7}$$

Multiply the first fraction by 7 over 7 and the second fraction by 5 over 5. (The 7 comes from the fraction $\frac{3}{7}$ while 5 from $\frac{4}{5}$.)

$$\frac{4}{5} \times \frac{7}{7} = \frac{28}{35}$$

$$\frac{3}{7} \times \frac{5}{5} = \frac{15}{35}$$

With both fractions having 35 as the common denominator, you can now clearly see that 28 must be greater than 15. Therefore, $\frac{4}{5}$ is greater than $\frac{3}{7}$.

2. Another way to go about this is through cross-multiplication. Using the same fractions as examples, you first multiply the numerator of the first fraction by the denominator of the second fraction. The product will then serve as the new numerator of the first fraction.

$$\frac{4}{5} \searrow \frac{3}{7} \Rightarrow 4 \times 7 = 28$$

Next, multiply the denominators of the two fractions. The product will now serve as the new denominator of the first fraction.

$$\frac{4}{5} \rightarrow \frac{3}{7} \Rightarrow 5 \times 7 = 35$$

The resulting new fraction would be $\frac{28}{35}$.

Now, let's work on the second fraction. To get its new numerator, this time, multiply the numerator of the second fraction by the denominator of the first fraction. Then

multiply the denominators of both fractions.

$$\frac{4}{5} \swarrow \frac{3}{7} \Rightarrow 3 \times 5 = 15$$

$$\frac{4}{5} \leftarrow \frac{3}{7} \Rightarrow 7 \times 5 = 35$$

The second fraction will now become $\frac{15}{35}$. Thus comparing the first and second fractions, we get the same result as we had in the first method.

Because $\frac{28}{35}$ is greater than $\frac{15}{35}$, therefore $\frac{4}{5}$ is greater than $\frac{3}{7}$.

Both procedures follow the same basic principles and prove to be efficient when dealing with two given fractions. But what if you were given more than two fractions (since DAT QR is multiple choice, this will happen from time to time)?

3. A much simpler way is to convert each fraction to decimals, and then compare the decimals. All you have to do is divide the numerator of the fraction by its own denominator. For big numbers, you can use the calculator provided during the exam. For smaller numbers, you could learn to do the calculations in your head or on your DAT noteboard. With a little practice, you can actually train your brain to work fast with arithmetic.

Now let's say a third fraction is introduced to our previous examples: $\frac{4}{5}, \frac{3}{7}, \frac{9}{13}$.

Working on the first fraction, simply divide 4 by 5; on the second fraction, 3 by 7; and on the last, 9 by 13 (you should try this yourself to ensure that you can perform these basic calculations quickly and correctly).

$$\frac{4}{5} = 4 \div 5 = 0.8$$

$$\frac{3}{7} = 3 \div 7 = 0.43$$

$$\frac{9}{13} = 9 \div 13 = 0.69$$

Comparing the three fractions in their decimal forms, 0.43 ($\frac{3}{7}$) is the smallest, 0.69 ($\frac{9}{13}$) is the next, and the largest is 0.8 ($\frac{4}{5}$).

NOTE

For the DAT, decimals should be the recourse of last resort. When needed, try to complete calculations using fractions which will improve your speed.

E. Reduction and Canceling

To make calculations easier, you should always avoid working with unnecessarily large numbers. To reduce fractions, you can cancel out any common factors in the numerator and denominator.

EXAMPLE

$$\frac{20}{28}$$

First, factor both the numerator and denominator.

$$= \frac{(4 \times 5)}{(4 \times 7)}$$

Since both have a factor of four, we can cancel.

$$= \frac{5}{7}$$

When multiplying fractions, it is possible to cross-cancel like factors before performing the operation. If there are any common factors between the numerator of the first fraction and the denominator of the second fraction, you can cancel them. Likewise, if there are common factors between the numerator of the second and the denominator of the first, cancel them as well.

EXAMPLE

$$\frac{5}{9} \times \frac{6}{25}$$

First, factor the numerators and denominators.

$$= \frac{5}{(3 \times 3)} \times \frac{(2 \times 3)}{(5 \times 5)}$$

Now, we see that we can cross-cancel 5's and 3's.

$$= \frac{1}{3} \times \frac{2}{5}$$

$$= \frac{2}{15}$$

F. Mixed Numbers

You may encounter numbers on the DAT that have both an integer part and a fraction part. These are called mixed numbers.

EXAMPLE

$$3\frac{1}{2}$$

Mixed numbers should be thought of as addition between the integer and the fraction.

EXAMPLE

$$3\frac{1}{2} = 3 + \frac{1}{2}$$

Now in order to convert a mixed number back to a fraction, all you have to do is consider the integer to be the fraction of itself over 1 and perform fraction addition.

EXAMPLE

$$3\frac{1}{2}$$

$$= \frac{3}{1} + \frac{1}{2}$$

Obtain a common denominator.

$$= \left(\frac{3}{1}\right)\left(\frac{2}{2}\right) + \frac{1}{2}$$

$$= \frac{6}{2} + \frac{1}{2}$$

$$= \frac{7}{2}$$

To add or subtract mixed numbers, you can deal with the integer and fraction portions separately. {*Notice above that parentheses side by side is shorthand for multiplication.*}

EXAMPLE

$$3\frac{1}{2} - 2\frac{1}{2}$$

$$= (3-2) + \left(\frac{1}{2} - \frac{1}{2}\right)$$

$$= 1$$

NOTE

To convert a mixed number to a fraction, keep the denominator of the fraction while multiplying the integer part of the mixed number by the denominator. Then add to the numerator of the mixed number.

EXAMPLE

$$6\frac{2}{5} = \frac{(6 \times 5) + 2}{5} = \frac{30 + 2}{5} = \frac{32}{5}$$

G. Fractions: Summary

Multiplying
$$\left(\frac{a}{b}\right)\left(\frac{c}{d}\right) = \frac{ac}{bd}$$

Addition
$$\frac{a}{b} + \frac{c}{d} = \frac{ad + bc}{bd}$$

Dividing
$$\frac{\left(a/b\right)}{\left(c/d\right)} = \frac{ad}{bc}$$

Subtraction
$$\frac{a}{b} - \frac{c}{d} = \frac{ad - bc}{bd}$$

2.4.3 Decimals and Percentages

There are two other ways to represent non-integer numbers that you will encounter on the DAT: As decimals and as percentages.

A. Decimals

Decimal numbers can be recognized by the decimal point (a period) that they contain. Whatever digits are to the left of the decimal point represent a whole number, the integer portion of the number. The digits to the right of the decimal point are the decimal portion.

EXAMPLE

12.34

The integer portion of the number is 12, and .34 is the fractional portion.

The value of the decimal portion of a number operates on a place-value system just like the integer portion. The first digit to the right of the decimal point is the number of tenths (1/10 is one tenth), two digits over is the number of hundredths (1/100 is one hundredth), three digits over is the number of thousandths, then ten-thousandths, etc.

For example, in the decimal 0.56789:

- the 5 is in the tenths position;
- the 6 is in the hundredths position;
- the 7 is in the thousandths position;
- the 8 is in the ten thousandths position;
- the 9 is in the one hundred thousandths position.

Thus, to convert a decimal into a fraction, just drop the decimal point and divide by the power of ten of the last decimal digit. To convert a fraction to a decimal, simply perform the long division of the numerator divided by the denominator.

EXAMPLE

$$0.34 = \frac{34}{100}$$

B. Operations with Decimals

Addition and Subtraction: Adding and subtracting decimals is the same as with integers. The only difference is that you need to take care to line up the decimal point properly. Just like with integers, you should only add or subtract digits in the same place with each other.

EXAMPLE

Add 3.33 to 23.6.

$$23.60$$
$$+ \ 03.33$$

Notice how we have carried the decimal point down in the same place. Also, to illustrate the addition more clearly, we have added zeros to hold the empty places. Now perform the addition as if there were no decimal points.

$$23.60$$
$$+ \ 03.33$$
$$\overline{26.93}$$

Multiplication: You can multiply numbers with decimals just as you would with integers, but placing the decimal point in the solution is a little tricky. To decide where the decimal point goes, first count the number of significant digits after the decimal points in each of the numbers being multiplied. Add these numbers together to obtain the total number of decimal digits. Now, count that number of digits in from the right of the solution and place the decimal point in front of the number at which you end.

EXAMPLE

Multiply 3.03 by 1.2.

$$3.03$$
$$\times \ 1.20$$

We have written in a zero as a placeholder at the end of the second number, but be careful not to include it in your decimal count. Only count up to the final nonzero digit in each number (the 0 in the first number counts because it comes before the 3). Thus our decimal digit count is $2 + 1 = 3$, and we will place our decimal point in the solution 3 digits in from the right; but first, perform the multiplication while ignoring the decimal.

$$3.03$$
$$\times \ 1.20$$
$$\overline{606}$$
$$+ \ 3030$$
$$\overline{3636}$$

Now, insert the decimal point to obtain the final solution.

$$= 3.636$$

When counting significant digits, remember to consider the following:

1. all zeros between nonzero digits

EXAMPLE

0.45078 → 5 significant figures

2. all zeros in front of a nonzero number

EXAMPLE

0.0056 → 4 significant figures

3. ignore all zeros after a nonzero digit

EXAMPLE

0.2500 → 2 significant figures

> **NOTE**
>
> Unfortunately, this last math rule is not so simple because in science labs, significant figures (= significant digits = sig figs) represent the accuracy of measurement. This is further discussed in the Appendix QR A.4 (*towards the end of this book*) and General Chemistry Chapter 12 in the Gold Standard DAT Masters Series.

Division: We can use our knowledge of the equivalence of fractions to change a decimal division problem into a more familiar integer division problem. Simply multiply each number by the power of ten corresponding to the smallest significant digit out of the two decimal numbers being divided, and then, perform the division with the integers obtained.

This operation is acceptable because it amounts to multiplying a fraction by 1.

EXAMPLE

Divide 4.4 by 1.6

$$\frac{4.4}{1.6}$$

Since the smallest decimal digit in either number is in the tenth place, we multiply the top and bottom by 10.

$$= \frac{4.4}{1.6} \times \frac{10}{10}$$

$$= \frac{44}{16}$$

$$= \frac{11}{4}$$

If you like, you can convert this back to a decimal.

$$= 2.75$$

Rounding Decimals: Rounding decimals to the nearest place value is just like rounding an integer. Look at the digit one place further to the right of the place to which you are rounding. If that digit is 5 or greater, add 1 to the previous digit and drop all the subsequent digits. If it is 4 or less, leave the previous digit alone and simply drop the subsequent digits.

Consider the number 5.3618:

(a) Round to the nearest tenth.

$$= 5.4$$

Since the digit after the tenth place is a 6, we add 1 tenth and drop every digit after the tenth place.

(b) Round to the nearest hundredth.

$$= 5.36$$

Since the digit after the hundredth place is a 1, we do not change any digits. Just drop every digit after the hundredth place.

Medium-level Importance

Fraction-Decimal Conversions to Know: Having these common conversions between fractions and decimals memorized will help you save valuable time on the test.

Fraction	Decimal
1/2	.5
1/3	~ .33
1/4	.25
1/5	.2
1/6	~.167
1/8	.125
1/10	.1

C. Percentages

Percentages are used to describe fractions of other numbers. One percent (written 1%) simply means 1 hundredth. This is easy to remember since "percent" can literally be broken down into "per" and "cent", and we all know that one cent is a hundredth of both a dollar and a euro.

We can use this conversion to hundredths when evaluating expressions containing percents of numbers. To find a percentage of a number, you can use ratios/proportions (QR 2.6), or it may be easier to convert to a decimal and then multiply. For example, 60% of x is $(0.6)x$. Of course, 100% of x is just $1 \times x$ which is x; maintaining the trend, 180% of x must be $1.8x$.

Be careful with the wording! A 10% *increase* is $(0.1)x$ but that is in addition to the original value of x, so if they ask for the *total value* then it must be $(1.1)x$.

EXAMPLE

What is 25% of 40?

$$= .25 \times 40$$
$$= 10$$

EXAMPLE

What is 350% of 2/5?

$$= 3.5 \times 2/5$$
$$= 7/5$$

To find what percentage a certain part of a value is of the whole value, you can use what is known as the **percentage formula**:

$$\text{Percent} = (\text{Part/Whole}) \times 100$$

EXAMPLE

What percentage of 50 is 23?

$$\text{Percentage} = (23/50) \times 100$$
$$= (46/100) \times 100$$
$$= 46\%$$

Combining percentages requires some nuance (i.e. 'it depends on the question' thus there are several possibilities). In word problems, which we will explore in greater detail in Chapter 8 (Applied Mathematics), often you need to add the given percentages to 100. Then, convert the percentages to decimals and multiply to the base value. Finally, use the new value and multiply it by the second percentage.

EXAMPLE

A store sells a pair of pants at a profit of 15%. A reseller buys the pants from the store and resells them at a 20% profit. If a supplier sold the pants to the store for $100, how much would a customer have to pay the reseller?

Step 1: 1.15 x $100 = $115

Step 2: 1.20 x $115 = $138

If this is new to you, don't worry, there are many more word problems awaiting you in Chapter 8!

2.5 Roots and Exponents

2.5.1 Properties of Exponents

An exponent is simply shorthand for multiplying that number of identical factors. So 4^3 is the same as (4)(4)(4) = 64, three identical factors of 4. Thus x^2 (i.e. 'x squared') is two factors of x, (x)(x), while x^3 (i.e. 'x cubed') is three factors of x, (x)(x)(x).

To multiply exponential values with the same base, keep the base the same and add the exponents.

EXAMPLE

$$a^2 \times a^3 = a^{2+3} = a^5$$

To divide exponential values with the same base, keep the base the same and subtract the exponent of the denominator from the exponent of the numerator.

EXAMPLE

$$\frac{x^5}{x^3} = x^{5-3} = x^2$$

To multiply exponential values with different bases but the same exponent, keep the exponent the same and multiply the bases.

EXAMPLE

$$2^x \times 3^x = (2 \times 3)^x = 6^x$$

To divide exponential values with different bases but the same exponent, keep the exponent the same and divide the bases.

EXAMPLE

$$\frac{6^x}{2^x} = \left(\frac{6}{2}\right)^x = 3^x$$

To raise an exponential value to another power, keep the base the same and multiply the exponents.

EXAMPLE

$$(x^3)^4 = x^{(3\times 4)} = x^{12}$$

Even though all of the preceding examples use only positive integer exponents, these properties hold true for all three of the types described in QR 2.5.3.

Medium-level Importance

2.5.2 Scientific Notation

Scientific notation, also called exponential notation, is a convenient method of writing very large (or very small) numbers. Instead of writing too many zeroes on either side of a decimal, you can express a number as a product of a power of ten and a number between 1 and 10. For example, the number 8,765,000,000 can be expressed as 8.765×10^9.

The first number 8.765 is called the coefficient. The second number should always have a base of ten with an exponent equal to the number of zeroes in the original numbers. Moving the decimal point to the left makes a positive exponent while moving to the right makes a negative exponent.

Questions involving scientific notation on the DAT basically boil down to multiplying and dividing the numbers. These problems can pose a challenge in the exam since you cannot input 10^x on the onscreen calculator. The only way to do it is by hand using your marker and noteboard.

In multiplying numbers in scientific notation, the general rule is as follows:

$$(a \times 10^x)(b \times 10^y) = ab \times 10^{x+y}$$

EXAMPLE

To multiply 2.0×10^4 and 10×10^2

{Whenever possible, when you see a practice question like the one above, consider using a sheet of paper or Post-It note to cover the solution while you try to answer the question yourself.}

(i) Find the product of the coefficients first.

$2.0 \times 10 = 20$

(ii) Add the exponents.

$4 + 2 = 6$

(iii) Construct the result.

20×10^6

(iv) Make sure that the coefficient has only one digit to the left of the decimal point. This will also adjust the number of the exponent depending on the number of places moved.

$= 2.0 \times 10^7$

Dividing numbers in scientific notation follows this general rule:

$$\frac{\left(a \times 10^x\right)}{\left(b \times 10^y\right)} = \frac{a}{b} \times 10^{x-y}$$

Going back to our preceding example, let's divide 2.0×10^4 and 10×10^2 this time:

(i) Divide the coefficients.

$2.0 \div 10 = 0.2$

(ii) Subtract the exponents.

$4 - 2 = 2$

(iii) Construct the result and adjust the values to their simplest forms.

$$0.2 \times 10^2 = 2 \times 10 = 20$$

In adding and subtracting numbers written in scientific notation, you need to ensure that all exponents are identical. You would need to adjust the decimal place of one of the numbers so that its exponent becomes equivalent to the other number.

EXAMPLE

Add 34.5×10^{-5} and 6.7×10^{-4}

(i) Choose the number that you want to adjust so that its exponent is equivalent to the other number. Let's pick 34.5 and change it into a number with 10^{-4} as its base-exponent term.

$$3.45 \times 10^{-4} + 6.7 \times 10^{-4}$$

(ii) Add the coefficients together:

$$3.45 + 6.7 = 10.15$$

(iii) The exponents are now the same, in this case 10^{-4}, so all you have to do is plug it in:

$$10.15 \times 10^{-4}$$

(iv) Adjust the end result so that the coefficient is a number between 1 and 10:

$$= 1.015 \times 10^{-3}$$

The same procedure basically applies to subtraction.

> **NOTE**
>
> Notice in the examples in this section, when you lower the power from the coefficient (i.e. by moving the decimal to the left), you must add to the exponent, and vice versa.

2.5.3 Types of Exponents

Positive Integer Exponents: This is the type of exponent you will encounter most often. Raising a base number b to a positive integer exponent x is equivalent to making x copies of b and multiplying them together.

EXAMPLE

$$2^4 = 2 \times 2 \times 2 \times 2 = 16$$

Fractional Exponents: Fractional exponents are also known as roots. Let x be the fraction. To raise a base number b to the x power we make use of the fifth property of exponents in QR 2.5.1.

We can write $b^{\frac{n}{d}}$ as $\left(b^{\frac{1}{d}}\right)^n$. The value $b^{\frac{1}{d}}$ is known as the d-th root of b. So the base b raised to the x power is the same as the d-th root of b raised to the n power.

EXAMPLE

$$8^{\frac{2}{3}}$$

$$= \left(8^{\frac{1}{3}}\right)^2$$

The expression inside the parentheses is the cube root of 8. Since $2 \times 2 \times 2 = 8$, the cube root of 8 is 2.

$$= 2^2$$
$$= 4$$

Consider the following: What is the cube root of 125, and separately, what is the cube root of -125? The number 5 multiplied by itself 3 times equals 125. Similarly, the number -5 multiplied by itself 3 times equals -125. Thus the answers are 5 and -5, respectively.

Negative Exponents: The value of a base raised to a negative power is equal to the reciprocal of the base, raised to a positive exponent of the same value. For any exponential value b^{-x}, b^{-x} is equivalent to $\frac{1}{\left(b^x\right)}$.

EXAMPLE

$$3^{-2}$$

Take the reciprocal and invert the sign of the exponent.

$$= \frac{1}{\left(3^2\right)}$$

$$= \frac{1}{\left(3 \times 3\right)}$$

$$= \frac{1}{9}$$

2.5.4 Zero and Exponents

Raising a Number to the Zero: Any number raised to the zero power is equal to 1.

We can see that this follows the rules of exponents (*see* section 1.5), because $a^0 = a^1 \times a^{-1} = a/a = 1$.

> **NOTE**
>
> The quantity 0^0 (read as zero to the zero power) is 1.

EXAMPLES

$$3^0 = 1$$
$$123.79^0 = 1$$
$$\left[1.2 + \left(37 - \sqrt{5}\right) \times 2.331\right]^0 = 1$$

As with multiplication and division, you should not waste time evaluating the parenthetical expression.

Medium-level Importance

2.5.5 Summary of the Rules for Exponents

$$a^0 = 1 \qquad\qquad a^1 = a$$

$$a^n\, a^m = a^{n+m} \qquad\qquad a^n/a^m = a^{n-m}$$

$$(a^n)^m = a^{nm} \qquad\qquad a^{\frac{1}{n}} = \sqrt[n]{a} \quad \{\text{note that } a^{\frac{1}{2}} \text{ is simply } \sqrt{a}\}$$

2.5.6 Recognizing Number Patterns

It is possible to save a lot of time during the real DAT by avoiding unnecessary calculations by the recognition of certain patterns. One helpful way to achieve this is by knowing at least the following relationships that are typically memorized in primary school math class (*see* the table below).

Test makers choose their numbers carefully. The moment you see 1.44 on the DAT, there would be a high likelihood that taking the square root, which gives 1.2, would be required (because, of course, the square root of 144 is 12, the square root of 1.44 must be 1.2). Likewise, the square root of 1.7, being an approximation of 1.69, must be 1.3 (the square root of 169 being 13).

x	1	2	3	4	5	6	7	8	9	10	11	12	13	14	15	20
x^2	1	4	9	16	25	36	49	64	81	100	121	144	169	196	225	400
x^3	1	8	27	64	125	-	-	-	-	1000	-	-	-	-	-	-

Table 1: Common squares and cubes that are helpful to know. Applying the rules of exponents (QR 2.5.3, 2.5.5), $5^2 = 25$, $5^3 = 125$; square root of 121 = $(121)^{1/2} = \sqrt[2]{121} = \sqrt{121} = 11$; cube (= 3rd) root of 64 = $(64)^{1/3} = \sqrt[3]{64} = 4$. These basic manipulations are commonly required for the real exam.

> **NOTE**
>
> Try to complete all the chapter warm-up exercises as quickly as possible. Preferably, you would do it without the use of a calculator, but of course you can practice using a mouse with an onscreen calculator.

Medium-level Importance

2.6 Ratio and Proportion

2.6.1 What is a Ratio?

A **ratio** is the relation between two numbers. There are multiple ways they can be written, but ratios can always be denoted as fractions.

These are all ways to represent the same ratio:

$$3 \text{ to } 4 \ = \ 3:4 \ = \ \frac{3}{4} \ = \ 3/4$$

If a ratio is written out in words, the first quantity stated should generally be placed in the numerator of the equivalent fraction and the second quantity in the denominator. Just make sure you keep track of which value corresponds to which category.

2.6.2 Solving Proportions

A **proportion** is a statement of equality between two or more ratios.

Solving for an unknown variable is the most common type of proportion problem. If you have just a ratio on either side of an equation, you can rewrite the equation as the numerator of the first times the denominator of the second equal to the denominator of the first times the numerator of the second. This allows you to find the missing information more easily.

EXAMPLE

Solve for x in the following equation.

$$\frac{2}{3} = \frac{5}{x}$$

Cross multiply to eliminate fractions.

$$2 \times x = 3 \times 5$$
$$2x = 15$$
$$x = \frac{15}{2} = 7\frac{1}{2}$$

This means that the ratio 2 to 3 is equivalent to the ratio 5 to $7\frac{1}{2}$.

Unless it is stated, a proportion does not describe a specific number of things. It can only give you information about quantities in terms of other quantities. But if it is explicitly stated what one of the two quantities is, the other quantity can be determined using the proportion.

A lot of the DAT QR questions on proportions are related to converting units to another type of unit. We will be doing many examples like this in QR Chapter 3.

GOLD STANDARD DAT QR PRACTICE QUESTIONS

CHAPTER 2: Numbers and Operations

> **NOTE**
>
> We suggest that you use the default calculator on your PC or Mac computer for all QR practice questions. Use only the features described in QR section 1.2. This will help you become accustomed to another element of the DAT QR. It is a good habit to aim to complete practice questions in under 1 minute per question. You will have a bit more time on the real DAT (i.e., 1.1 min./question) but ideally you would leave some time at the end of the exam to review your work.

1) What is the approximate value of

$$0.125 + \sqrt{\frac{1}{9}} \ ?$$

   A. 0.40
   B. 0.46
   C. 0.50
   D. 0.45
   E. 0.30

2) 0.8 is to 0.9 as 80 is to:

   A. 9
   B. 100
   C. 8
   D. 10
   E. 90

3) Board C is 3/4 as long as Board B. Board B is 4/5 as long as Board A. What is the sum of the lengths of all three Boards if Board A is 100 m long?

   A. 255 m
   B. 225 m
   C. 240 m
   D. 235 m
   E. 250 m

4) If you invest in Bank A, you will receive 19% interest on the amount you invest. If you invest in Bank B, you will receive 21% interest. The maximum amount you can invest in Bank A is $6,430, and the maximum amount you can invest in Bank B is $5,897. How much more interest will you earn if you invest the maximum amount in Bank B than if you invest the maximum amount in Bank A?

   A. $16.67
   B. $16.30
   C. $101.27
   D. $111.93
   E. $533.00

5) The proportion of the yellow marbles in a jar of yellow and green jars is 7 out of 9. If there are 999 marbles in the jar, how many of these are yellow?

   A. 111
   B. 777
   C. 2
   D. 222
   E. 0

Medium-level Importance

6) If 0.25 months is equal to one week, what fraction of a month is equal to one day?

   A. 1/7

   B. 4/7

   C. 7/4

   D. 1/30

   E. 1/28

7) Which of the following is 6.4% of 1,000?

   A. $64^{\frac{3}{4}}$

   B. $256^{\frac{3}{4}}$

   C. $\left(\dfrac{64}{100}\right)^2$

   D. 0.8^2

   E. $6.4/100$

8) $2+\left[71-8\left(\dfrac{6}{2}\right)^2\right]$ is what percent of $\sqrt{2500}$?

   A. 50%

   B. 1%

   C. 44%

   D. 2%

   E. 6%

9) Which is the largest?

   A. 0.636

   B. 0.136

   C. 0.46

   D. 0.163

   E. 0.3

10) Determine the sum of 9, -5, and 6.

   A. 20

   B. -20

   C. -10

   D. 10

   E. -6

11) Determine the value of 1.5×10^7 divided by 3.0×10^4.

   A. 5.0×10^3

   B. 0.5×10^3

   C. 5.0×10^{-2}

   D. 0.5×10^{-3}

   E. 0.5×10^2

12) Determine the value of 1.5×10^7 subtracted by 3.0×10^4.

   A. 1.497×10^7

   B. -1.5×10^3

   C. 1.2×10^3

   D. 1.47×10^7

13) Determine the value of $|(-3)(6)|$.

   A. 3

   B. -3

   C. 18

   D. -18

14) Determine the value of $-|2-5|$.

   A. 3

   B. -3

   C. 7

   D. -10

Medium-level Importance

15) Try to complete the following calculation in under 30 seconds: Determine the value of .333 × .125. {*Try using your noteboard or scratch paper in under 30 seconds; then try with your onscreen calculator using the mouse to compare your accuracy, timing and comfort.*}

A. 0.02   C. 0.04
B. 0.03   D. 0.05

16) Which of the following is the greatest number?

A. $\dfrac{31}{50}$ C. $\dfrac{3}{5}$

B. $\dfrac{31}{51}$ D. $\dfrac{16}{25}$

17) Which of the following is the greatest number?

A. $\dfrac{96}{5}$ C. $\dfrac{230}{15}$

B. $\dfrac{53}{3}$ D. $\dfrac{147}{9}$

18) Simplify the expression: $(x^2)(y^2)(x^3)(y)(x^0)$.

A. 0
B. x^6y^3
C. x^5y^3
D. x^5y^2

19) Simplify the expression:
$(x^{2a+b})(x^{a-2b}) / (x^{2a-b})$.

A. x^a
B. x^{ab}
C. x^{5a-2b}
D. x^{5a+2b}

20) Let $x = 4$ and $y = 8$. Evaluate the expression: $((y^{-2/3})^{1/2}) / (x^{-1/2})$.

A. 8   C. 2
B. 1   D. 1/2

21) Which of the following is equal to x if $(0.16/0.4)(100/32)x = 1$?

A. 4/5   C. 5/4
B. 40/5   D. 5/40

22) If $[\sqrt{w}\,(x - y) - v]\,z = 21.4$, then which of the following variables cannot be zero?

A. v D. y
B. w E. z
C. x

23) Consider a decrease of 40% followed by an increase of 60%. What is the total percentage change?

A. Decrease of 4%
B. Increase of 10%
C. Increase of 20%
D. Decrease of 24%
E. None of the above

24) If $x = 3$, then $x + 6$ is what percent of $x^2 - 6$?

A. 3   C. 100
B. 33.3   D. 300

25) If $x = 1/3$ and $y = 13/25$, then which of the following is equal to $1/x \div y$?

A. 13/75
B. 75/13
C. 13/15
D. 15/13

Medium-level Importance

26) If $(a + b)(c + d) + e = 0$ and $e \neq 0$, which statement CANNOT be true?

   A. $a = b$
   B. $(a + b) = (c + d)$
   C. $(c + d) > e$
   D. $(a + b) = 0$
   E. $(a - b) = 0$

27) Simplify the expression: $[(3.3 \times 10^4 - 6.2 \times 10^4)/(5.8 \times 10^2)]^3$.

   A. 5.0×10^{-2}
   B. 5.0×10^{-1}
   C. -1.25×10^2
   D. -5.0×10^3
   E. -1.25×10^5

28) If $x = 7/28$, $y = 1/3$, and $z = 3/4$, then which is equal to $[(zy) - 2x] \div x$?

   A. 1   D. $-1/16$
   B. $1/16$ E. -1
   C. 0

29) Which represents 20% of 15% of 3/5?

   A. .018   D. 18
   B. .18   E. 180
   C. 1.8

30) If $[(a + b)(c + d) + e][f - g] = 80$, which CANNOT be true?

   A. $(a + b) = 0$
   B. $a = b$
   C. $e = 1$
   D. $(a + b) = (c + d)$
   E. $f = g$

31) Which is the value of $\sqrt{.000081}$?

   A. .9
   B. .09
   C. .009
   D. .0009
   E. .00009

32) Simplify the expression: $(2x)^{-2}(((2x^2)^3)^2)$.

   A. $16x^5$
   B. $16x^6$
   C. $16x^8$
   D. $16x^{10}$
   E. $16x^{12}$

33) Evaluate the expression $(3 \times 10^{-4})(8 \times 10^9)/(2 \times 10^3)$.

   A. 1.2×10^2
   B. 1.2×10^3
   C. 1.2×10^4
   D. 1.2×10^7
   E. 1.2×10^8

34) What is the approximate value of $(3/5 + \sqrt{.09})(.2)^2$?

   A. .036   D. 36
   B. .36   E. 360
   C. 3.6

35) If $x = 1/4$, $y = 3/2$, and $z = 1/2$, then which is equal to $[(zy) - 2x] \div x$?

   A. 1   D. $-1/16$
   B. $1/16$ E. -1
   C. 0

Medium-level Importance

CHAPTER REVIEW SOLUTIONS: CHAPTER 2

Question 1   B

See: QR 2.2.3, 2.4.3

According to the rules of order of operations, we work with the square root first: $0.125 + \sqrt{\frac{1}{9}} = 0.125 + \frac{1}{3}$. Since the answers are in decimal form, this problem is easiest to solve if all values are in decimal form. From the list of fraction-to-decimal conversions, $\frac{1}{3} \approx 0.33$, and so, $0.125 + \frac{1}{3} \approx 0.125 + 0.33 = 0.455$. All of the answers have only two decimal places, so we must round this answer off to the hundredths decimal place. The digit in the thousandths decimal place is a 5, and so the digit in the hundredths decimal place increases by 1 to become 6. 0.455 therefore rounds off to 0.46.

Quick Solution:

$$0.125 + \sqrt{\frac{1}{9}} = 0.125 + \frac{1}{3} \approx 0.125 + 0.333$$

$$= 0.458 \approx 0.46.$$

Question 2   E

See: QR 2.6.2

This is a proportion problem, so there will be two equivalent ratios. We construct the first ratio as $\frac{0.8}{0.9}$ and the second as $\frac{80}{x}$. If we set them equal, we get $\frac{0.8}{0.9} = \frac{80}{x}$, and cross-multiplication gives us $0.8x = (0.9)(80)$, or $0.8x = 72$. Therefore, $x = \frac{72}{0.8} = 90$.

Quick Solution: 80 differs from 0.8 by a factor of 100. This means that the answer must be related to 0.9 by the same factor: $x = 100(0.9) = 90$

Question 3   C

See: QR 2.4.2

We must work backwards to find the lengths of boards B and C. Board B is 4/5 as long as Board A, which is

$\frac{4}{5}(100m) = 80m$. Board C is 3/4 as long as this, which is $\frac{3}{4}(80m) = 60m$. To find the sum of these lengths, we add the three values: $100m + 80m + 60m = 240m$.

Question 4   A

See: QR 2.4.3

The interest earned by investing \$5,897 in Bank B is 21% of \$5,897, or $(0.21)(\$5,897) = \$1238.37$. The interest earned by investing \$6,430 in Bank A is 19% of \$6,430, or $(0.19)(\$6,430) = \$1221.70$. Subtracting the smaller from the larger, we get $\$1238.37 - \$1221.70 = \$16.67$.

Question 5   B

See: QR 2.6.2

This is a proportion problem in which the following are given: The proportion of the yellow marbles in the jar of yellow and green marbles is 7 out of 9. This makes the ratio of the number of yellow marbles to green marbles 7:2. The total number of marbles is 999. Therefore, the number of yellow marbles = $(7/9) \times 999$ = 777 marbles.

Question 6   E

See: QR 2.6.1

This is a ratio problem involving different units. The given ratio is 0.25 months per week. We need to re-write this as a fraction: 0.25 months per week $= \frac{25}{100}$ months/week $= \frac{1}{4}$ months/week.

This ratio tells us that there are four weeks in one month. We can express the number of months corresponding to one day using an intermediate relationship. There are 7 days in one week, which we can express with the ratio $\frac{1}{7}$ weeks/day. To express the number of months per day, we must multiply the first ratio by the second: $(\frac{1}{4}$ months/week$)$ $(\frac{1}{7}$ weeks/day$) = \frac{1}{28}$ months/day. Notice that the weeks units cancel so that the only units left are months and days. If we had used a ratio expressing the number of days per week

Medium-level Importance

(the reciprocal of weeks per day), $\frac{7}{1}$ days/week, this cancellation would not occur and the final answer would not have the correct units of months per day.

> **Quick Solution:** To convert a ratio that expresses a relationship between months and weeks to one that expresses a relationship between months and days, multiply it by a ratio that expresses a relationship between weeks and days:

$$\left(\frac{1}{4} \text{ months/week}\right)\left(\frac{1}{7} \text{ weeks/day}\right) = \frac{1}{28} \text{ months/day}.$$

Question 7   B

See: QR 2.2.3, 2.4.3, 2.5.2

The first step in this problem is to find the value of 6.4% of 1,000. We convert the percentage to a decimal (0.064) and multiply by one thousand: $0.064(1,000) = 64$. Next, we find which of the answer choices is equal to this value. Choice A is obviously incorrect because 64 taken to any power besides 1 does not equal 64. The order of operations tells us that we must perform the calculation inside the parentheses first in choice C, which is a decimal (0.64). Squaring this value does not give us 64. It is easy to see that choice D will also be a decimal. Choice E begins with a small number (6.4) and divides it by a much larger number, so we know that the answer will be even smaller, and therefore not equal to 64. The correct choice is B. To check this, note that $256^{3/4} = (256^{1/4})^3 = (4)^3$ (because $4 \times 4 \times 4 \times 4 = 256$) and $(4)^3 = 64$.

Question 8   D

See: QR 2.2.3, 2.4.3

First, simplify the expressions according to the rules of the order of operations:

$$2 + \left[71 - 8\left(\frac{6}{2}\right)^2\right] = 2 + (70 - 8(3)^2)$$
$$= 2 + (71 - 8(9))$$
$$= 2 + (71 - 72)$$
$$= 2 + (-1) = 1$$

and $\sqrt{2500} = 50$. So, we need to find the percentage of 50 that is constituted by 1. Using the formula

Percent = Part/Whole × 100

$$\frac{1}{50} \times 100 = 0.02 \times 100 = 2,$$

we see that the answer is 2%.

Question 9   A

See: QR 2.4.3

The tenths decimal place is the largest occupied in each number. Comparing the digits in this decimal place, it is clear that the .6 in .636 is the largest.

Question 10   D

See: QR 2.2.1

Following the rule of adding like and unlike signs:

$$= 9 + -5 + 6$$
$$= 4 + 6$$
$$= 10$$

Question 11   B

See: QR 2.5.2

Dividing the coefficients 1.5 and 3.0 gives an answer of 0.5. Then the correct exponent value is determined by subtracting the exponents involved, which are 7 and 4. The final answer in scientific notation is 0.5×10^3.

Question 12   A

See: QR 2.5.1, 2.5.2

Convert so that both numbers have the same power of 10, then and only then can subtraction (or addition) be accomplished.

$$1.5 \times 10^7 = 1500 \times 10^4$$
$$1500 \times 10^4 - 3.0 \times 10^4 =$$
$$1497 \times 10^4 = 1.497 \times 10^7$$

Medium-level Importance

Question 13   C

See: QR 2.2.1.1, 2.1.3

Vertical bars mean 'absolute value'. First we calculate what is within the vertical bars, then to take the absolute value, we convert to a positive number.

$$|(-3)(6)| = |-18| = 18$$

Question 14   B

See: QR 2.2.1.1, 2.1.3

Vertical bars mean 'absolute value'. First we calculate what is within the vertical bars, then to take the absolute value, we convert to a positive number. Note that there is a negative symbol *outside* the vertical lines which will ensure that the answer becomes negative.

$$-|2-5| = -|-3| = -|3| = -3$$

{Recall: $2-5 = -3$, $|-3| = 3$, and then the first minus gets you -3}

Question 15   C

See: QR 2.4.3

It is usually easier to calculate using fractions than decimals. You should instantly recognize .333 as 1/3 and .125 as 1/8 (QR 2.4.3).

$1/3 \times 1/8 = 1/24$ which is approximately $1/25 = 4/100 = 0.04$.

Of course, you can solve the question with a longhand calculation and compare with using an onscreen calculator with a mouse (*which is not always the most efficient process*).

Question 16   D

See: QR 2.4.2D

When comparing answer choice A and B, you can immediately notice that answer choice B has the same numerator but a slightly larger denominator which means that 31/51 is a smaller number than 31/50. Answer choice C can be converted to a form that can easily be compared to the highest number so far (answer choice A): so 3/5

= 30/50 which has a smaller numerator but the same denominator as answer choice A, thus B is smaller. Now let's convert answer choice D so we can compare with A: 16/25 = 32/50 which is slightly higher than 31/50 and thus D is the winner.

Question 17   A

See: QR 2.4.2D

Choose the method that you are most comfortable with. As decimals: A is 19.2, B is 17.7, C is 15.3, D is 16.3. Thus the answer is A. If you did not complete the decimal calculations, see if you can do them now with speed. If you did not try reducing (as below), also see if you can do that now with speed.

You could choose to reduce: A = 96/5 = 19 1/5 (notice that 96 is close to 100 and 100/5 is clearly 20; so you could try 19 x 5 to get to 95 with 1 remainder); B = 53/3 (again, 60/3 is easily 20 but we are a few 3's below 60: try 17 x 3 = 51 with 2 remainder thus 17 2/3; C = 230/15 = 15 5/15 = 15 1/3 (recall that 15 x 15 is on your list for rote learning, QR 2.5.6, and is 225); D = 147/9 = 16 1/3. And so answer choice A has the greatest number.

Please note: there are dozens of other ways to solve these questions (including estimating to achieve rounder numbers). Choose your technique.

Question 18   C

See: QR 2.5

First rearrange the expression and group like terms:

$$(x^2)(y^2)(x^3)(y)(x^0) = (x^2\ x^3\ x^0)(y^2 y)$$

When multiplying powers with the same base, you can combine them by adding the exponents. For example:

$$y^2 y = (y)(y)(y) = y^{2+1} = y^3$$

So the expression becomes:

$$(x^2\ x^3\ x^0)(y^2 y)$$

$$= x^{2+3+0} y^{2+1}$$

$$= x^5 y^3$$

Question 19   A

See: QR 2.5

First simplify the numerator:

$(x^{2a+b})(x^{a-2b}) / (x^{2a-b})$

$= (x^{2a+b+a-2b}) / (x^{2a-b})$

$= (x^{3a-b}) / (x^{2a-b})$

Then combine the numerator and denominator using the properties of exponent division.

$= (x^{3a-b-2a+b})$

$= x^{a}$

Question 20   B

See: QR 2.5

First combine the exponents where possible, and rearrange so they are all positive:

$((y^{-2/3})^{1/2}) / (x^{-1/2})$

$= (y^{-1/3}) / (x^{-1/2})$

$= (x^{1/2}) / (y^{1/3})$

Now plug in x = 4 and y = 8. Notice that $4 = 2^2$ and $8 = 2^3$.

$= (4^{1/2}) / (8^{1/3})$

$= (2^{(2)1/2}) / (2^{(3)1/3})$

$= 2^1/2^1$

$= 1$.

Question 21   A

See: QR 2.4

$(0.16/0.4)(100/32)x = 1$

but $0.16/0.4 \times 100/100 = 16/40 = 2/5$, so:

$(2/5)(100/32)x = 1$, cancel to get:

$(1/1)(20/16)x = 1$, reduce to get:

$(5/4)x = 1$, thus:

$x = 4/5$

Question 22   E

See: QR 2.2.3, 2.3.2

This question is about respecting the order of operations and knowing the rule of zero. If *w* is 0, we have a reasonable equation left: $-vz = 21.4$ (of course, either variable could be negative to give a positive answer 21.4). If *x*, *y* or *v* is zero, we still have variables left that would equal 21.4. However, if *z* is zero, the entire left part of the equation becomes zero which produces the impossible equation: $0 = 21.4$.

Side note: If 2 squared is 4, then the square root of 4 is 2. If 0 squared is 0, then the square root of 0 is 0. Division by zero is undefined, but the square root of 0 is 0.

Question 23   A

See: QR 2.4.3 C

Percentage is calculated from a specific base value. After the first percentage change, the base changes, and the second percentage does not have the same base. Two percentages that have different base values cannot be directly combined by addition! Instead, we have to work out the percentage changes separately.

Decrease of 40% means that we have 60% of the original value *x*: $0.6x$.

Now the new base value $0.6x$ will have a 60% increase which is the same as multiplying the base by 1.60 (i.e. 1.6): $1.6(0.6x) = 0.96x$. So, we end up with 96% of the original *x* which is a 4% decrease from the full amount (100%). More word problems in Chapter 8!

Question 24   D

See: QR 2.4.3 C.

Percent = (Part/Whole) × 100

Part = $x + 6 = 3 + 6 = 9$

Whole = $x^2 - 6 = 3^2 - 6 = 9 - 6 = 3$

Percent = $(9/3) \times 100 = 3 \times 100 = 300\%$

Question 25   B

See: QR 2.4

$1/x \div y = 1/(1/3) \div 13/25 =$

$3 \div 13/25 = 3 \times 25/13 = 75/13$

Question 26   D

See: QR 2.3.2

Since e ≠ 0, we know that $(a + b)(c + d) = -e \neq 0$. This tells us that $(a + b) \neq 0$ and $(c + d) \neq 0$, because this would contradict the requirement that $(a + b)(c + d) \neq 0$. Therefore choice D. $(a + b) = 0$ cannot be true.

Question 27   E

See: QR 2.5.2

Follow the order of operations, beginning inside the parentheses and working your way out:

$[(3.3 \times 10^4 - 6.2 \times 10^4)/(5.8 \times 10^2)]^3$

$= [(3.3 \times 10^4 - 6.2 \times 10^4)/(5.8 \times 10^2)]^3$

$= [(-2.9 \times 10^4)/(5.8 \times 10^2)]^3$

$= (-.5 \times 10^2)^3$

$= (-50)^3$

$= -125,000$

$= -1.25 \times 10^5.$

Question 28   E

See: QR 2.2.3, 2.4

Plug the values given for x, y, and z into the expression, then evaluate:

$[(zy) - 2x] \div x = [(3/4)(1/3) - 2(7/28)] \div 1/4$

$= [(3/12) - (14/28)] \div 1/4 = [(1/4) - (2/4)] \div 1/4$

$= -(1/4) \div 1/4 = -1 .$

Question 29   A

See: QR 2.4.3

Convert the given values to decimals and multiply:

$(20\%)(15\%)(3/5) = (.2)(.15)(.6) = 0.018.$

Question 30   E

See: QR 2.2.3, 2.3.2

For this problem, you can begin testing each solution to see if the equation results in a contradiction. There is a way to focus this process, though. Since none of the possible solutions give you actual values for all the variables, you will not be able to determine the exact value of the left side (or even whether it is positive or negative) except in a case where it is guaranteed to equal 0. So, all you really need to do is find the solution that makes the left hand side equal to 0. This is the one that cannot be true. In this case, it is (E.) since when f = g, f − g = 0 and the left hand side is 0.

Question 31   C

See: QR 2.5

Simply test each of the possible solutions by squaring them and checking if the result is .000081. To speed up the process, you can begin testing with the choice that you guess is most likely. For example, you can rule out .9 and .00009 without testing them, since you can intuitively see that $.9^2$ will not have enough zeroes in the decimal, and $.00009^2$ will have too many zeros. .009 seems like a likely choice, so begin there:

$.009^2 = .000081$

So .009 is, in fact, the solution.

Alternatively, convert the problem to scientific notation (QR 2.5.2): $(81 \times 10^{-6})^{1/2}$ which easily reduces to 9×10^{-3} which is .009.

Question 32   D

See: QR 2.2.3

We can break this problem two chunks: $(2x)^{-2}$ and $(((2x^2)^3)^2)$. First consider $(2x)^{-2}$. Because the exponent is negative, this is equal to the inverse of the positive power.

$(2x)^{-2} = 1/(2x)^2$

Next, distribute the exponent throughout the parenthetical expression:

$1/(2x)^2 = 1/(2^2 x^2)$

Now let's move to our second chunk, $(((2x^2)^3)^2)$. When you raise a power to another power, multiply the exponents together. And don't forget to distribute through the parenthetical expression.

$(((2x^2)^3)^2) = ((2^3 x^{(2)(3)})^2) = (2^{(3)(2)} x^{(2)(3)(2)}) = 2^6 x^{12}$

Finally, let's multiply the two chunks together to get back to the original expression:

$(2x)^{-2}(((2x^2)^3)^2)$

$= [1/(2^2x^2)](2^6x^{12})$

$= (2^6x^{12})/(2^2x^2)$

When dividing powers, subtract the exponents:

$= (2^{6-2}x^{12-2})$

$= 2^4x^{10}$

$= 16x^{10}.$

Question 33   B
See: QR 2.5
Begin by combining the product in the numerator:

$(3x10^{-4})(8x10^9) = (24x10^5) = (2.4x10^6)$

Remember to reduce the number on the left so that it is between 1 and 10. Now divide by the denominator:

$(2.4x10^6)/(2x10^3) = (2.4/2)x10^{(6-3)} = 1.2x10^3.$

Question 34   A
See: QR 2.2.3, 2.4, 2.5
In this case it is convenient to convert all numbers to decimal form. This makes them easy to combine.

$(3/5 + \sqrt{.09})(.2)^2 = (.6 + .3)(.04) = (.9)(.04) = .036.$

Question 35   A
See: QR 2.2.3, 2.4, 2.5
Plug the values given for x, y, and z into the expression, then evaluate:

$[(zy) - 2x] \div x = [(1/2)(3/2) - 2(1/4)] \div 1/4$

$= [(3/4) - (1/2)] \div 1/4$

$= (1/4) \div 1/4$

$= 1.$

If you have any questions or concerns regarding your DAT practice questions, or the solutions, access the free Gold Standard Masters Series Forum for clarification: www.dat-prep.com/forum.

Medium-level Importance

(SPOILER ALERT ⚠)

Gold Standard has cross-referenced the content in this chapter to examples from the ADA's official DAT practice materials. It is for you to decide when you want to explore these questions since you may want to preserve DAT practice tests for timed mock-exam practice.

We suggest that you acquire the free 2007 DAT practice test from ada.org (digital document format), as well as the 2009 exam or, even better, the most recent online practice test. The online DAT Quantitative Reasoning practice test from the ADA is available through prometric.com and includes content from 2007 (35%), 2009 (10%), and newly added questions (55%). Note below that "Q" is followed by the question number, and cross-references to this chapter are in parentheses.

Examples –

2007 and 2022: Simplify an expression with exponents (QR 2.5): 2007 Q1; simplify a fraction with exponents (QR 2.4, 2.5): 2007 Q3; compare fractions to determine the smallest one (QR 2.4): 2007 Q4; manipulate multiple fractions (QR 2.4): 2007 Q6 and 2022 Q25 (*one answer choice is deleted in the 2022 version*); determine the square root of a decimal (QR 2.4.3, 2.5): 2007 Q7; manipulate fractions and then take the percentage (QR 2.4.1, 2.4.3 C.): 2007 Q8; apply the rule for zero during multiplication while respecting the brackets (QR 2.2.3, 2.3.2): 2007 Q11; solve a simple proportion (QR 2.6.2): 2007 Q13 and 2022 Q28; take the percentage of a number twice (QR 2.4.3 C.): 2007 Q16; plug in a value and then take the percentage (QR 2.4.3 C.): 2007 Q27 and 2022 Q32 (*one answer choice is deleted in the 2022 version*); set up a simple proportion (*knowing any conversion is unnecessary*; QR 2.6.2): 2007 Q31.

2009: Simplify a fraction with fractions in the numerator and denominator (QR 2.2.3, 2.4): 2009 Q3; solve a simple proportion (QR 2.6.2): 2009 Q7; solve a suspiciously (!!) similar simple proportion (QR 2.6.2): 2009 Q16; simplify a fraction with exponents (QR 2.4, 2.5.1, 2.5.2): 2009 Q20; percentage calculation (QR 2.4.3 C.): 2009 Q23; basic multiplication with decimals (QR 2.4.3): 2009 Q25; convert a long form number to scientific notation (QR 2.5.2): 2009 Q29.

2022: Solve for *x* with fractions and decimals (*first order polynomial*; QR 2.2.3, 2.4, 2.4.3): 2022 Q3; understanding fractions, substitute numbers (QR 2.2.3, 2.4): 2022 Q8.

Note: **The ADA practice tests are composed of questions which have previously appeared on real, past DATs, but have been retired.** Also, note that most of the 2022 ADA DAT practice test questions have had one answer choice removed. In other words, most questions have 4 answer choices instead of 5, which was standard in 2007 and 2009.

Chapter Checklist

- [ ] Sign up or access your free online account at www.dat-prep.com for discussion boards for any content from this chapter including chapter-ending practice questions.

- [ ] Reassess your 'learning objectives' for this chapter: Go back to the first page of this chapter and re-evaluate the top 3 boxes and the Introduction.

- [ ] Complete 1-2 pages of notes using symbols/abbreviations to represent the entire chapter based on your learning objectives. These are your Gold Notes.

- [ ] Consider your multimedia options based on your optimal way of learning:

    - [ ] Download the free Gold Standard DAT app for your Android device or iPhone. Create your own, tangible study cards or try the free app: Anki.

    - [ ] Record your voice reading your Gold Notes onto your smartphone (MP3s) and listen during exercise, transportation, etc.

    - [ ] Try some online math videos on YouTube like Khan Academy or Leah4sciMCAT playlist for Math Without a Calculator (the latter was produced for MCAT preparation but it remains helpful for DAT QR basics).

- [ ] Schedule your full-length DAT practice tests: ADA and/or GS exams and/or other free or paid third-party resources. Schedule one full day to complete a practice test and 1-2 days for a thorough assessment of answers and explanations while adding to your abbreviated Gold Notes.

- [ ] Schedule and/or evaluate stress reduction techniques such as regular exercise (sports), yoga, meditation and/or mindfulness exercises (*see* YouTube for suggestions).

Medium-level Importance

Memorize	Understand	Importance
* Conversions between units in the same system (whenever applicable) * Conversions between certain units in different systems	* Metric prefixes * How to convert between units, dimensional analysis	**Medium level: 3 of 40** **DAT Quantitative Reasoning questions** are based on content in this chapter (avg. based on past testing patterns). * Note that approx. **70%** of the questions in DAT QR are from just 3 of 8 chapters: 2, 4 and 8.

DAT-Prep.com

Introduction

While scientific measurement is not a primary focus of the Quantitative Reasoning Test, the DAT does use problems involving specific measurements. In order to solve these problems effectively, you must be familiar with British, Metric, and SI units, and some of the relationships between them.

Multimedia Resources at DAT-Prep.com

Free Online Forum

Special Guest

3.0 DAT Has a *Need for Speed*!

Section	DAT Quantitative Reasoning *Need for Speed* Exercises	
3.1.1	There are _____ inches in every foot.	
	There are _____ feet in every yard.	
	There are _____ feet in every mile. (*DAT-30, low yield*)	
	There are _____ ounces in every pound.	
3.1.2	How much is 36 liters in milliliters? _____	
	What is 6.3 cm in km? _____	
3.1.3 Table 1: Important Prefixes for the Metric and SI Systems	Write the base 10 value, e.g., tera: 10^{12}	deci:
	giga:	centi:
	mega:	milli:
	kilo	micro:
	hecto:	nano:
	deca:	pico:
3.2.1	1 inch = _____ cm	
	1 mile = _____ yards	
	1 mile = _____ km	
	To convert Celsius to Fahrenheit: °C × _____ + 32 = °F	
3.2.2	How many inches are there in 5.08 meters? _____	
	Calculate the number of seconds in a day. _____	

Medium-level Importance

3.1.1 British Units (Imperial System of Measurement)

You are probably already familiar with several of these units of measurement, but we recommend reviewing them at least once. If you don't know the following information backwards and forwards, you risk losing time on the test.

A. Length: These units are used to describe things like the length of physical objects, the displacement of a physical object, the distance something has traveled or will travel, etc. Area and volume are also measured as the square and cube (respectively) of these units.

Inches	The *inch* is the smallest measurement of length in the British System.
Feet	There are 12 inches in every foot. 1 ft. = 12 in.
Yards	There are 3 feet in every yard. 1 yd. = 3 ft.
Miles	The *mile* is the largest unit of length in the British System. There are 5,280 feet in every mile. 1 mi. = 5,280 ft.

B. Time: These units describe the passage of time.

Seconds	The *second* is the smallest unit of time in the British System.
Minutes	There are 60 seconds in every minute. 1 min. = 60 s.
Hours	There are 60 minutes in every hour. 1 h. = 60 min.
Days	There are 24 hours in every day. 1 day = 24 h.
Years	The *year* is the largest unit of time in the British System. There are 365 days in every year. 1 yr. = 365 days

C. Mass/Weight: Though not technically the same, we can consider mass and weight to be interchangeable for the DAT. The following units describe the amount of matter in an object.

Ounces	The *ounce* is the smallest unit of mass in the British System.
Pounds	There are 16 ounces in every pound. 1 lb. = 16 oz.
Tons	The *ton* is the largest unit of mass in the British System. There are 2,000 pounds in every ton. 1 ton = 2,000 lb.

> **NOTE**
>
> Make sure you memorize the conversions between the different units in each category. You will most likely be required to supply some of this information in order to solve problems on the test.

Medium-level Importance

3.1.2 Metric Units

Medium-level Importance

Measuring with Powers of 10: Unlike the British System, the Metric System has only one unit for each category of measurement. In order to describe quantities that are much larger or much smaller than one of the base units, a prefix is chosen from a variety of options and added to the front of the unit. This changes the value of the unit by some power of 10, which is determined by what the prefix is. The following are the most common of these prefixes:

Milli	One thousandth (10^{-3}) of the base unit
Centi	One hundredth (10^{-2}) of the base unit
Deci	One tenth (10^{-1}) of the base unit
Deca	Ten (10^{1}) times the base unit
Kilo	One thousand (10^{3}) times the base unit

There is a mnemonic that may be used to identify these prefixes:

King	Kilometer	Kilo
Henry	Hectometer	Hecto
Died	Decameter	Deca
Unexpectedly	Unit Base	Unit
Drinking	Decimeter	Deci
Chocolate	Centimeter	Centi
Milk	Milimeter	Milli

As you go down, you divide by 10 and as you go up, you multiply by 10 in order to convert between the units.

EXAMPLE

How many meters is 1 kilometer?

$$1 \text{ km} = 1{,}000 \text{ m}$$

From general knowledge, we know that kilo means one thousand. This means there are 1,000 meters in a kilometer. But just in case you get confused, you can also use the clue from the mnemonic. Now we know that **K**ilo is three slots upward from the **U**nit base. Hence we multiply 10 to itself three times: $10 \times 10 \times 10 = 1000$.

An even less confusing way to figure out how to do the metric conversions quickly and accurately, is to use a metric conversion line. This is quite handy with any of the common units such as the *meter*, *liter*, and *grams*.

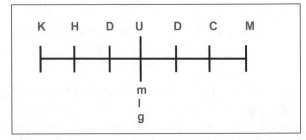

Fig QR 3.1: The Metric Conversion Line. The letters on top of the metric line stands for the "King Henry" mnemonic. On the other hand, the letters below the metric line - **m**, **l**, **g** – stand for the unit bases, **m**eter, **l**iter, or **g**ram, respectively.

To use this device, draw out the metric line as shown in Fig QR 3.1. From the centermost point **U**, the prefixes going to the left represent those that are larger than the base unit (kilo, hecto, deca). These also correspond to the decimal places that you will be moving from the numerical value of the unit to be converted. Those going to the right are for the ones smaller than the unit (deci, centi, milli).

EXAMPLE

How much is 36 liters in milliliters?

Step 1: Place your pen on the given unit, in this case L (liter). Then count the number of places it takes you to reach the unit being asked in the problem (milliliter).

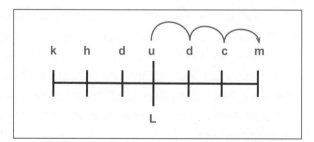

Fig QR 3.2: Converting liter to milliliter using the metric conversion line.

Step 2: Because it took you three places going to the right to move from the liter to the milliliter units, you also need to add three places from the decimal point of the number 36.0.

$$36 \text{ L} = 36{,}000 \text{ mL}$$

Now, let's try converting centimeter to kilometer: What is 6.3 cm in km?

1. Place your pen on the **c** (centi) point in the metric line.

2. Moving from **c** to **k** (kilo) takes five places going to the left. This also means moving five places from the decimal point of the number 6.3.
   $$6.3 \text{ cm} = .000063 \text{ km}$$

Using this method definitely makes doing the metric conversions so much faster than the fraction method!

There are other prefixes that are often used scientifically and may be found in the DAT:

Tera	10^{12}	times the base unit
Giga	10^{9}	times the base unit
Mega	10^{6}	times the base unit
Micro	10^{-6}	of the base unit
Nano	10^{-9}	of the base unit
Pico	10^{-12}	of the base unit

A. Length: As with British length units, these are used to measure anything that has to do with length, displacement, distance, etc. Area and volume are also measured as the square and cube (respectively) of these units.

Meters	The *meter* is the basic unit of length in the Metric System.
Other Common Forms	millimeter, centimeter, kilometer

B. Time: These are units that quantify the passage of time.

Seconds	Just as in the British System, the *second* is the basic unit of time in the Metric System. Minutes, hours, and the other British units are not technically part of the Metric System, but they are often used anyway in problems involving metric units.
Other Common Forms	millisecond

C. Mass: These are units that describe the amount of matter in an object.

Grams	The *gram* is the basic metric unit of mass.
Other Common Forms	milligram, kilogram

3.1.3 SI Units

SI units is the **International System of Units** (abbreviated **SI** from the French *Le Système International d'Unités*) and is a modern form of the metric system. They are used to standardize all the scientific calculations that are done anywhere in the world. The base units are meters, kilograms and seconds. These are the only SI units that may appear on the Quantitative Reasoning Test:

Meters	Same as Metric meters
Seconds	Same as Metric and British seconds
Grams	Same as Metric grams (will usually appear as kilograms)

All of these SI units are duplicates from other systems of measurement. There are other distinct units in this system, but it is highly unlikely that they will appear on the QR because they are chemistry and physics units (i.e., moles, kelvin, amperes and candelas).

> **NOTE**
>
> The values of these SI units can be modified by powers of 10 using the same prefixes as in the metric system.

Table 1: Important Prefixes for the Metric and SI Systems

Prefix Name	Symbol	Base 10	Decimal	English Word
tera	T	10^{12}	1000000000000	trillion
giga	G	10^{9}	1000000000	billion
mega	M	10^{6}	1000000	million
kilo	k	10^{3}	1000	thousand
hecto	h	10^{2}	100	hundred
deca	da	10^{1}	10	ten
BASE UNIT	-	10^{0}	1	one
deci	d	10^{-1}	0.1	tenth
centi	c	10^{-2}	0.01	hundredth
milli	m	10^{-3}	0.001	thousandth
micro	μ	10^{-6}	0.000001	millionth
nano	n	10^{-9}	0.000000001	billionth
pico	p	10^{-12}	0.000000000001	trillionth

3.2 Conversions

3.2.1 Quick Conversion Formulas

In many instances, having a ready set of memorized formulas saves you time in the test. Here is a quick list of those that you should know for the DAT:

1 inch = 2.54 cm

1 meter = 1.0936 yd

1 mile = 1,760 yards

1 mile = 1.6 km

1 kg = 2.2 lbs

1 kg = 35.27396 oz

1 g = 1000 mg = 0.0353 oz

1 oz = 0.0295735 liter

1 gallon = 128 fl oz

1 hr = 60 min = 3,600 seconds

3 feet = 1 yard = 0.9144 m

12 inch = 1 foot = 0.3048 m

Formula for converting Fahrenheit to Celsius: $\dfrac{(°F - 32)}{1.8} = °C$

Celsius to Fahrenheit: $°C \times 1.8 + 32 = °F$

Medium-level Importance

3.2.2 Mathematics of Conversions

While it is possible to memorize the conversions between every possible set of units, this would require much more effort than it would be worth. You do need to memorize the basic conversions but there is no point in knowing how many millimeters there are in a mile, for example. Odds are, these obscure conversions won't come up on the test; if they do, the math is simple enough to do without difficulty.

Whether you are converting units between different systems of measurement or simply within a single system, the math involved is the same.

A. The Process: In order to convert a quantity from one type of unit to another type of unit, all you have to do is set up and execute multiplication between ratios. Each conversion that you have memorized from the preceding sections is actually a ratio.

Let's look at the conversion from feet to inches.

"There are 12 inches in 1 foot."

This can be rewritten as a ratio in two ways:

"12 inches to 1 foot" or "1 foot to 12 inches."

$$= \frac{12 \text{ in}}{1 \text{ ft}} \text{ or } \frac{1 \text{ ft}}{12 \text{ in}}$$

When you are performing a conversion, you should treat the units like numbers. This means that when you have a fraction with a certain unit on top and the same unit on bottom, you can cancel out the units leaving just the numbers.

You can multiply a quantity by any of your memorized conversions, and its value will remain the same as long as all of the units, but one, cancel out.

EXAMPLE 1

How many inches are there in 3 feet?

First, determine which memorized conversion will help. Of course we have a conversion directly between feet and inches, so that is what we'll use.

Next, determine which of the two possible conversion ratios we should use. The goal is to be able to cancel out the original units (in this case, feet), so we want to use whichever ratio has the original units in the denominator (in this case, inches/feet).

$$3 \text{ ft} = 3 \text{ ft} \times \frac{12 \text{ in}}{1 \text{ ft}}$$

Now perform the unit cancellation.

$$= 3 \times \frac{12 \text{ in}}{1}$$
$$= 36 \text{ in}$$

In many instances, you will not have a direct conversion memorized. All you have to do in such a case is multiply by a string of ratios instead of just one.

Medium-level Importance

EXAMPLE 2

How many inches are there in 5.08 meters?

We cannot convert meters directly into inches, but we can convert meters to centimeters and then centimeters into inches. We can set up both these conversions at the same time and evaluate.

$$5.08 \text{ m} = 5.08 \text{ m} \times \frac{100 \text{ cm}}{1 \text{ m}} \times \frac{1 \text{ in}}{2.54 \text{ cm}}$$

Next, cancel the units.

$$= 5.08 \times \frac{100}{1} \times \frac{1 \text{ in}}{2.54}$$

$$= \frac{508 \text{ in}}{2.54}$$

$$= 200 \text{ in}$$

NOTE

Make sure you check and see that all of your units cancel properly! A lot of unnecessary errors can be avoided simply by paying attention to the units. "Dimensional analysis" is the formal term given to these types of calculations that are solved while keeping an eye on the relations based on units.

EXAMPLE 3

Calculate the number of seconds in a day.

1) Check the units of the answer: Convert the English "seconds in a day" to the math, seconds/day or s/day.

2) Next, assess what you already know. You know that there are 60 seconds in one minute, 60 minutes in an hour, and 24 hours in one day. But to convert to math, should you use, for example, 60 seconds/minute, or, 1 minute/60 seconds? They are equivalent expressions so we can use either, but only one of the two will help solve this problem.

3) Choose the conversion that takes you towards your answer. In our first step, we determined that seconds was in the numerator, so we must choose a matching conversion, 60 seconds/minute has the correct unit in the numerator. Let's begin to set up the equation:

$$\frac{60 \text{ seconds}}{\text{minute}} \times A \times B = \frac{X \text{ seconds}}{\text{day}}$$

4) Now the new problem that we have is to get rid of "minute" in the denominator and replace it with "day". Should "A" be 60 minutes/hour, or, 1 hour/60 minutes. Only if we choose a conversion with minutes in the numerator could it cancel the "minute" in the denominator. We do the same analysis for 24 hours/day and we get:

$$\frac{60 \text{ seconds}}{\text{minute}} \times \frac{60 \text{ minutes}}{\text{hour}} \times \frac{24 \text{ hours}}{\text{day}} = \frac{X \text{ seconds}}{\text{day}}$$

Now we can cancel the units to confirm that our analysis was correct (i.e. that the units on the left of the equal sign are exactly equal to the units on the right):

$$\frac{60 \text{ seconds}}{\cancel{\text{minute}}} \times \frac{60 \cancel{\text{minutes}}}{\cancel{\text{hour}}} \times \frac{24 \cancel{\text{hours}}}{\text{day}} = \frac{X \text{ seconds}}{\text{day}}$$

Since the units on both sides of the equation are equal, we are left with the following calculation:

$$60 \times 60 \times 24 = X$$

Try to quickly complete the calculation above.

If your method gets you the correct answer, well done! When you have completed hundreds of practice questions in DAT QR and DAT General Chemistry,

you will begin to notice number patterns. In the preceding calculation, you can set the 2 zeros aside, and complete $6 \times 6 \times 24$. In the next step, rather than calculating 36×24, which is perfectly fine, you might notice that 6×24 is 144. You might find 6×144 faster than 36×24. $6 \times 144 = 864$, now return those 2 zeros, and we have 86 400 seconds/1 day (8.64×10^4 s/day).

On the real exam, you will rarely need to be so precise and you would likely just use the calculator. Nonetheless, it is helpful to first assess the units of the answer choices, then assess how close the numbers are, then you would have determined the degree of precision necessary for your calculation (how much can you safely estimate in order to increase speed?).

GOLD STANDARD DAT QR PRACTICE QUESTIONS

CHAPTER 3: Scientific Measurement and Dimensional Analysis

1) How many millimeters are there in 75 meters?

   A. 750 mm

   B. 75 mm

   C. 1000 mm

   D. 75,000 mm

   E. 7,500 mm

2) Which of the following is the shortest distance?

   A. 10 m

   B. 1,000 mm

   C. 10 cm

   D. 0.5 km

   E. 0.1 km

Medium-level Importance

3) A triathlon has three legs. The first leg is a 12 km run. The second leg is a 10 km swim. The third leg is a 15 km bike ride. How long is the total triathlon in meters?

A. 37,000 m

B. 3,700 m

C. 1,000 m

D. 37 m

E. 0.037 m

4) If a paperclip has a mass of one gram and a staple has a mass of 0.05 g, how many staples have a mass equivalent to the mass of one paperclip?

A. 10

B. 100

C. 20

D. 25

E. 2

5) Which of the following is the number of minutes equivalent to $17\frac{5}{6}$ hours?

A. 1,080

B. 1,056

C. 1,050

D. 1,020

E. 1,070

6) The three children in a family weigh 67 lbs. 1 oz., 93 lbs. 2 oz., and 18 lbs. 5 oz. What is the total weight of all three children?

A. 178.8 lbs.

B. 178.5 lbs.

C. 178.08 lbs.

D. 179.8 lbs.

7) A lawyer charges clients $20.50 per hour to file paperwork, $55 per hour for time in court, and $30 per hour for consultations. How much will it cost for a 90-minute consultation, $\frac{8}{6}$ hours time filing paperwork, and 1 hour in court?

A. $110.28

B. $100.75

C. $88.25

D. $127.33

E. $95.25

8) If a car moving at a constant speed travels 20 centimeters in 1 second, approximately how many feet will it travel in 25% of a minute?

A. 10

B. 15

C. 12

D. 9

E. 39

9) The Dounreay Nuclear Power Station has been in operation for quite some time. Over the last six years, they have turned out a total of two megawatt-years of energy. Assuming that operations were continuous over a six year period at a constant rate, what was its power in watts (W)?

A. 3.3×10^5 W

B. 6.6×10^5 W

C. 3.3×10^2 W

D. 6.6×10^2 W

Medium-level Importance

10) A novel medication is found to have a density of 7.8 µg/mL. What is the mass of 295 mL of the novel medication?

A. 2.3 g
B. 2.3 mg
C. 2.3 µg
D. 2.3 pg

11) What is the approximate number of minutes in 1 year?

A. 5.3×10^3
B. 5.3×10^5
C. 5.3×10^7
D. 5.3×10^9

12) Which of the following is the Fahrenheit equivalent of -28.3 °C?

A. -18.9
B. -19.6
C. 16.4
D. -14.3

13) Which of the following is the number of pounds equivalent to 40 ounces?

A. 1.33
B. 1.5
C. 2
D. 2.5
E. 4

14) If 1 meter is equal to 3.3 feet, then a velocity of 35 km/hr is equal to a velocity of approximately how many feet per second?

A. 32
B. 35
C. 42
D. 50
E. 78

15) How many inches are there in 2 1/3 yards?

A. 28
B. 50
C. 72
D. 84
E. 100

16) How many decimeters are there in 12 kilometers?

A. 120
B. 1,200
C. 12,000
D. 120,000
E. 1,200,000

17) A movie has a run time of 1 hour and 46 minutes. What is the run time of the movie in seconds?

A. 6360
B. 6300
C. 6240
D. 6100
E. 6000

18) A bicyclist travels down a slope at a rate of 20 mph. About how many feet will the cyclist travel in 6 seconds?

A. 120
B. 144
C. 160
D. 170
E. 176

19) If a marble weighs .25 ounces and a bowling ball weighs 11 pounds, how many marbles are required to equal the weight of two bowling balls?

A. 88

B. 704

C. 1408

D. 1446

E. 2028

20) An amoeba has a diameter of 15 micrometers. If 2.5×10^3 amoebas are placed side by side, how many meters would the chain stretch?

A. 3.75×10^{-1}

B. 3.75×10^{-2}

C. 3.75×10^{-3}

D. 3.75×10^{-4}

E. 3.75×10^{-5}

CHAPTER REVIEW SOLUTIONS: CHAPTER 3

Question 1   D

See: QR 3.2.2

Construct a ratio comparing millimeters to meters using the definition of the prefix "milli." Remember that we want to convert from meters to millimeters, so the denominator of the fraction we use for this ratio must contain the units of meters: $\frac{1000\,mm}{1\,m}$. Now multiply this ratio and the given value: $75\,m\left(\frac{1000\,mm}{1\,m}\right) = 75,000\,mm.$

Question 2   C

See: QR 3.1.2

Start with any of the choices and compare it to the rest:

$0.1 km = 100m > 10\ m$

$0.5\ km > 0.1\ km > 10\ m$

$10\ cm < 10\ m$

$1000 mm = 1m > 10\ cm$

Question 3   A

See: QR 3.2

The total length of the triathlon is 12 km + 10 km + 15 km = 37 km. Express the ratio of kilometers to meters as a fraction, with kilometers in the denominator to cancel the units of 37 km: $\frac{1000\ m}{1\ km}$. Now multiply: $37\ km\left(\frac{1000\ m}{1\ km}\right) = 37,000\ m.$

Question 4   C

See: QR 3.1

Construct an equation that expresses an unknown number of staples, times the weight of each, equals the weight of one paperclip:

$$0.05x = 1$$

$$x = \frac{1}{0.05} = 20$$

Question 5   E

See: QR 3.2.2

Convert the mixed number to an improper fraction:

$$17\frac{5}{6} = \frac{107}{6}$$

Convert using the fact that 60 minutes equals 1 hour:

$$\left(\frac{107}{6}\ hours\right)\left(\frac{60\ minute}{1\ hour}\right) = 1,070\ minutes$$

Question 6   B

See: QR 3.2.2
Add like units:

$$67 \text{ lbs.} + 93 \text{ lbs.} + 18 \text{ lbs.} = 178 \text{ lbs.}$$

$$1 \text{ oz.} + 2 \text{ oz.} + 5 \text{ oz.} = 8 \text{ oz.}$$

Convert to pounds the part of the total weight that is in ounces and add to the rest of the weight:

$$(8 \text{ oz.})\left(\frac{1 \text{ lbs.}}{16 \text{ oz.}}\right) = 0.5 \text{ lbs.}$$

$$178 \text{ lbs.} + 0.5 \text{ lbs.} = 178.5 \text{ lbs.}$$

Question 7   D

See: QR 3.1.1, 3.2
Given that the charges are:

$20.50 per hour to file paper,
$55 per hour for time in court,
$30 per hour for consultations,

a 90-minute consultation = $30 + $15 = $45.
8 /6   hours = 80 minutes time filing paper work = $20.50 + $6.83 = $27.33

Since 20 minutes = $6.83

1 hour in court = $55

Total charges = $45 + $27.33 + $55 = $127.33

Question 8   A

See: QR 3.2.2
Multiply by all ratios necessary to convert centimeters to feet (via inches) and seconds to minutes, and divide by 4 to calculate the speed for only 25% of a minute:

$$(20 \text{ cm/sec.})\left(\frac{1}{2.54} \text{ in./cm}\right)$$

$$\left(\frac{1}{12} \text{ ft./in.}\right)(60 \text{ sec./min.})\left(\frac{1}{4}\right) \approx 10 \text{ ft./min.}$$

Question 9   A

See: QR 3.1, 3.2; dimensional analysis
This problem is strictly a matter of dimensional analysis.

In the SI system, "mega" means 10^6

$$1 \text{ Megawatt} = 10^3 \text{ kW} = 10^6 \text{ W}$$

Therefore, power in watts = (Total number of watt-years)/(Number of years)

Notice that the equation is constructed to allow "years" to cancel (i.e. it is in the numerator and in the denominator).
2×10^6 watt-years/6 years = 0.33×10^6 W = 3.3×10^5 W

Question 10   B

See: QR 3.1.3, 3.2
Even if you have never heard of 'density', even if you have never known that density is mass divided by volume (DAT CHM 4.1.8), you can just examine the units provided and dimensional analysis (QR 3.2) will lead you to the correct answer. All of the answers are in a form of grams (QR 3.1.3), we are given µg/mL so in order to get g we need to multiply µg/mL by mL and then mL cancels and we will have µg. Then we can convert to mg by using our SI Unit Prefix knowledge. If you have not considered the preceding then try to answer the question before looking at the solution.

7.8 µg/mL × 295 mL = (7.8 × 295) µg = approx. (8 × 300) µg = 2400 µg = 2.4 mg

Notice that the answer choices are at least 1000 times apart and so small approximations can be done with confidence.

Question 11   B

See: QR 3.1, 3.2
X minutes/year = 60 minutes/hour × 24 hours/day × 365 days/year

Cancel units on the right side (hours, days) and we are left with:

X minutes/year = 60 × 24 × 365 minutes/year = approx. 60 × (25 × 400) m/y

X minutes/year = 60 × 10 000 = 600 000 m/y = 6×10^5 m/y which is a reasonable approximation of answer choice B, especially when all of the other choices are 100 times apart.

Medium-level Importance

Question 12   A

See: QR 3.2.1

To convert Celsius to Fahrenheit:

$°C × 1.8 + 32 = °F$

$-28.3 × 1.8 + 32 = °F$

$-50.94 + 32 = °F$

$-18.94 = °F$

Some students prefer to memorize 9/5 instead of 1.8 but either is clearly fine.

Question 13   D

See: QR 3.1.1, 3.2.1

Remember that 1 lb = 16 oz, so:

40 oz = (40 oz)(1 lb/16 oz) = 40/16 lbs = 5/2 lbs = 2.5 lbs.

Question 14   A

See: QR 3.2

Dimensional analysis! We must multiply the given fraction (in km/hr) by all relevant conversion ratios to obtain a fraction in ft/sec.

(35 km/hr)(1000 m/km)(3.3 ft/m)(1 hr / 60 min)(1 min / 60 sec)

All of the units cancel except ft/sec and we are left with:

$≈ 32$ ft/sec.

Question 15   D

See: QR 3.1.1, 3.2.1

There are 3 feet in 1 yard and 12 inches in 1 foot, so there are:

(12 in/1ft)(3 ft/1 yd) = 36 in/1 yd.

Now we can convert 2 1/3 yards to inches, multiplying it by this conversion ratio:

(2 1/3 yd)(36 in/1 yd) = 72 36/3 in = 84 in.

Question 16   D

See: QR 3.1.2, 3.2.2

There are 1,000m in 1km and 10 decimeters in 1m, so:

(12km)(1,000m/1km)(10 decimeters/1m)

= (12)(1,000)(10) decimeters

= 120,000 decimeters.

Question 17   A

See: QR 3.1.1B, 3.2.2

First find the total run time in minutes:

t = 1hr(60min/1hr) + 46min

t = 106min

Now convert minutes to seconds:

t = 106min(60sec/1min)

t = 6360 seconds.

Question 18   E

See: QR 3.1.1A, 3.2.2

Convert 20 mph to feet per second:

(20mile/1hr)(5,280ft/1mile)(1hr/60min)(1min/60sec)

= 105,600ft/3,600sec

$≈ 29.33$ ft per second

So to obtain distance traveled over 6 seconds, multiply by 6:

(29.33 ft/sec)(6 sec) ≈ 176 feet.

Question 19   C

See: QR 3.1.1C, 3.2.2

Think of this problem in terms of converting 2 bowling balls (BB) into marbles (M).

(2 BB)(11lb/1BB)(16oz/1lb)(1M/.25oz)

= (352/.25)M

= 1408 marbles.

Question 20   B

See: QR 2.5.2, 3.1.2

The prefix "micro" represents 10^{-6}, meters = m, the solution is:

$(15 × 10^{-6}$ m/amoeba)(2.5 × 10^3 amoebas)

$= 37.5 × 10^{-3}$ m $= 3.75 × 10^{-2}$ m.

If you have any questions or concerns regarding your DAT practice questions, or the solutions, access the free Gold Standard Masters Series Forum for clarification: www.dat-prep.com/forum.

Medium-level Importance

⚠ SPOILER ALERT ⚠

Gold Standard has cross-referenced the content in this chapter to examples from the ADA's official DAT practice materials. It is for you to decide when you want to explore these questions since you may want to preserve DAT practice tests for timed mock-exam practice.

We suggest that you acquire the free 2007 DAT practice test from ada.org (digital document format), as well as the 2009 exam or, even better, the most recent online practice test. The online DAT Quantitative Reasoning practice test from the ADA is available through prometric.com and includes content from 2007 (35%), 2009 (10%), and newly added questions (55%). Note below that "Q" is followed by the question number, and cross-references to this chapter are in parentheses.

Examples –

2007 and 2022: Solve a simple proportion with a basic conversion (QR 2.6.2, 3.1.3): 2007 Q18; take the average of 3 weights in lb. and oz. (QR 3.1.1, 3.2, 7.2.1): 2007 Q26 and 2022 Q32 (*one answer choice is deleted in the 2022 version*).

2009 and 2022: Conversions, dimensional analysis (QR 3.2): 2009 Q13; very basic dimensional analysis (QR 3.2): 2009 Q18 and 2022 Q4 (*though the question is the same, some answer choices were different in 2022*); convert kg to g (*yes, that basic!* QR 3.1.3): 2009 Q21; convert ounces to pounds (QR 3.1.1, 3.2): 2009 Q26; convert days to minutes (QR 3.1.1, 3.2): 2009 Q27; convert Fahrenheit to Celsius (QR 3.2): 2009 Q28; convert inches to yards (QR 3.1.1, 3.2): 2009 Q33; adding times with hours and minutes (QR 3.1.1, 3.2): 2009 Q38.

2022: Dimensional analysis, manipulate units that are provided (QR 3.2): 2022 Q23.

Note that the free DAT practice test (GS-Free) and the additional Gold Standard online exams at DAT-prep.com contain specific cross-references to this chapter within the answers and explanations.

Note: **The ADA practice tests are composed of questions which have previously appeared on real, past DATs, but have been retired.** Also, note that most of the 2022 ADA DAT practice test questions have had one answer choice removed. In other words, most questions have 4 answer choices instead of 5, which was standard in 2007 and 2009.

Chapter Checklist

☐ Sign up or access your free online account at www.dat-prep.com for discussion boards for any content from this chapter including chapter-ending practice questions.

☐ Reassess your 'learning objectives' for this chapter: Go back to the first page of this chapter and re-evaluate the top 3 boxes and the Introduction.

☐ Complete 1-2 pages of notes using symbols/abbreviations to represent the entire chapter based on your learning objectives. These are your Gold Notes.

☐ Consider your multimedia options based on your optimal way of learning:

    ☐ Download the free Gold Standard DAT app for your Android device or iPhone. Create your own, tangible study cards or try the free app: Anki.

    ☐ Record your voice reading your Gold Notes onto your smartphone (MP3s) and listen during exercise, transportation, etc.

    ☐ Try some online math videos on YouTube like Khan Academy or Leah4sciMCAT playlist for Math Without a Calculator (the latter was produced for MCAT preparation but it remains helpful for DAT QR basics).

☐ Schedule your full-length DAT practice tests: ADA and/or GS exams and/or other free or paid third-party resources. Schedule one full day to complete a practice test and 1-2 days for a thorough assessment of answers and explanations while adding to your abbreviated Gold Notes.

☐ Schedule and/or evaluate stress reduction techniques such as regular exercise (sports), yoga, meditation and/or mindfulness exercises (*see* YouTube for suggestions).

Medium-level Importance

Memorize	Understand	Importance
* The #1 Rule of Algebra * Slope-Intercept Form for Linear Equations * The Quadratic Formula * Gold Standard 5-step Graph Analysis Technique	* Multiplying Polynomials; Basic Concepts of Functions; Manipulating Inequalities * Basic Equations and Methods of Equation Solving; Simplifying Equations * Solving One or More Linear Equations * Graphing Linear Equations (Cartesian) * Factoring and Completing the Square * Graph Analysis; Quantitative Comparison	**High level: 12 of 40** DAT Quantitative Reasoning questions are based on content in this chapter (avg. based on past testing patterns). * Note that approx. 70% of the questions in DAT QR are from just 3 of 8 chapters: 2, 4 and 8.

DAT-Prep.com

Introduction

Becoming comfortable with manipulating and solving algebraic equations is perhaps the single most important skill to have when tackling the Quantitative Reasoning Test. This section covers a breadth of important information that will help you deal with any algebraic problem that is thrown at you on the DAT. Almost every problem requires some form of algebra and consequently, you should make it your goal to be confident in all of these concepts.

Graph analysis is a relatively new section which has quickly evolved in the last few years. The ADA's earlier released questions had 0 DAT QR graph analysis questions (e.g. pie charts, histograms and line graphs; *not* referring to y = mx + b questions), yet the 2022 ADA practice exam has 4 such questions out of 40. The ADA has made graph analysis an integral part of DAT QR (*still no calculus!*). Note that 2 of the 4 ADA graph-based questions are mixed with another relatively new question type: Quantitative Comparison, which presents standard options to compare sets of data. Also note that we will have more practice questions in Chapter 8 (Word Problems) using the skills that you will be perfecting within this chapter . . .

Multimedia Resources at DAT-Prep.com

Free Online Forum

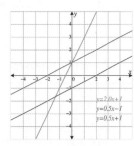

Special Guest

4.0 DAT Has a *Need for Speed*!

As you have done before, answer any or all of the questions/exercises in the table now. Or, after completing this chapter, return to the table below to ensure that you can complete all entries. Subsequently, you can proceed to answer the additional DAT QR multiple-choice questions at the end of this chapter. Good luck!

Section	DAT Quantitative Reasoning *Need for Speed* Exercises
4.1.1C	Solve for x: $2x + 3 = 5$
	Solve for x: $2x + 2/3 = 3x - 2$
4.1.3	Expand the following expressions: $(a + b)^2 =$ $(a - b)^2 =$
4.1.3.1	Evaluate the following expression: $(2x + 1)(x^2 - 3x + 2) =$
4.1.4	$f(x) = 2x$, therefore $f(-1/2) =$
4.2.2A	Solve the following inequality for x: $2 - 3x \leq .5x - 1$
4.2.2B	Solve: $|x + 2| < 7$
4.2.2C	Solve the following inequality for x: $12 > 3x > 6$
4.3.1	Simplify: $3x + 4xy - 2 = xy + 1$

4.3.2	Simplify: $\dfrac{3}{2x} + 5x = 4$
	Solve for x: $\dfrac{5}{(x+3)} = \dfrac{2}{x} - \dfrac{1}{3x}$
4.3.3	Factor the following: $2x^3 - 4x^2 + 4x$
4.4.1	Circle the correct response. This equation is (linear / not linear): $3x + 2y = z + 5$ This equation is (linear / not linear): $3x^2 - 2xy = 1$
4.4.2A	Solve for y: $4y - 3x = 2y + x - 6$
4.4.2B	Solve the following system of equations for x and y: $4y - 3x = 2y + x - 6$ $3x + y = 12$
	Use equation addition or subtraction to solve the following for x and y: $2x - 2y = 1$ $4x + 5y = 11$
4.5.1	Rewrite $3y - 2x = 6$ as a function of x
4.5.3	Graph the line using the grid to the right defined by the equation: $2x + y = 3$

High-level Importance

4.5.4	Rewrite the following equation in slope-intercept form: $2y + 5x = 8$
	Find the equation for the line passing through (1, 1) and (2, 3)

4.6.5	Consider Figure 1 and then circle the correct response.
	
	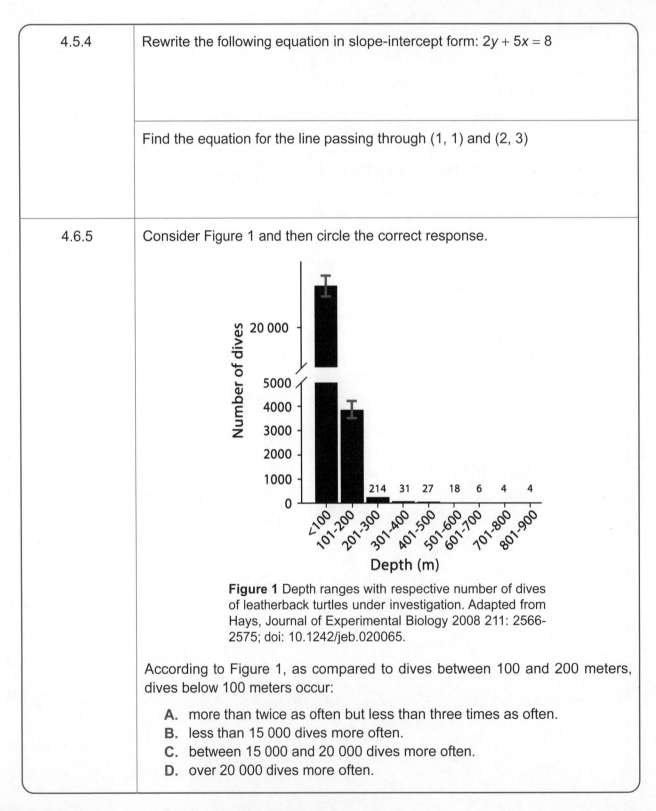
	
	Figure 1 Depth ranges with respective number of dives of leatherback turtles under investigation. Adapted from Hays, Journal of Experimental Biology 2008 211: 2566-2575; doi: 10.1242/jeb.020065.
	
	According to Figure 1, as compared to dives between 100 and 200 meters, dives below 100 meters occur:
	
	  A. more than twice as often but less than three times as often.
	  B. less than 15 000 dives more often.
	  C. between 15 000 and 20 000 dives more often.
	  D. over 20 000 dives more often.

| 4.7 | Which of the following is most consistent with the peak absorbance in Figure IV.3.2b?

A. Less than 1.2
B. Exactly 1.2
C. Above 1.2
D. None of the above | 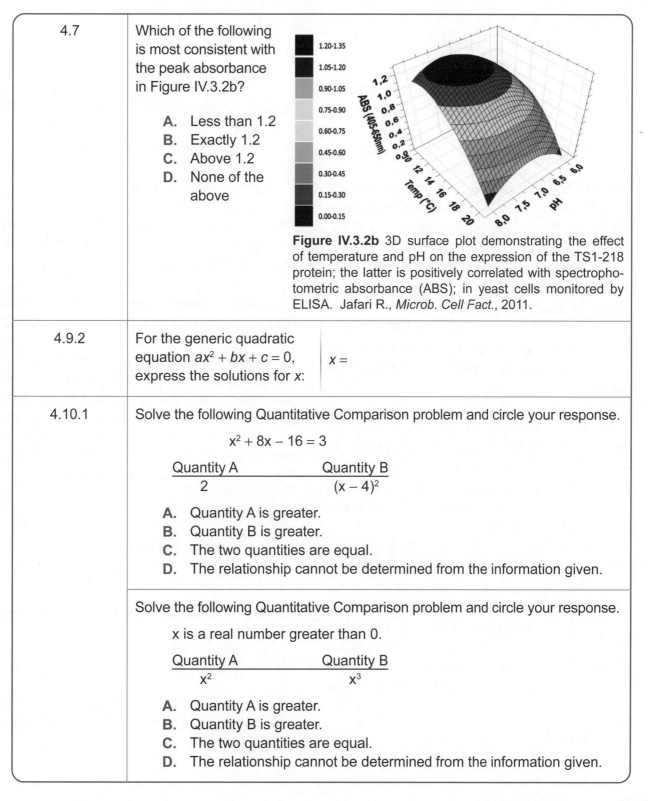

Figure IV.3.2b 3D surface plot demonstrating the effect of temperature and pH on the expression of the TS1-218 protein; the latter is positively correlated with spectrophotometric absorbance (ABS); in yeast cells monitored by ELISA. Jafari R., *Microb. Cell Fact.*, 2011. |

| 4.9.2 | For the generic quadratic equation $ax^2 + bx + c = 0$, express the solutions for x: | $x =$ |

| 4.10.1 | Solve the following Quantitative Comparison problem and circle your response.

$$x^2 + 8x - 16 = 3$$

Quantity A   Quantity B
2      $(x - 4)^2$

A. Quantity A is greater.
B. Quantity B is greater.
C. The two quantities are equal.
D. The relationship cannot be determined from the information given. |

Solve the following Quantitative Comparison problem and circle your response.

x is a real number greater than 0.

Quantity A   Quantity B

x^2 x^3

A. Quantity A is greater.
B. Quantity B is greater.
C. The two quantities are equal.
D. The relationship cannot be determined from the information given.

4.1 Equation Solving and Functions

4.1.1 Algebraic Equations

Before we jump into more complicated algebra, let's review the basics.

A. Terms

Variable: A variable is a symbol - usually in the form of a small letter - that represents a number. It can take on any range of values.

Most problems that are strictly algebraic in nature will provide you with an equation (or equations) containing one or more unknown variables. Based on the information given, the values of the variables will most likely be fixed. Your job is to solve for those values.

Constant: A constant is a fixed value. A constant can be a number on its own, or sometimes it is represented by a letter such as a, b, k, π, e, etc. In the chapters to come, you will discover that there are many constants in nature.

Polynomial: A polynomial is an expression (usually part of a function or an equation) that is composed of the sum or difference of some number of terms. Please note that some of the terms can be negative. The **order** of a polynomial is equal to the largest exponent to which a variable is raised in one of the terms.

EXAMPLE $3x^2 + x + 5$

This expression is a polynomial. The variable here is x, and the order of the polynomial is 2 ("2nd order") because that is the largest exponent to which x is raised.

B. Preserving Equality

The #1 Rule of Algebra: Whatever you do to one side of an equation, you *must* do to the other side also!

The equals sign implies equality between two different expressions. When you are given an equation, the equality established must be considered to be always true for that problem (unless you are told otherwise). So if you change one side of the equation and you do not also change the other side in the same way, you fundamentally alter the terms of the equation. The equation will no longer be true.

EXAMPLE

Consider this equation:

$$2x + 3 = 5$$

The following manipulation violates the above rule:

$$(2x + 3) - 3 = 5$$

Here, we have subtracted three from one side but not the other, so the equality no longer holds.

This manipulation, however, does not violate the rule:

$$(2x + 3) - 3 = 5 - 3$$

Here, we have subtracted three from both sides, so the equality still holds true.

> **NOTE**
>
> If two sides of an equation are equal, you can add or subtract the same amount to/from both sides, and they will still be equal.
>
> **EXAMPLE**
>
> $a = b$
>
> $a + c = b + c$
>
> $a - c = b - c$
>
> The same rule applies to multiplication and division.
>
> **EXAMPLE**
>
> $a = b$
>
> $ac = bc$
>
> $a \div c = b \div c$

C. Solving Basic Equations

We can use the rule of algebra described in Part B to help solve algebraic equations for an unknown variable. Keep in mind that addition and subtraction, along with multiplication and division, are inverse operations: They undo each other. First decide the operation that has been applied and then use the inverse operation to undo this (make sure to apply the oper-

ation to both sides of the equation). The idea is to isolate the variable on one side of the equation. Then, whatever is left on the other side of the equation is the value of the variable.

EXAMPLE

Solve: $2x + 3 = 5$

$$2x + 3 - 3 = 5 - 3$$
$$2x = 2$$

Subtracting 3, however, has not isolated the variable x. Hence, we need to continue undoing by dividing 2 on both sides.

$$2x \div 2 = 2 \div 2$$
$$x = 1$$

Here's a little more complicated equation for you to try: $2x + 2/3 = 3x - 2$

Objective: isolate the variable in order to provide a solution to the equation. When you have an equation with the variable on both sides, choose whichever you think will be easier to focus on. In this case, we will isolate x on the right. First, subtract $2x$ from both sides.

$$(2x + 2/3) - 2x = (3x - 2) - 2x$$
$$\Rightarrow 2/3 = x - 2$$

Next, add 2 to both sides to isolate x.

$$(2/3) + 2 = (x - 2) + 2$$
$$\Rightarrow 8/3 = x$$

4.1.2 Addition and Subtraction of Polynomials

When adding or subtracting polynomials, the general rules for exponents are applied and like terms are grouped together. You can think of it as similar to collecting the same things together.

EXAMPLE

$$4x^3y + 5z^2 + 5xy^4 + 3z^2$$

$$= 4x^3y + 5xy^4 + (5+3)z^2$$
$$= 4x^3y + 5xy^4 + 8z^2$$

By grouping the similar terms, seeing which terms may be added or subtracted becomes easier.

4.1.3 Simplifying Algebraic Expressions

Algebraic expressions can be factored or simplified using standard formulae:

$$a(b + c) = ab + ac$$
$$(a + b)(a - b) = a^2 - b^2$$
$$(a + b)(a + b) = (a + b)^2 = a^2 + 2ab + b^2$$
$$(a - b)(a - b) = (a - b)^2 = a^2 - 2ab + b^2$$
$$(a + b)(c + d) = ac + ad + bc + bd$$

4.1.3.1 Multiplying Polynomials

When multiplying two polynomials, you must multiply every term of the first polynomial with every term of the second. The order of this multiplication doesn't matter, but most people find it easiest to keep track by starting with the first term of the first polynomial, multiplying it by every term in the second from left to right, then taking the second term of the first polynomial and doing the same, and so on until all terms have been used. Following this pattern will ensure that every combination of multiplication is done.

EXAMPLE

Evaluate the following expression:

$$(2x + 1)(x^2 - 3x + 2)$$

Begin with the term $2x$ and multiply it by every term of the second polynomial, then do the same with the term 1. To make this clearer, we can even rewrite the expression as follows:

$$(2x)(x^2 - 3x + 2) + (1)(x^2 - 3x + 2)$$
$$= (2x^3 - 6x^2 + 4x) + (x^2 - 3x + 2)$$

Combining like terms, we get the following:

$$= 2x^3 - 5x^2 + x + 2$$

4.1.4 Function Basics

Before we can start working with functions, here are some basic definitions, terminology and examples with which you should be familiar.

Function: At its most basic, a function is a mathematical relation that outputs a unique number for every input.

EXAMPLE $f(x) = 2x$

In this case, the function is f; the input variable is x; and the output is $2x$. The notation used here is standard for functions. The denotation of the function (f) comes first, followed by a set of parentheses containing the input variable.

(a) Evaluate f for $x = 2$.

We need to solve for $f(2)$ (pronounced "f of two").

$$f(2) = 2 \times 2$$
$$= 4$$

(b) Find $f(-1/2)$.

$$f(-1/2) = 2 \times (-1/2)$$
$$= -1$$

Domain: The domain of a function is the set of possible values that the independent variable or variables (the input) of the function can have.

Range: The range of a function is the set of possible values that the output of the function can have.

EXAMPLE

(a) Find the domain and range of the function f defined by $f(x) = 2x$.

Remember, on the DAT we only need to worry about real numbers. So the largest domain or range we could possibly have is "all real numbers."

To find the domain of the function, look at its output expression (in this case "$2x$") and determine if there are any real number values of the variable (x) for which the expression is not defined. In this case, there are none. For any number x, we can always multiply it by 2 and obtain a new real number value.

High-level Importance

Domain = All Real Numbers

To find the range of the function, you also need to look at its output expression. Are there any numbers the output cannot equal? In this case, no; because for any number you can think of, simply inputting half of it will output that number.

Range = All Real Numbers

(b) Find the domain and range of the function f defined by $f(x) = x^2$.

First, find the domain. Is there any number we cannot input into this function? Since x^2 is defined for all real numbers, there are none.

Domain = All Real Numbers

Now, find the range. Are there any numbers we cannot obtain as an output from this function? Since x^2 is always positive for real numbers x, we can never obtain a negative output.

Range = All Non-negative
Real Numbers

Remember, this range does include 0. We can also write this as shown in the expression that follows.

Range = $[0 , \infty)$

The "[" bracket means that 0 is included in the set and the ")" bracket means that ∞ is not included in the set (because infinity is not actually a number). So this notation means the set of all real numbers between 0 and infinity, including 0.

4.2 Inequalities

4.2.1 Inequality Basics

An **inequality** is a statement that describes the relative size of two quantities. This is similar to an equation; except that instead of only saying that two quantities are equal, an inequality can also mean that one quantity is always larger than another.

Inequality Symbols

> is the symbol for "greater than." The quantity on the left of this symbol is always greater than the quantity on the right.

< is the symbol for "less than." The quantity on the left of the symbol is always less than the quantity on the right.

≥ is the symbol for "greater than or equal to." The quantity on the left of this symbol is always either greater than or equal to the quantity on the right.

≤ is the symbol for "less than or equal to." The quantity on the left of the symbol is always either less than or equal to the quantity on the right.

$|x|$ is the symbol for absolute value. It represents the numerical value of x and disregards its sign. Therefore, the absolute value of any real number will always be positive (QR 1.1.3).

EXAMPLE $x > 3$

This inequality states that the variable x is greater than 3. So x can have any value that is larger than 3, such as 4 or 100.

EXAMPLE $3 \leq x \leq 4$

This is an example of how multiple inequalities can be used in the same statement. It states that x is both less than or equal to 4 and greater than or equal to 3. So x can have any value between (and including) 3 and 4, such as 3 or 3.5.

4.2.2 Solving Inequalities

A. One-Sided Inequalities

Solving inequalities is almost identical to solving equations. The same rule applies: You always have to do the same thing to both sides. The only difference is that the symbols of inequality are sensitive to inversions of the sign (flipping from positive to negative). Whenever you multiply or divide both sides by a negative number, the inequality symbol changes direction (remember, squaring a negative number falls into this category because you are multiplying by that same negative number). This will never happen with addition and subtraction.

Here is a quick example that might help you understand why the inequality symbol flips for multiplication by a negative number.

EXAMPLE

Say there are two people, person A and person B. Person A has 3 dollars and person B has 2 dollars. In inequality form, we know that $3 > 2$.

Now, instead of having money, let's say for some reason person A now *owes* 3 dollars and person B *owes* 2 dollars. As you can see, we have simply multiplied both quantities by −1. Now, which person has more money and which has less? Obviously −3 dollars is less than −2 dollars; so as an inequality, this reads as $-3 < -2$.

So, simply multiplying by a negative number has caused the direction of the inequality symbol to switch.

With this principle in mind, we can now solve inequalities. Just like with equations, all we have to do is isolate the variable on one side.

EXAMPLE

Solve the following inequality for x:

$2 - 3x \leq .5x - 1$.

First, choose the side on which you want to isolate the variable. We'll use the left side.

$$(2 - 3x) - 2 \leq (.5x - 1) - 2$$
$$\Rightarrow (-3x) - .5x \leq (.5x - 3) - .5x$$
$$\Rightarrow (-7/2)x \leq -3$$
$$\Rightarrow (-2/7)(-7/2)x \geq -3 \times (-2/7)$$
$$\Rightarrow x \geq 6/7$$

B. Absolute Inequalities

In solving absolute inequalities, the inequality symbol used ($<, \leq, >, \geq$) is a significant consideration in writing the solution set. The following rules should apply:

- If the symbol is $>$ (or $\geq$), meaning that the absolute value is greater than the number on the other side of the inequality, the connecting word is "or."

  If $a > 0$, then the solutions to $|x| > a$ are $x > a$ or $x < -a$.

EXAMPLE

Solve for the following inequality:

$|x + 2| > 7$.

In this case, the absolute value $|x + 2|$ is greater than 7. Hence,

$$\Rightarrow x + 2 > 7 \text{ or } x + 2 < -7$$
$$\Rightarrow x > 5 \text{ or } x < -9$$

You can think of "great-or" as a way of memorizing this rule.

- If the symbol is $<$ (or $\leq$), meaning that the absolute value is less than the number on the other side of the inequality, the connecting word is "and."

  If $a < 0$, then the solutions to $|x| < a$ are $x < a$ and $x > -a$. This can also be written as $-a < x < a$.

Similarly, in the inequality $|x + 2| < 7$, the side containing the absolute value (QR 2.1.3) is less than 7 and should thus indicate the connective "and" in the solution.

EXAMPLE

Solve: $|x + 2| < 7$.

$\Rightarrow x + 2 < 7$ and $x + 2 > -7$

$\Rightarrow x < 5$ and $x > -9$

$\Rightarrow -9 < x < 5$

This time, you can think of "less th-and" to remember this rule.

C. Two-Sided Inequalities

Though it is odd to see equations with more than one equals sign, two-sided inequalities are common. You can solve them by splitting them up into two one-sided inequalities and solving these individually.

EXAMPLE

Solve the following inequality for x:

$$12 > 3x > 6.$$

Breaking this inequality into two, we obtain $12 > 3x$ and $3x > 6$. We must solve these:

(i) $(12)/3 > (3x)/3$

            $\Rightarrow 4 > x$

(ii) $(3x)/3 > (6)/3$

            $\Rightarrow x > 2$

These two inequalities can be recombined to form the new two-sided inequality $4 > x > 2$.

4.3 Simplifying Equations

In order to make solving algebraic equations easy and quick, you should simplify terms whenever possible. The following are the most common and important ways of doing so.

4.3.1 Combining Terms

This is the most basic thing you can do to simplify an equation. If there are multiple terms being added or subtracted in your equation that contain the same variables, you can combine them.

EXAMPLE

Simplify the equation: $3x + 4xy - 2 = xy + 1$

Notice that there are two terms we can combine that contain xy and two terms we can combine that are just constants.

$$(3x + 4xy - 2) - xy = (xy + 1) - xy$$
$$\Rightarrow 3x \quad 3xy - 2 = 1$$

$$(3x + 3xy - 2) + 2 = 1 + 2$$
$$\Rightarrow 3x + 3xy = 3$$

$$\Rightarrow \left(\frac{3x + 3xy}{3} \right) = \frac{3}{3}$$
$$\Rightarrow x + xy = 1$$

Always make sure to look for like terms to combine when you are solving an algebra problem.

4.3.2 Variables in Denominators

When you are trying to manipulate an equation, having variables in the denominators of fractions can make things difficult. In order to get rid of such denominators entirely, simply multiply the entire equation by the quantity in the denominator. This will probably cause other terms to become more complicated, but you will no longer have the problem of a variable denominator.

EXAMPLE

Simplify the expression: $\dfrac{3}{2x} + 5x = 4.$

The problem denominator is $2x$, so we multiply both sides by $2x$.

$$(\frac{3}{2x} + 5x)2x = (4)2x$$
$$\Rightarrow 3 + 10x^2 = 8x$$

When there are different denominators containing variables, cross multiply the denominator to cancel out. Try the following example.

EXAMPLE

$$\frac{5}{(x+3)} = \frac{2}{x} - \frac{1}{3x}$$

Multiply 3x on both sides:

$$\frac{5}{(x+3)}(3x) = \frac{2}{x} - \frac{1}{3x}(3x)$$

$$\frac{15x}{(x+3)} = 6 - 1$$

Multiply (x+3) on both sides:

$$\frac{15x}{(x+3)}(x+3) = 5(x+3)$$

$$15x = 5x + 15$$

$$15x - 5x = 5x + 15 - 5x$$

$$10x = 15$$

$$x = \frac{15}{10} = \frac{3}{2}$$

High-level Importance

4.3.3 Factoring

If every term of a polynomial is divisible by the same quantity, that quantity can be factored out. This means that we can express the polynomial as the product of that quantity times a new, smaller polynomial.

EXAMPLE

Factor the following expression:

$$2x^3 - 4x^2 + 4x$$

Every term in this polynomial is divisible by $2x$, so we can factor it out of each term. The simplified expression, then, is

$$2x(x^2 - 2x + 2).$$

To verify that you have properly factored an expression, multiply out your solution. If you get back to where you started, you've done it correctly.

4.4 Linear Equations

4.4.1 Linearity

Linear equation is an equation between two (or three) variables that gives a straight line when plotted on a graph (QR 4.6.1). In a linear equation, there can neither be variables raised to exponents nor variables multiplied together.

(a) $3x + 2y = z + 5$

This equation is linear.

(b) $3x^2 - 2xy = 1$

This equation is not linear. The terms $3x^2$ and $2xy$ cannot appear in a linear equation.

The reason such equations are called "linear" is that they can be represented on a Cartesian graph as a straight line (*see* QR 4.5). "Cartesian" is the basic coordinate system composed of an x-axis and a y-axis (and sometimes z-axis as well) which we will review shortly.

High-level Importance

4.4.2 Solving Linear Equations with Multiple Variables

In the previous sections we have only considered equations with single variables. In some cases though, DAT QR problems will require you to deal with a second variable.

> **NOTE**
>
> Everything in this section applies to inequalities as well as equations. Just remember to be wary of multiplication and division by negative numbers!

A. Isolating a Variable

When you have a single equation with two variables, you will not be able to solve for specific values. What you can do is solve for one variable in terms of the other. To do this, pick a variable to isolate on one side of the equation and move all other terms to the other side.

EXAMPLE

Solve the following for y: $4y - 3x = 2y + x - 6$.

Let's isolate y on the left side:

$$(4y - 3x) + 3x - 2y = (2y + x - 6) + 3x - 2y$$

$$\frac{(2y)}{2} = \frac{(4x - 6)}{2}$$

$$y = 2x - 3$$

Now we know the value of y, but only in relation to the value of x. If we are now given some value for x, we can simply plug it in to our solution and obtain y. For example, if $x = 1$ then $y = 2 - 3 = -1$.

B. Solving Systems of Equations

How do you know if you will be able to solve for specific values in an equation or not? The general rule is that if you have the same number of unique equations as variables (or more equations), you will be able find a specific value for every variable. So for the example in Part A, since we have two variables and only one equation, in order to solve for the variables, we would need one more unique equation.

In order for an equation to be unique, it must not be algebraically derived from another equation.

EXAMPLE

$$300 = 30x - 10y$$
$$30 = 3x - y$$

From the above example, the two equations describe the same line and therefore are not unique since they are scalar multiples of each other.

There are two strategies you should know for solving a system of equations (AKA, *simultaneous equations*):

I. **Substitution.** This strategy can be used every time, although, it will not always be the fastest way to come up with a solution. You begin with one equation and isolate a variable as in Part A. Next, wherever the isolated variable appears in the second equation, replace it with the expression this variable is equal to. This effectively eliminates that variable from the second equation.

If you only have two equations, all you need are two steps. Once you have followed the procedure above, you can solve for the second variable in the second equation and substitute that value back into the first equation to find the value of the first variable. If you have more than two variables and equations, you will need to continue this process of isolation and substitution until you reach the last equation.

EXAMPLE

Solve the following system of equations for x and y.

$$4y - 3x = 2y + x - 6$$
$$3x + y = 12$$

We have already isolated y in the first equation, so the first step is done. The new system is as follows:

$$y = 2x - 3$$
$$3x + y = 12$$

Next, we substitute $2x - 3$ for y in the second equation.

$$3x + (2x - 3) = 12$$
$$\Rightarrow 5x - 3 = 12$$
$$\Rightarrow 5x = 15$$
$$\Rightarrow x = 3$$

Now, we have a value for x, but we still need a value for y. Substitute 3 for x in the y-isolated equation.

$$y = 2(3) - 3$$
$$y = 3$$

So our solution to this system of equations is $x = 3$, $y = 3$.

II. **Equation Addition or Subtraction.** You will not always be able to apply this strategy, but in some cases, it will save you from having to do all of the time-consuming substitutions of Strategy I. The basic idea of equation addition or subtraction is exactly what you would expect: Addition or subtraction of equations directly to each other.

Say you have two equations, A and B. Because both sides of any equation are by definition equal, you can add, say, the left side of equation A to the left side of equation B and the right side of equation A to the right side of equation B without changing anything. In performing this addition, you are doing the same thing to both sides of equation B.

The purpose of performing such an addition is to try and get a variable to cancel out completely. If you can accomplish this, you can solve for the other variable easily (assuming you only have two variables,

High-level Importance

of course). Before adding the equations together, you can manipulate either of them however you like (as long as you maintain equality) in order to set up the cancellation of a variable.

If the only way to cancel out a variable is by subtracting the equation, this may be done as well.

EXAMPLE

Use equation addition or subtraction to solve the following for x and y.

$$2x - 2y = 1$$
$$4x + 5y = 11$$

If we multiply the first equation by two, we will have $4x$ present in each equation. Then if we subtract, the $4x$ in each equation will cancel.

$$4x - 4y = 2$$
$$- (4x + 5y = 11)$$
$$\overline{0x - 9y = -9}$$
$$\Rightarrow y = 1$$

Now, we can substitute this value of y into whichever equation looks simpler to solve for x (either one will work though).

$$2x - 2(1) = 1$$
$$\Rightarrow 2x = 3$$
$$\Rightarrow x = \frac{3}{2}$$

So our solution to this system of equations is $y = 1$, $x = \frac{3}{2}$.

NOTE

A 'classic' DAT General Chemistry type question requires an understanding of Strategy II to solve Hess' Law problems (CHM 8.3). For OAT candidates studying Physics, we will also apply Strategy II to solve simultaneous equations for a pulley system (PHY 3.4).

4.5 Graphing Linear Functions

4.5.1 Linear Equations and Functions

Every linear equation can be rewritten as a linear function. To do so, simply isolate one of the variables as in QR 4.1.1C. This variable is now a function of the variables on the other side of the equation.

EXAMPLE

Rewrite the equation $3y - 2x = 6$ as a function of x.

$$3y - 2x = 6$$
$$\Rightarrow 3y = 2x + 6$$
$$\Rightarrow y = \frac{2}{3}x + 2$$

Now that we have isolated y, it is actually dependent on, or a *function* of, x. For every input of x, we get a unique output of y. If you like, you can rewrite y as $f(x)$.

$$f(x) = \frac{2}{3}x + 2$$

4.5.2 Cartesian Coordinates in 2D

The Cartesian coordinate system is the most commonly used system for graphing. A Cartesian graph in two dimensions has two axes: The x-axis is the horizontal one, and the y-axis is the vertical one. The independent variable is always along the x-axis and the dependent variable is along the y-axis. The independent variable is controlled and the output depends on the independent variable.

The further right you go on the x-axis, the larger the numbers get; and on the y-axis, the numbers get larger the further up you go. A point on the graph is specified as an ordered pair of an x value and a y value like this: (x, y). This point exists x units from the origin (the point $(0, 0)$ where the axes cross) along the x-axis, and y units from the origin along the y-axis.

EXAMPLE

A *grid* is a network of lines that cross each other to form a series of squares or rectangles. Find the point $(3, -1)$ on the 8x8-grid Cartesian graph shown. To plot this point, simply count three units to the right along the x-axis and one unit down along the y-axis.

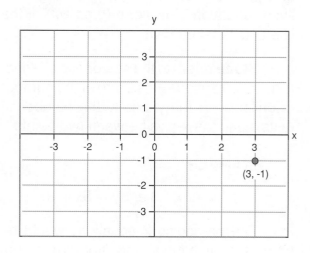

4.5.3 Graphing Linear Equations

In order to graph a straight line in Cartesian coordinates, all you need to know is two points. Every set of two points has only one unique line that passes through both of them.

To find two points from a linear equation, simply choose two values to plug in for one of the variables. It is best to pick values that will make your calculations easier, such as 0 and 1. Plugging in each of these values, we can solve for y and obtain two points.

EXAMPLE

Graph the line defined by $2x + y = 3$.

First, let's plug in $x = 0$ and $x = 1$ to find two points on the line.

$$2(0) + y = 3 \qquad\qquad 2(1) + y = 3$$
$$\Rightarrow y = 3 \qquad\qquad\qquad \Rightarrow y = 1$$

Now, we have two points: (0, 3) and (1, 1). To graph the line, all we have to do is plot these points on a graph and draw a straight line between them.

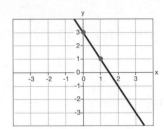

4.5.4 Slope-Intercept Form

There are two pieces of information that are very useful in the graphing of a linear equation: The slope (*gradient*) of the line and its y-intercept.

Slope refers to the steepness of a line. It is the ratio (slope = rise/run) of the number of units along the y-axis to the number of units along the x-axis between two points.

EXAMPLE

$$y = 5x + 3 \text{ and } y = 5x + 10$$

The preceding 2 equations would be parallel to each other since both slopes (m) = 5.

$$y = 3x + 6 \text{ and } y = -\frac{1}{3x} + 3$$

These two equations are perpendicular. The line of the first equation has a positive slope and the perpendicular line has a decreasing slope and therefore both slopes have opposite signs. In fact, the general rule is that when slopes are negative reciprocals of each other, the 2 lines in question must be perpendicular to each other.

The y-**intercept** of a line is the y-coordinate of the point at which the line crosses the y-axis. The value of x where the line intersects, is always zero and its coordinates will be (0, y).

One of the standard forms of a linear equation is the slope-intercept form, from which the slope and the y-intercept of the line are immediately obvious. This form resembles $y = mx + b$. Here m and b are

High-level Importance

constants such that m is the slope of the line and b is the y-intercept.

EXAMPLE

Rewrite the following equation in slope-intercept form: $2y + 5x = 8$.

$$\Rightarrow 2y = -5x + 8$$
$$\Rightarrow y = -\frac{5}{2}x + 4$$

This is now in slope-intercept form. In this case, the slope m is $-5/2$ and the y-intercept is 4.

Slope-intercept form is also useful for constructing the equation of a line from other information. If you are given the slope and the intercept, obviously you can simply plug them in to $y = mx + b$ to get the equation. It is also very simple to obtain the slope and intercept if you know two points on the line, (x_1, y_1) and (x_2, y_2). The slope can be obtained directly from this information:

Slope = rise/run = $(y_2 - y_1)/(x_2 - x_1)$

Once the slope m is obtained, you only need to solve for b. To do so, plug in one of the points as well as m into the slope-intercept equation. You can then solve for b.

EXAMPLE

Find the equation for the line passing through (1, 1) and (2, 3).

First, determine the slope.

$$m = \frac{(3-1)}{(2-1)} = 2$$

Now plug m and a point into the slope-intercept equation to find b.

$$y = mx + b$$
$$\Rightarrow 1 = 2(1) + b$$
$$\Rightarrow -1 = b$$

Plugging in all of this information, we now have a complete equation.

$$y = 2x - 1$$

4.6 Basic Graphs

4.6.1 The Graph of a Linear Equation

Given any two points (x_1, y_1) and (x_2, y_2) on the line, we have:

$$y_1 = ax_1 + b$$

and

$$y_2 = ax_2 + b.$$

Subtracting the upper equation from the lower one and dividing through by $x_2 - x_1$ gives the value of the slope,

$$a = (y_2 - y_1)/(x_2 - x_1)$$
$$= \Delta y/\Delta x = \text{rise/run}$$

Lines that have positive slopes slant "up hill" (as viewed from left to right), like the graph on this page. Lines that have negative slopes slant "down hill" (as viewed from left to right). Lines that are horizontal have no slope (= a slope of zero).

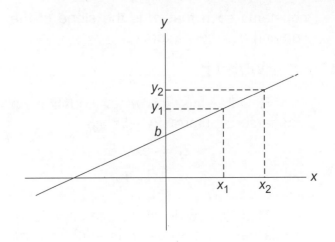

4.6.2 Illustrations of Common Graphs

For the graphs in this section (QR 4.6.2), please consider replacing x by 0, 1 and 2 (or other values) to ensure that the graph behaves in a way that makes sense to you. In the following graph, note that the red and blue lines have the same slope (gradient); the red and green lines have the same y-intercept:

For any real number x, there exists a unique real number called the multiplicative inverse or *reciprocal* of x denoted $1/x$ or x^{-1} such that $x(1/x) = 1$. The graph of the reciprocal $1/x$ for any x is:

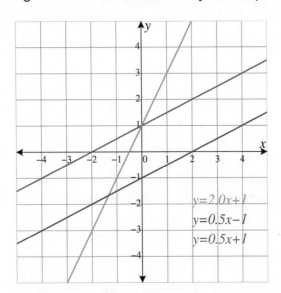

$y = 2.0x + 1$
$y = 0.5x - 1$
$y = 0.5x + 1$

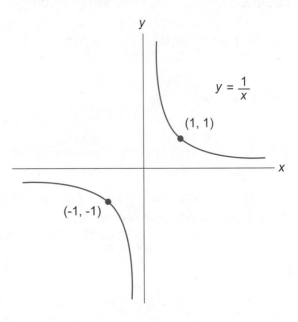

$y = \dfrac{1}{x}$

(1, 1)

(-1, -1)

A quadratic equation (e.g. CHM 6.6.1) is a polynomial (QR 4.1.1) in which the highest-order term is 'to the power of 2'. For example, $y = ax^2$. A quadratic equation describes a parabola which is approximately U-shaped:

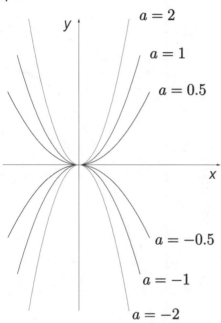

Interestingly, there are important graphs and shapes, including a parabola, that can be obtained by taking a simple cone and cutting it at various angles. This only requires a bit of imagination:

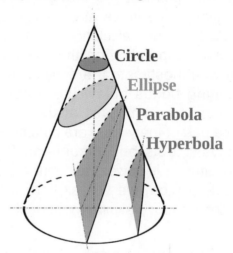

4.6.3 Common Graphs Found in Other Sections or Chapters

There are classic curves which are represented or approximated in the science text as follows: Sigmoidal curve (CHM 6.9.1, BIO 7.5.1), sinusoidal curve (QR 6.2.3), hyperbolic curves (CHM 9.7 Fig III.A.9.3, BIO 1.1.2), exponential rise (QR Appendix A.2, CHM 9.8.1) and decay (CHM 9.2).

If you were to plot a set of experimental data, often one can draw a line or curve which can "best fit" the data. The preceding defines a *regression* line or curve (QR 7.3.1).

One purpose of the regression graph is to predict what would likely occur outside of the experimental data. The skill to extend a graph by inferring unknown values from trends in the known data is *extrapolation* (e.g., BIO 14, Q7).

4.6.4 Tangential Slope and Area under a Curve (DAT-30)

Calculating a slope based on a curve (i.e. the slope of the straight line must just glance the curve at a specific point = *tangential*), and calculating the area under a curve (depending on the presentation, you would estimate the answer by either counting boxes below the graph or by multiplying some part of the x-axis by some part of the y-axis) are common graph analysis tools but uncommon for DAT QR. Since it is 'lower yield' but a possible question type, we will explore it in this section for those aiming for perfect scores.

This form of graph analysis is really based on dimensional analysis (QR 3.2). Let's examine a velocity vs. time graph of a bullet fired from a gun (side note: notice that the curve resembles ½ of an upside-down parabola). The y-axis is velocity which is in the SI units of meters/second (m/s). The x-axis is time in the SI units of seconds (s). Here are 2 questions that you can try to work out before looking at the solutions:

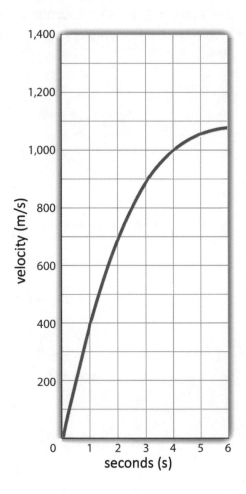

EXAMPLES

(1) Given that acceleration is in units of m/s^2, calculate the instantaneous acceleration at time = 3 seconds.

(2) Given that displacement is in the units of meters (m), calculate the displacement of the bullet in the first 2 seconds of being fired.

> **Hints if required:**
>
> (1) **Hint:** try to calculate the slope of a straight line off the curve at 3 seconds. Why does the slope solve the problem? Take a look at the units. A slope is the change of y divided by the change of x. In terms of units, this would make m/s/s = m/s^2 = acceleration.
>
> (2) **Hint:** determine the area of the curve below that segment of the graph (i.e. the first 2 seconds). One way to do so is to calculate the area of one box and then estimate how many boxes are below the curve. Why the area? Again, the units: the area of a square or rectangle is one side times the other side. For a graph, it is x times y. So here is what happens to the units: m/s x s = m = meters which is displacement.

ANSWERS

(1) To calculate the slope at a point, the line that you draw needs to be tangential to the curve as described previously (*see* the graphs on the following page, *au verso*). The line can be as long or as short as you want (basically, you choose the length to make the calculation as easy as possible).

We chose a change in x (i.e. from points A to B as seen from the x-axis) which is easy to calculate = 2 seconds (i.e. 4 − 2 = 2). The change in y (i.e. from points A to B as seen from the y-axis) is also easy = 300 m/s (1050 − 750 = 300). The slope is the change in y divided by the change in x so: (300 m/s)/(2 s) = 150 m/s².

Notice that point A in the graph is our point (x_1, y_1) and point B is (x_2, y_2); *see* QR 4.6.1.

(2) As explained in the "hint", we are trying to calculate the area under the curve in the first 2 seconds. If you put your pen in the line (0, 0) to (2, 700), you will notice that your pen approximates the green line.

In other words, if we were to imagine a rectangle that includes the points (0, 0) to (2, 700), then the area under the curve seems to be about ½ that value. Because a rectangle is simply one side times the other, we can multiply 2 seconds x 700 m/s = 1400 meters. The area below the green graph is about ½ that or 700 meters, which is thus the displacement.

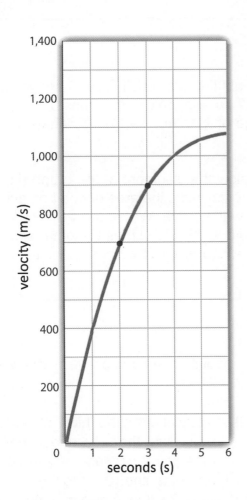

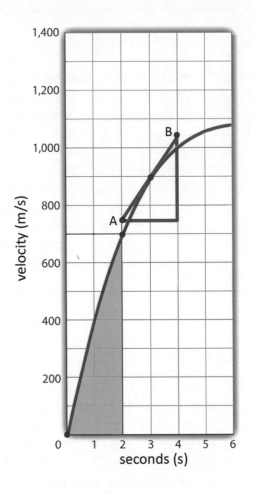

Of course, it depends on the multiple choice answers. Careful observation will show you that the area under the curve is slightly more than 700 m.

An alternative way to calculate the area in blue would be to calculate the area of one single small box from the graph: 100 m/s times 1 s = 100 meters. If you carefully count the boxes in the blue shaded area (which you can see better from the graph

on the left), you will be able to count about 7 complete boxes (i.e. approx. 700 m; of course, sometimes you need to add 2 incomplete boxes to make one full box).

Yet another alternative may have been the first choice of some students: estimate the area in blue as a triangle (which we will discuss in QR 5.2.2) which is 1/2(base)(height) = 1/2(2)(700) = 700 m.

High-level Importance

Among the many reasons that an axis could be broken would be if the missing part of the graph is not key to understanding the trend, and/or when the trend is obvious which allows more data to be shown in a smaller graph.

The following represents 3 different symbols for a broken axis.

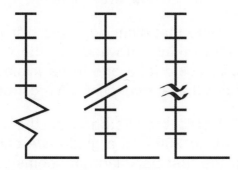

EXAMPLE 1

Consider the following diagram. The break in the *x*-axis does not change the scale; however, the break in the *y*-axis clearly permits the scale to jump from 0 to 0.5 in a way that is remarkably different from the rest of the *y*-axis.

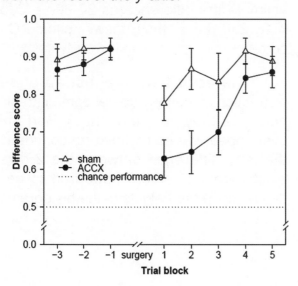

Error bars show the variability of data and indicate the error or *uncertainty* in a measurement. Error bars often represent one standard deviation of uncertainty (QR 7.3.2), or a particular confidence interval (e.g., a 95% chance that the actual data point falls within the extremes of the error bar). From the preceding graph, it can be seen that the error bars for the measurements for Trial block 3 are longer than for Trial block 1, meaning the latter has an average (*mean*) value that is more representative of the data (= more reliable). Also notice that only 2 trials (Trial block 1 and 2) have non-overlapping error bars. This means that in all of the other trials, because of the overlap, the difference between the data points of the sham versus ACCX trials may not be statistically significant.

Thus, even though you are not provided any details, the graph informs us that ACCX (whatever that means) has a statistically significant post-surgical 'difference score' within the first two trial blocks as compared to the sham group. Of course, 'sham' implies 'fake' and in science that implies a group (= *control* group; BIO 2.5) that is exposed to the same conditions as the experimental group, except that the control group does not receive the treatment (e.g. no ACCX).

Mathematically, we can describe a data point's error as 'plus or minus' the point seen in the graph. For example, for ACCX trial block 3, the data point is approximately 0.7 with a range given by the error bar of about 0.64 to 0.76. Thus the point can be described as 0.7 plus or minus 0.06 (i.e. 0.7 ± 0.06).

Let us consider another example of a broken axis but in this case the data is presented using rectangular bars of different heights (= a *histogram*, AKA bar graph or chart). Please note that the following histogram is presented with error bars and is using a linear scale.

EXAMPLE 2

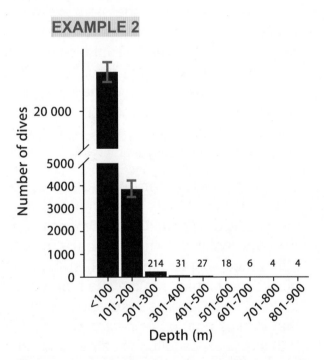

Figure 1 Depth ranges with respective number of dives of leatherback turtles under investigation. Adapted from Hays, Journal of Experimental Biology 2008 211: 2566-2575; doi: 10.1242/jeb.020065.

According to Figure 1, as compared to dives between 100 and 200 meters, dives below 100 meters occur:

A. more than twice as often but less than three times as often.
B. less than 15 000 dives more often.
C. between 15 000 and 20 000 dives more often.
D. over 20 000 dives more often.

Note that glancing at the histogram, without taking into account the broken *y*-axis, could lead one to be misled into thinking that answer choice A is correct.

Using the distance on the *y*-axis from 0 to 2000 as a guide, we can see that the first bar diagram seems to end approximately 2000 dives above 20 000 (i.e. 22 000; we can only make this conclusion because the increments are linear).

The second bar diagram seems to be between 3500 and 4000, which we can approximate as 3750. Thus we can estimate the difference as 22 000 − 3750 = 18 250 dives, thus answer choice C is correct.

The error bars are just an added distraction since they do not come into play here (i.e. they do not overlap). Had they overlapped, we could have no confidence that any difference between the 2 dives exists − even if there appeared to be a difference in the heights of the histograms.

4.7 Cartesian Coordinates in 3D

If you do get a 3D (3-dimensional) graph in DAT QR, relax, the analysis will be very basic.

EXAMPLE 1

Consider the following illustration of a 3D Cartesian coordinate system. Notice the origin O and the 3 axis lines X, Y and Z, oriented as shown by the arrows. The tick marks on the axes are one length unit apart. Look carefully at the black dot. What coordinate (x, y, z) would you give to identify the position of that dot? (2,2,3)? (3,2,4)? (4,3,2)? (2,4,3)? (2,3,4)? The black dot represents a point with coordinates x = 2, y = 3, and z = 4, or (2,3,4).

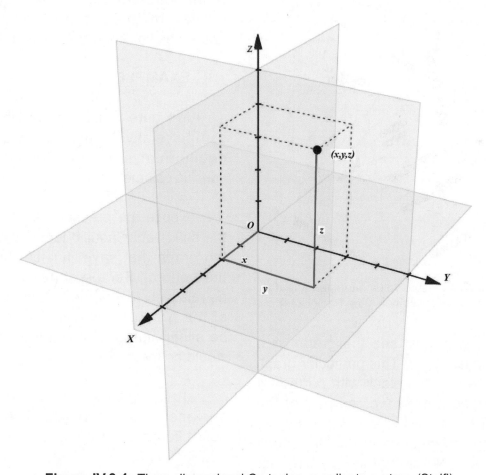

Figure IV.3.1: Three-dimensional Cartesian coordinate system. (Stolfi)

EXAMPLE 2

We will be looking at phase diagrams in DAT General Chemistry Chapter 4. For now, we'll ignore the chemistry and just focus on graph analysis. So as an exercise to read 3D graphs, comment on the relative magnitudes of temperature and pressure for the SOLID (only) portion of the curve in Figure IV.3.2.

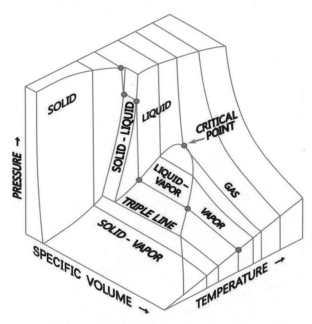

Figure IV.3.2: Pressure-volume-temperature diagram for a pure substance. (Lee/Padleckas)

First, you must see the graph as a 3-dimensional object. This particular graph looks like a wooden block with parts of 4 sides gouged out, as well as part of the middle. The 3 arrows in the graph indicate increasing magnitudes in the directions of the arrows. Notice that the pressure for

solids could be either high or low. However, the specific volume is always relatively low as is the temperature in the region where the graph shows only solid (of course, it makes sense that something that is solid takes up less volume than the gaseous state; also, because of our experience with water - for example, ice and steam - we expect solids to be at low temperatures and gas to be at high temperatures with liquid somewhere in between).

In conclusion, the relative magnitude of the temperature for the SOLID (only) portion of the curve is low while the pressure can range from high to low.

EXAMPLE 3

In Figure IV.3.2, which of the following can be relatively high at the solid-vapor equilibrium: pressure, temperature or specific volume?

Notice the pressure is always low at the solid-vapor equilibrium (i.e. the part of the graph that says SOLID-VAPOR near the bottom). Temperature also seems to be relatively low at the SOLID-VAPOR part of the graph. However, the volume can be either high or low and thus the volume would be the correct answer.

Just as an aside, the line on the surface called a **triple line** is where solid, liquid and vapor can all coexist in equilibrium.

EXAMPLE 4

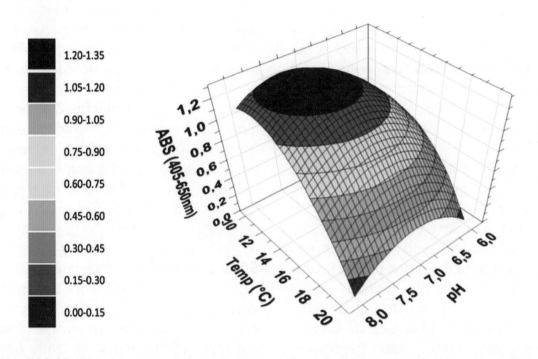

Figure IV.3.2b 3D surface plot demonstrating the effect of temperature and pH on the expression of the TS1-218 protein; the latter is positively correlated with spectrophotometric absorbance (ABS); in yeast cells monitored by ELISA. Jafari R., *Microb. Cell Fact.*, 2011.

QUESTION 1

According to the data presented in Figure IV.3.2b, approximately what pH and temperature is best for TS1-218 expression?

A. 7.5, 9.5 °C
B. 7.5, 14 °C
C. 6.5, 11 °C
D. 7.0, 11 °C

QUESTION 2

Which of the following is most consistent with the peak absorbance in Figure IV.3.2b?

A. Less than 1.2
B. Exactly 1.2
C. Above 1.2
D. None of the above

High-level Importance

EXPLANATION

You should develop a standard way to approach all DAT graphs. Here is our **Gold Standard 5-step Graph Analysis Technique** which you can modify to your liking. With experience, it should take you about 30 seconds:

Step 1) Quickly read the labels for all axes (i.e. ABS, Temp, pH) and, most importantly, the caption below the graph, *if present*. "3D surface plot" suggests that although it is a 3D diagram, we only need to be concerned with the surface of the graph (e.g. it seems to be shaped like a segment of an egg but we only need to be concerned with the eggshell); the rest of the caption can be reasonably interpreted to mean that pH and temperature affects TS1-218 expression which increases with increasing ABS. Thus high ABS = high TS1-218 expression (though the preceding could be inferred, for more about positive correlation: QR 7.3.1). {Note: Sometimes the ADA will not have a caption for a diagram, if there is none, make one up! Taking 5-10 seconds to consider your own description of a diagram can focus your mind on the 'big picture'.}

As part of your routine for reading the labels for a graph, you must consider any *key* if present. A key or *legend* is an explanatory list of symbols and/ or categories used in a graph, map or table. The key for Figure IV.3.2b is to the left of the graph and clearly shows that

the darkest shading at the top refers to values of 1.20-1.35 which means that for the second question, answer choice C is correct. Had you chosen otherwise, it is likely because you did not identify the key and/or fully appreciate the 3D aspect of the diagram. You can tell by the 3 axes that we must be looking at the "top of the eggshell" from the top down, and at an angle. In other words, you can't just read the ABS value (1.2) from the top of the curve because we are not looking at the graph head-on.

Step 2) Always double check the units (e.g. nm, °C, pH) and the graph's intervals. The latter can be the source of many trick questions, so always check the regularity of the actual distance between the lines on each axis; the unit distance between those lines; as well as the point of origin for each axis to identify cases where the axis begins at a number other than zero.

The intervals for our particular 3D graph are linear. Notice that from pH 6 to 8, each major interval is regular at 0.5 pH units. Also note that the surface graph has a grid (QR 4.5.2), and although you do not have to be too precise, you can count - more or less - 30 lines by 30 lines for the grid. That means that to correspond to a pH of 7 (half way between 6 and 8), you would follow a line at approximately 15 on the grid (half of 30, which is due to the graph's visual symmetry; note: you could be off by 3 grid lines - higher or lower - and you would still get the correct answer which is D).

We have placed red asterisks on the 3D graph for you to follow a line from pH 7.0 to the imaginary (approx.) apex of the diagram.

Thus pH has determined that the answer for the first question must be D. The temperature does not need to be precisely calculated but it appears that the Temp axis ranges from about 9 to 21, or about 12 degrees; 30 lines/12 degrees, about 2.5 lines per degree so 11 degrees is about 5 3D-grid lines from the back of the graph, counting along the axis for Temp.

We have already answered both questions, but we will continue with the GS 5-step Graph Analysis Technique which you may need for other types of questions.

Step 3) Recheck the axes to ensure there is not a second labeling system (note that the second graph in QR 4.8 has 2 different labels for the same x-axis), nor any broken axes (i.e. QR 4.6.5).

Step 4) Double check for logarithmic or exponential changes.

Step 5) Depending on the question type (i.e. QR 4.6.4), assess what the slope or area under the curve would give. This stage may require the equation of a line (QR 4.6.1) and/or dimensional analysis (QR 3.2.2).

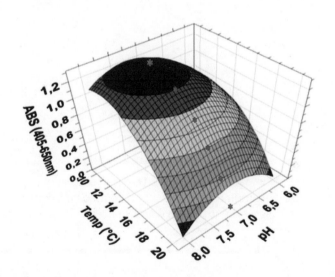

4.8 Nomograms: The Art of Unusual Graphs (*DAT-30*)

A **nomogram** is a diagram representing the relations between three or more changing variables using several scales. Each scale is arranged so that the value of one variable can be found by simple geometry, for example, by drawing a straight line intersecting the other scales at the appropriate values.

High-level Importance

EXAMPLE 1

Consider the following nomogram. Using a straight pencil as a guide, you can join a point from the water temperature on the upper scale to the dissolved oxygen reading (ppm) on the bottom scale. You can then read the percentage oxygen saturation from the point at which your pencil crosses the middle scale. For example, at 7 °C and 12 ppm of dissolved oxygen, the result is approximately 100% saturation.

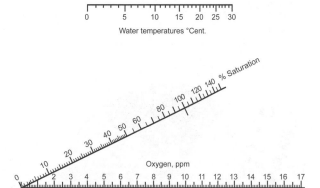

Nomogram for dissolved oxygen saturation.
Ref. Environments in Profile, an aquatic perspective, W Kaill and J Frey, Canfield Press, 1973.

What is the % saturation for 1.5 ppm of dissolved oxygen at a water temperature of 18 °C?

A. Less than 10%
B. 15%
C. 20%
D. More than 20%

Side note: Although there is no assumed knowledge for the preceding question, the nomogram teaches an important point about gases dissolved in water which comes up frequently on the real exam. Hopefully, after you study General Chemistry, you will understand why the same concentration of oxygen (in this case, ppm) results in lower saturation in water at lower temperatures. Consequently, more gas can "fit" in water when the temperature is low (like a can of Coke or champagne, the gas bubbles are lost faster at higher temperatures). The answer for EXAMPLE 1 is upside down below.

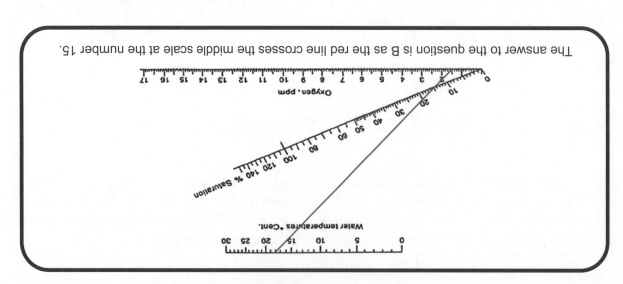

The answer to the question is B as the red line crosses the middle scale at the number 15.

EXAMPLE 2

Nomograms can appear to be more complex than the preceding straight lines as will be illustrated next.

The following represents normal values for arterial blood in humans: pH 7.4, bicarbonate 24 mmol/L, pCO_2 40 mmHg.

Consider Figure IV.3.7.

QUESTION 1

According to Figure IV.3.7, an arterial blood pH of 7.5 with a pCO_2 of 25, corresponds best with which of the following?

A. Metabolic alkalosis

B. Acute respiratory alkalosis

C. Chronic respiratory alkalosis

D. Chronic respiratory acidosis

QUESTION 2

Consider a patient with metabolic alkalosis. Based on Figure IV.3.7, which of the following would be most consistent with returning the patient back to normal?

A. Increase in arterial $[H^+]$, decrease arterial bicarbonate

B. Increase arterial pH, increase arterial bicarbonate

C. Decrease pCO_2, decrease arterial $[H^+]$

D. Increase pCO_2, decrease arterial bicarbonate

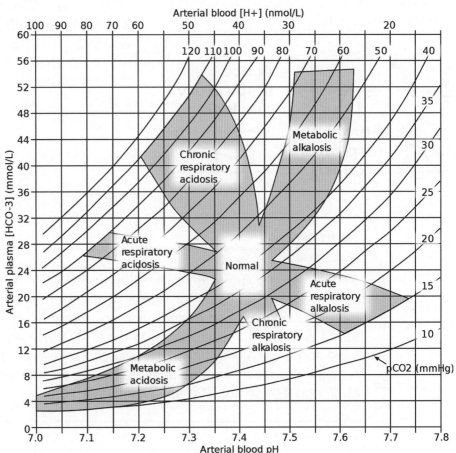

Figure IV.3.7 Human arterial blood acid-base balance and disorders

High-level Importance

EXPLANATION

For Question 1, you must begin with the example provided in the preamble and trace the lines of pH 7.4, bicarbonate 24 mmol/L, and the curved line of pCO_2 40 mmHg which all intersect in the graph at one point – basically, in the middle of 'Normal'.

Notice that the bottom right corner of the diagram points to a curved line which says pCO_2 (mmHg) to suggest that all the curved lines represent pCO_2.

Now our attention turns towards the two lines in the question: pH of 7.5 with a pCO_2 of 25 which just manage to intersect at 'Acute respiratory alkalosis'. The answer is B for Question 1.

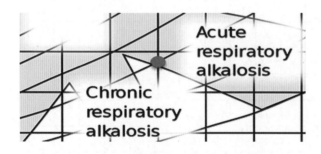

For Question 2, note that 'metabolic alkalosis' is in the top right portion of the graph. 'Normal' is, comparatively, down and to the left of 'metabolic alkalosis'. Looking at the y-axis to the left, we can see that going down means that we would have a decrease in arterial bicarbonate. Now be careful to notice that the x-axis at the top of the graph has arterial $[H^+]$ decreasing from left to right, which means that moving to the left results in an increase in arterial $[H^+]$. The answer is A for Question 2.

Of course, from your DAT General Chemistry studies, you are aware that as a result of the equation for pH ($pH = -\log_{10}[H^+]$), because of the negative sign, when pH rises, $[H^+]$ must decrease, and vice versa. This point is confirmed by the nomogram (Fig. IV.3.7). We review the pH scale in CHM 6.5 of the Masters Series.

NOTE

Please avoid trying to think: 'I will memorize this or that graph for the exam'. The better long-term strategy would be: 'I need to have a reliable method to approach novel graphs so when I see one, I will have the confidence to break it down (and hopefully have some fun along the way!)'. You can try the Gold Standard 5-step Graph Analysis Technique (QR 4.7), or develop your own approach, but do not let graphs intimidate you!

4.9 Quadratic Equations

A **quadratic equation** is an equation that can be written in the form $ax^2 + bx + c = 0$ where a, b, and c are constants. This is a second-degree polynomial set equal to zero, and it will always have two solutions, although they are not always unique. Being asked to solve a quadratic equation is a standard type of algebra problem, so you should be very familiar with the techniques listed in the following subsections.

4.9.1 Factoring and Completing the Square

A. Factoring

Factoring is the simplest and easiest way to solve a quadratic equation, but you will not always be able to use this method. Only special quadratics can be solved this way. Still, you should always try and use this method first.

The goal is to factor the quadratic into two first-degree polynomials so you have $(ax + b)(cx + d) = 0$. Once you have obtained this form, you know that either $(ax + b) = 0$ or $(cx + d) = 0$, so the two solutions are $x = -\dfrac{b}{a}$ and $x = -\dfrac{d}{c}$.

There is no single quick way to factor a quadratic this way. Instead, you should do many sample exercises to develop the ability to think logically and come up with the solution. As a guide, think about what values must be multi-plied to obtain the constants a, b, and c of your quadratic.

More specifically, for $ax^2 + bx + c$, if the value of a is 1, your two polynomials will be $(x + m)$ and $(x + n)$ where $b = m + n$ and $c = m \times n$. Therefore, try to think about what numbers multiply together to give c and add together to give b.

EXAMPLE

Solve the quadratic equation:

$$x^2 + 3x + 2 = 0$$

To factor, we need two numbers that add to 3 and multiply to 2. We know that these numbers must both be positive since a positive and a negative number would yield a negative number when multiplied, and two negative numbers would yield a negative number when added.

Also, the two numbers must be less than 3 because otherwise their sum would have to be larger than 3. After some thought, it is clear that the numbers we are looking for are 1 and 2 since $1 + 2 = 3$ and $1 \times 2 = 2$.

$$\Rightarrow (x + 1)(x + 2) = 0$$
$$\Rightarrow (x + 1) = 0 \text{ and } (x + 2) = 0$$
$$\Rightarrow x = -1 \text{ and } x = -2$$

B. Completing the Square

This method can be a little tricky. The basic idea is to manipulate the quadratic so that you can write the portion with the variables as the square of a first-order polynomial. Then you can take the square root and find the solutions. To accomplish this for a generic quadratic $ax^2 + bx + c = 0$, follow these steps:

Step 1 Move c to the other side of the equation.

$$ax^2 + bx = -c$$

Step 2 Divide through by the leading coefficient a.

$$x^2 + \left(\frac{b}{a}\right)x = -\frac{c}{a}$$

Step 3 Take half of $\left(\frac{b}{a}\right)$, i.e., the coefficient of x. Square it, and add it to both sides of the equation.

$$x^2 + \left(\frac{b}{a}\right)x + \left(\frac{b}{2a}\right)^2 = -\frac{c}{a} + \left(\frac{b}{2a}\right)^2$$

This allows you to write the polynomial as a square, namely $\left(x + \frac{b}{2a}\right)^2$.

$$\left(x + \frac{b}{2a}\right)^2 = -\frac{c}{a} + \left(\frac{b}{2a}\right)^2$$

Step 4 Take the square root of both sides and solve for x.

$$x + \frac{b}{2a} = \pm\sqrt{\left[-\frac{c}{a} + \left(\frac{b}{2a}\right)^2\right]}$$

$$x = -\frac{b}{2a} \pm \sqrt{\left[-\frac{c}{a} + \left(\frac{b}{2a}\right)^2\right]}$$

Following the variables in this general version can be difficult, so let's look at an example.

EXAMPLE

Solve the following quadratic by completing the square:

$$2x^2 + 4x - 8 = 0$$

Step 1 $\quad 2x^2 + 4x = 8$

Step 2 $\quad x^2 + 2x = 4$

Step 3 $\quad x^2 + 2x + 1 = 4 + 1 = 5$

$$\Rightarrow \sqrt{(x + 1)^2} = \sqrt{5}$$

Step 4 $\quad x + 1 = \pm\sqrt{5}$

$$\Rightarrow x = -1 \pm \sqrt{5}$$

If you do not want to or cannot use one of the methods in QR 4.9.1 to solve your quadratic equation, you can simply plug numbers into the quadratic formula to come up with a solution (CHM 6.6.1).

For a generic quadratic equation $ax^2 + bx + c = 0$, these are the solutions:

$$x = \frac{-b \pm \sqrt{b^2 - 4ac}}{2a}$$

Sometimes, doing the arithmetic necessary to compute this formula can take a lot of time, so factoring and completing the square are usually better options if you feel comfortable with them. They will save you time on the test.

When there is no first degree term $ax^2 + c = 0$, we can solve the equation by isolating x^2. Such that,

$$x^2 = -\frac{c}{a}.$$

Therefore, $x = \pm\sqrt{-\dfrac{c}{a}}$.

4.10 Quantitative Comparison

Quantitative Comparison (QC) is a relatively new type of problem that was added to the DAT QR Section. It is important to be familiar with the format in order to quickly answer the question. The QC format includes two quantities and four standard answer choices. The two quantities are Quantity A and Quantity B (*with a certain variation in formats*):

Quantity A	Quantity B
x	y

The answer choices have the format:

A. Quantity A is greater.
B. Quantity B is greater.
C. The two quantities are equal.
D. The relationship cannot be determined from the information given.

Many QC questions involve algebra; however, algebra is just one of the topics that is tested using QC. It is important to keep in mind it is not the only topic the DAT can test. Sometimes it is used for graph analysis (e.g. 2 of 40 of the DAT QR questions in the ADA's 2022 practice test are graph analysis with QC), or it could be in the context of word problems (Chapter 8).

Let's explore some basic examples…

EXAMPLE

Quantity A	Quantity B
5 + 3	7 + 4

Using addition, we see that Quantity A is 8 and Quantity B is 11. As Quantity B is greater, answer choice B. is correct.

The question stem can also give additional information that applies to both quantities.

EXAMPLE

$$y = 1$$

Quantity A	Quantity B
y^1	$y/1$

The question stem ("y=1") gives a value to y that can be applied to both Quantity A and Quantity B.

Solve:

Quantity A	Quantity B
1^1	$1/1$
$= 1$	$= 1$

As Quantity A and Quantity B are equal, answer choice C. is correct.

4.10.1 Quantitative Comparison Strategy

Solving Algebraic Equations: Some QC questions can have an algebraic equation in the question stem or one of the quantities. The most efficient way to tackle this problem is by solving the equation.

EXAMPLE

$$3x - 10 = 2$$

Quantity A	Quantity B
x	2

A. Quantity A is greater.
B. Quantity B is greater.
C. The two quantities are equal.
D. The relationship cannot be determined from the information given.

Choose your response before continuing.

Solve: $3x - 10 = 2$
           $3x = 12$
           $x = 4$

As Quantity A is much easier to compare to Quantity B, it is clear to see that Quantity A is greater and choice A. is correct.

EXAMPLE

$$x^2 + 8x - 16 = 3$$

Quantity A	Quantity B
2	$(x - 4)^2$

A. Quantity A is greater.
B. Quantity B is greater.
C. The two quantities are equal.
D. The relationship cannot be determined from the information given.

Solve (QR 4.1.3):

$$(x - 4)^2 = (x - 4)(x - 4)$$
$$= x^2 + 8x - 16$$

When solving the algebraic equation of Quantity B, we see that Quantity B is equal to the equation in the question stem and therefore is equal to 3. For that reason, Quantity B. is greater than 2 (Quantity A), and thus answer choice B. is correct.

Plugging in Numbers: Plugging in numbers is a great strategy to solve QC questions with variables in both quantities. However, keep in mind that although plugging in one number gives two values for Quantity A and Quantity B, it does not definitively give the exact relationship between Quantity A and Quantity B. Rather, it eliminates certain relationships between the two quantities and therefore cancels out certain answer choices.

For example, one number could find that Quantity A and Quantity B are equal. However, this doesn't mean that all values will make Quantity A and Quantity B equal. Therefore, it is crucial to evaluate multiple numbers to get the answer.

As the DAT is a timed test, it is valuable to use the time wisely and not just plug and chug random numbers. For this reason, there are some key numbers that should be utilized:

- 10
- 1
- 0.5
- 0
- -0.5
- -1
- -10

These key numbers ensure there is variety and efficiency when using this strategy. This specific variety of numbers ensures all the bases are covered by using whole numbers and fractions, as well as positive and negative numbers. These key numbers are also very efficient as they are easy to plug into equations. Note: It is almost impossible that you will need to plug in more than just a few of these numbers.

EXAMPLE

x is a real number greater than 0.

Quantity A	Quantity B
x^2	x^3

A. Quantity A is greater.
B. Quantity B is greater.
C. The two quantities are equal.
D. The relationship cannot be determined from the information given.

Solve:

	Quantity A	Quantity B
x = 10	$10^2 = 100$	$10^3 = 1000$

By plugging in the key number 10, it is shown that Quantity B is greater than Quantity A. However, unlike previous examples this solution does not find the answer, but only eliminates certain answer choices. This eliminates answer choices A. and C. but leaves answer choices B. and D. When another key number is plugged in:

	Quantity A	Quantity B
x = 1	$1^2 = 1$	$1^3 = 1$

High-level Importance

It can be seen that with the key number 1, Quantity A and Quantity B are equal. As two key numbers give two different outcomes, the relationship cannot be determined from the information given. Therefore, the correct answer is D.

Note that it is crucial to evaluate multiple numbers when using this method to get the correct answer.

Note that we will explore QC again in QR Chapter 8, Word Problems.

GOLD STANDARD DAT QR PRACTICE QUESTIONS

CHAPTER 4: Algebra, Graph Analysis and Quantitative Comparison

1) If $\dfrac{x}{2} - 1 < x,$ then which must be true?

   A. $\quad 2 > x$

   B. $\quad -\dfrac{1}{2} < x$

   C. $\quad -2 < x$

   D. $\quad -2 > x$

   E. $\quad 2 < x$

2) If $f(x) = \dfrac{12}{4x^3 - 6x + 5}$, then $f(2)$ equals:

   A. 12/17

   B. 12/49

   C. 12/9

   D. 12/15

   E. 12/25

3) $13xy^2z$ is to $39y$ as $9xyz^6$ is to:

   A. $3z^5$

   B. $27z$

   C. $9y$

   D. $27z^5$

   E. $9z^6$

4) At what point do the two lines $y = 2x - 1$ and $6x - 5y = -3$ intersect?

   A. (2, 3)

   B. (0.5, 0)

   C. (−1,−3)

   D. (−0.5, −2)

   E. (1/4,-3/4)

5) Loubha has a total of $.85. If she has two less dimes than nickels, how many dimes and nickels does she have?

   A. 5 nickels, 7 dimes

   B. 6 nickels, 4 dimes

   C. 1 nickel, 8 dimes

   D. 4 nickels, 2 dimes

   E. 7 nickels, 5 dimes

6) If $2.5 \times 10^3 (3 \times 10^x) = 0.075$, then x equals:

   A. −3

   B. −5

   C. 0

   D. −4

   E. 2

7) If $y = 3x^2 - 5x - 7$, then which of the following represents x?

A. $\dfrac{-5 \pm \sqrt{3y + 46}}{3}$

B. $\dfrac{5 \pm \sqrt{12y + 109}}{6}$

C. $\dfrac{-5 \pm \sqrt{12y + 109}}{6}$

D. $\dfrac{5 \pm \sqrt{12y + 109}}{36}$

E. $\dfrac{5 \pm \sqrt{3y + 46}}{3}$

8) A plank of wood is leaning against the left side of a house with vertical walls. Both are on level ground. If the plank touches the ground 7 feet away from the base of the house, and touches the house at a point 5 feet above the ground, at what slope is the plank lying?

A. –5/7

B. 7/5

C. –7/5

D. 5/7

E. 2

9) If $n + n = k + k + k$ and $n + k = 5$, then $n = ?$

A. 9   D. 3

B. 6   E. 2

C. 5

10) Let x = 4 and y = 8. Evaluate the expression: $((y^{-2/3})^{1/2}) / (x^{-1/2})$.

A. 8   C.   1

B. 4   D.   1/2

11) Which of the following Physics equations would not be expected to represent the graph of a straight line? (note: you do not need to understand any of the equations in order to answer the question)

A. F = ma

B. M = mv

C. W = Fd

D. E = ½ mv²

12) Consider Figure 1.

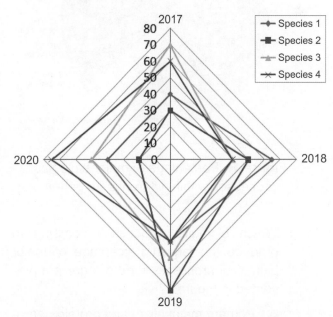

Figure 1: Radar chart displaying the population of 4 bird species in thousands of individuals on an isolated island during a 4-year period. As an example, Species 2 had a population of 40 000 in 2018.

Which bird species shows the maximum change in population numbers from 2017 to 2020?

A. Species 1   C.   Species 3

B. Species 2   D.   Species 4

High-level Importance

13) Consider Figure 1.

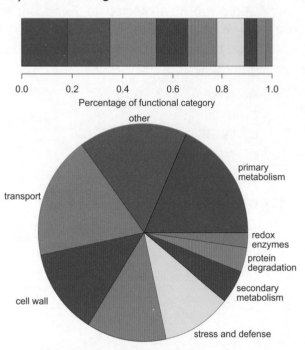

Figure 1: Percentage of major biological processes within differentiated genes.

Which biological processes combine to produce the largest percentage of major biological processes for the organism presented in Figure 1?

A. Primary metabolism and protein degradation

B. Redox enzymes and transport

C. Stress, defense and 'other' processes

D. Cell wall and stress and defense

14) A tephigram is a type of nomogram used for weather analysis and forecasting. Temperatures (Celcius, C, and Absolute, A) are marked on the x-axes, while entropy and potential temperatures (pot temp) are marked along the y-axes. Other features such as pressure are marked as shown.

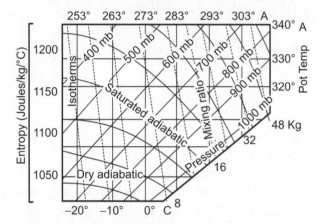

Figure 1: Tephigram. Note that temperature along the bottom x-axis is in degrees Celcius (C) and corresponds precisely and vertically with the absolute temperature (A; these are isothermal lines). For example, 0 °C corresponds to 273 on the absolute (A) temperature scale. Entropy, along the left-most y-axis, runs horizontally.

According to Figure 1, if the entropy is 1150 Joules/kg/°C and the pressure is 800 mb, the expected temperature in degrees Celcius would be in the range of which of the following?

A. 0-10

B. 10-20

C. 20-30

D. 30-40

High-level Importance

15) The total annual snowfall among 7 US states is 800 cm.

   A: The difference in the annual snowfall between S3 and S6 in cm.

   B: 52

   When comparing the two quantities, the:

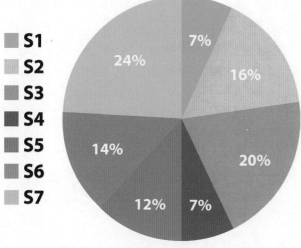

   S1
   S2
   S3
   S4
   S5
   S6
   S7

   7%
   24%
   16%
   20%
   14%
   12%
   7%

   Percent Annual Snowfall Among Seven US States

   A. quantity of A is greater than the quantity of B.
   B. quantity of B is greater than the quantity of A.
   C. relationship cannot be determined from the information given.
   D. two quantities are equal.

16) If $f(x) = 2x^3 - .25x^2 - (1/x)$, what is $f(1) - f(2)$?

   A. −15.25
   B. −13.75
   C. 13.75
   D. 15
   E. 15.25

17) If $2y^2 - 12 = 2y$, which of the following represents possible values of y?

   A. (2, 3)
   B. (−2, 3)
   C. (2, −3)
   D. (−2, −3)
   E. All of the above

18) What is the y-intercept of the line passing through points (1, 4) and (−1, 1)?

   A. 0
   B. 1
   C. 2
   D. 2.5
   E. 3.5

19) Solve the following system of equations for x and y:

   $$5x - 2y = 3$$
   $$2x + 2y = 4y - x + 1$$

   A. (.5, 1)
   B. (−1, 1)
   C. (1, 1)
   D. (1, −1)
   E. (2, 2)

20) Which of the following is not a possible solution to the inequality $|2 - 3x| > 4$?

   A. x = −1
   B. x = −2
   C. x = 5
   D. x = 3
   E. x = 1

High-level Importance

21) Find the x-intercepts of $y = 3x^2 - 3x - 5$.

   A. $1/2 \pm \sqrt{(23/12)}$

   B. $\pm 1/2$

   C. $0, 1$

   D. $1/4 \pm \sqrt{(23/12)}$

   E. $\pm\sqrt{(23/12)}$

22) If $x^2 - 3x + 5 = 3$, which is a possible value for x?

   A. -3

   B. -2

   C. -1

   D. 2

   E. 3

23) If $\sqrt{[(1/x^2) + 3]} = 5$, then $x = ?$

   A. $1/\sqrt{22}$

   B. $1/\sqrt{2}$

   C. $1/22$

   D. $1/2$

   E. 2

24) If $x = (2y - 1)/(y + 3)$, then which of the following represents y?

   A. $(3x - 1)/(x + 2)$

   B. $(3x - 1)/(x - 2)$

   C. $(3x + 1)/(x - 2)$

   D. $-(3x + 1)/(x - 2)$

   E. $-(3x + 1)/(x + 2)$

25) If $f(y) = y^3/2 + 2y^2 + 3y$, then $f(-2)$ equals

   A. -18 D. 10

   B. -2 E. 18

   C. 6

26) Expand the expression: $(x - y + 3)^2$.

   A. $x^2 - y^2 + 9$

   B. $x^2 + y^2 + 9$

   C. $x^2 + y^2 + 2xy + 6x + 6y + 9$

   D. $x^2 + y^2 - 2xy + 6x - 6y + 9$

   E. $x^2 - y^2 - 2xy + 6x - 6y + 9$

27) If $(2/x) + 3 > 5 - (1/x)$, then which must be true?

   A. $(1/x) > (2/3)$

   B. $(1/x) < (2/3)$

   C. $(3/2) > x$

   D. $(3/2) < x$

   E. A and C

28) Which of the following is the value of x if $x \neq -2$, $x \neq 3$, and $2/[3(x + 2)] + 3/(x - 3) = (5x - 1)/(x^2 - x - 6)$?

   A. $3/4$

   B. $15/4$

   C. 15

   D. -2

   E. -6

29) Which of the following equations describe a line passing through points $(-1, 3)$, $(1, 0)$ and $(5, -6)$ in the Cartesian plane?

   A. $y = -(3/2)x + 1$

   B. $y = (3/2)x + 3/2$

   C. $3y + 3x = 5$

   D. $y + 2x = 2/3$

   E. $2y + 3x = 3$

30) This is a *DAT-30* question.

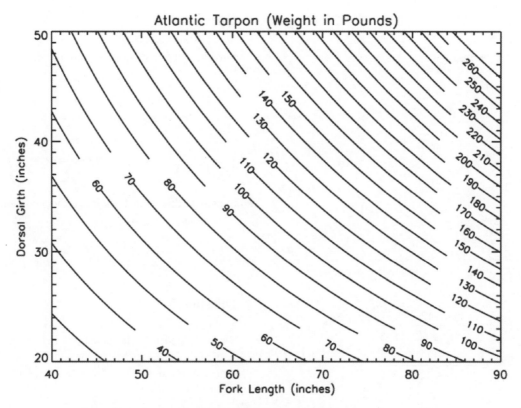

Atlantic Tarpon Weight Related to Dorsal Girth and Fork Length

A: Dorsal girth in inches of a 210-pound tarpon with a fork length of 83 inches

B: 40

When comparing the two quantities, the:

A. quantity of A is greater than the quantity of B.

B. quantity of B is greater than the quantity of A.

C. relationship cannot be determined from the information given.

D. two quantities are equal.

Chapter Review Solutions: Chapter 4

Question 1   C

See: QR 4.2.2A
Combine like terms:

$$\frac{x}{2} - 1 - \frac{x}{2} < x - \frac{x}{2}$$

$$-1 < \frac{x}{2}$$

$$-1(2) < \left(\frac{x}{2}\right)(2)$$

$$-2 < x$$

Question 2   E

See: QR 4.1.4
Substitute 2 for x in the function:

$$f(2) = \frac{12}{4(2)^3 - 6(2) + 5}$$

$$= \frac{12}{4(8) - 12 + 5}$$

$$= \frac{12}{32 - 12 + 5} = \frac{12}{25}$$

Question 3   D

See: QR 4.3.2, 4.3.3
Create a ratio with the first two values and simplify:

$$\frac{13xy^2z}{39y} = \frac{xyz}{3}$$

The unknown ratio must also be equal to this value. Let k represent the variable and cross-multiply:

$$\frac{9xyz^6}{k} = \frac{xyz}{3}$$

$$3(9xyz^6) = (xyz)k$$

$$\frac{27xyz^6}{xyz} = k$$

$$27z^5 = k$$

Question 4   A

See: QR 4.4.2A, 4.4.2B
Substitute the first equation into the second, replacing y:

$$6x - 5y = -3$$
$$6x - 5(2x - 1) = -3$$
$$6x - 10x + 5 = -3$$
$$-4x + 5 = -3$$
$$-4x = -8$$
$$x = 2$$

Substitute this value back into either equation to find y:

$$y = 2x - 1$$
$$y = 2(2) - 1$$
$$y = 3$$

Question 5   E

See: QR 4.4.2B
We will need to write equations that correspond to the sentences. Let d represent the number of dimes, and n represent the number of nickels. Since there are two less dimes than nickels,

$$d = n - 2.$$

The amount of money a group of coins is worth is equal to the value of the coins times the number of coins. The total value of Loubha's nickels is $\$0.05n$ and the total value of her dimes is $\$0.10d$. These add up to all of the money she has:

$$\$0.05n + \$0.10d = \$0.85.$$

Substitute the first equation into the second for n:

$$\$0.05n + \$0.10(n - 2) = \$0.85$$
$$\$0.05n + \$0.10n - \$0.20 = \$0.85$$
$$\$0.15n = \$0.85 + \$0.20$$
$$\$0.15n = \$1.05$$

$$n = \$1.05 / \$0.15$$
$$n = 7$$

There are 7 nickels. We can plug this into either of the two original equations, but the first is easiest to use:

$$d = n - 2$$
$$d = 7 - 2$$
$$d = 5$$

NOTE: In this particular problem, the fastest way is to just try the different answers until one fits the requirements. We have shown the work in case it was a different question type then you would still know the approach.

Question 6   B

See: QR 4.3.1
Simplify the expression:

$$(2.5 \times 10^3)(3 \times 10^x) = 0.075$$
$$(2.5 \times 3)(10^3 \times 10^x) = 0.075$$
$$(7.5)(10^{3+x}) = 0.075$$

Divide both sides of the equation 7.5, or simply note that 0.075 is one-hundredth $\left(\frac{1}{100}\right) = 10^{-2}$ of 7.5:

$$10^{3+x} = 10^{-2}$$
$$3 + x = -2$$
$$x = -5$$

Question 7   B

See: QR 4.9.2
y is a quadratic equation, so we can use the quadratic formula to solve for x, but, first, the equation must be in standard form:

$$3x^2 - 5x - 7 - y = 0$$

The term $-y$ does not have any powers of x, so it becomes part of the constant term: $a = 3, b = -5, c = -7 - y$. Applying the quadratic formula,

$$\frac{-(-5) \pm \sqrt{(-5)^2 - 4(3)(-7-y)}}{2(3)}$$
$$= \frac{5 \pm \sqrt{25 + 84 + 12y}}{6}$$
$$= \frac{5 \pm \sqrt{109 + 12y}}{6}$$

Question 8   D

See: QR 4.5.4
If we think of the plank as a straight line in a coordinate system, we can use the points at which its ends are located to find its slope. The origin can be anywhere we choose, and the base of the house's left wall is a good choice. This point of the house must be located at (0, 0), and so the base of the plank, 7 feet to the left, is located at (-7, 0). The point at which the plank touches the left wall is 5 feet above the origin, at (0, 5). The slope of the plank is therefore

$$m = \frac{0 - 5}{-7 - 0} = \frac{-5}{-7} = \frac{5}{7}$$

Question 9   D

See: QR 4.3.1, 4.4.2A, 4.4.2B
It is given that $2n = 3k$, which implies that $\frac{2}{3}n = k$. $n + k = 5$ can therefore be rewritten:

$$n + \frac{2}{3}n = 5$$
$$\frac{5}{3}n = 5$$
$$n = 3$$

Question 10   C

See: QR 2.5
First combine the exponents where possible, and rearrange so they are all positive:

$$((y^{-2/3})^{1/2}) / (x^{-1/2})$$
$$= (y^{-1/3}) / (x^{-1/2})$$
$$= (x^{1/2}) / (y^{1/3})$$

Now plug in x=4 and y=8. Notice that $4=2^2$ and $8=2^3$.

$$= (4^{1/2}) / (8^{1/3})$$
$$= (2^{(2)1/2}) / (2^{(3)1/3})$$
$$= 2^1/2^1$$
$$= 1.$$

High-level Importance

Question 11   D

See: QR 4.4, 4.5

Of course, y = mx + b is the equation of a straight line. Notice that b can equal 0, meaning that the line intersects at the point (0, 0), and so y can be equal to mx. Answer choices A, B and C have the same format as y = mx. Answer choice D has a variable raised to the power of 2 which is not consistent with the format: y = mx + b. Identifying whether or not an equation could produce a straight line is an important DAT skill.

And for students studying OAT Physics, A: Newton's 2nd Law; B: Momentum; C: Work; D: Kinetic energy.

Spelling out some examples: A graph of F vs a, has m as a slope. A graph of W vs d, has F as a slope. A graph of E vs v would be an exponential curve (QR Appendix A; notice the word 'exponent' in exponential!).

Question 12   C

See: QR 4.8

On the Surface: The increments are linear (0, 10, 20, etc., nothing exponential) and there are 4 axes for the 4 different years. We just need to identify, from 2017 to 2020 (only look at the upper left of Figure 1), which line crosses the most space between lines: Green, Species 3, answer C.

For this question, you were given a strong hint in the caption. You can see that Species 2 is the small red square on a grey line. Now you need to think: How does that point near 2018 give me 40 000? Now just look for a way to get to 40 and you notice that the increments of 10 are for all directions along the grey lines, and the caption states "in thousands."

Going Deeper: Figure 1 is a radar chart (AKA, web chart, spider chart, star plot, polar chart). Just read it as though you have 4 different x-axes. Notice where 0 must be for each direction, then 10 and so on. From 2017 to 2020, write down on your scratch paper the values in thousands for each species: answer choice A: 30 to 30 (notice how 'blue' just stays on the 30 line in the top left of Figure 1); B: 20 to 10; C: 60 to 40; D: 50 to 65. Clearly the biggest change is the 20 000 drop in population for Species 3, answer C.

Other questions that could have been asked? 1) Biggest percent change: B (a whopping 50% decrease!); Largest decrease: C; Largest increase: D.

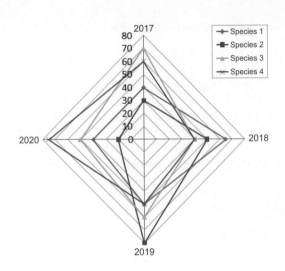

Question 13   C

See: QR 4, deduce

If you are skilled at noticing differences, since there is no log scale, you can find the answer visually. Notice that answer choices C and D both have 'stress and defense' so you only have to compare: other vs cell wall, and other is visually bigger.

If not visually, this question requires discipline and patience. Don't worry if you made +/− 10% approximations, your answers would be the same. Estimate based on the legend (key), keeping in mind that all of the processes, according to the legend, add up to 1 (the components of the pie chart add up to 100%):

primary metabolism: 0.18	A. 0.21
redox enzymes: 0.03 (a little less?)	B. 0.22
protein degradation: 0.03	C. 0.27
secondary metabolism: 0.05	D. 0.23
transport: 0.19	
stress and defense: 0.10	
other processes: 0.17	
cell wall: 0.13	

Reference: Image adapted from Horn F. et al, Front. Genet., 2014.

Question 14   C

See: QR 4.8

Let's start with the information we are given in this 'unit': Entropy represents horizontal lines which means that the value of 1150 can be traced horizontally to see what it meets. Next, pressure? We are not told anything specific, but, similar to carbon dioxide in the QR 4.8 nomogram, Fig. IV.3.7, we can see the label for Pressure on the graph which suggests that lines which are oblique (*slanting*) and have a number ending with mb represent the pressure.

OK, so we can make a point with the entropy of 1150 and the pressure of 800 mb (oblique line). We are told that straight vertical lines have the same temperature (isotherms) so we follow that line up and see a number just above 293. Well, let's follow that number straight down and it looks like it is around 16, but we have a problem: the direction and labeling seems to have changed. Before temperature was increasing by 10 and now by 16, at an angle, and ending with 48 Kg, which is NOT temperature!

Now we need to reason that from 253 to 273, the absolute temperature clearly followed Celcius by increments of 10 (linear, no logs). If 273 is 0, then 283 must be 10, 293 must be 20, and thus the point represents 20-30 degrees Celcius.

Side note: The absolute (A) scale actually refers to the (big K) Kelvin scale, and 0 °C is indeed 273 K, but (small k) kelvin is not technically regarded as degrees. We will explore this more in CHM 7.4.

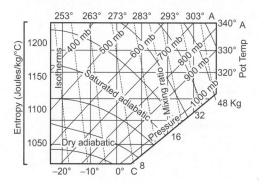

Reference: Image redrawn from aviation_dictionary. enacademic.com/6690/tephigram.

Dear DAT QR,

Please stop asking me to find your x.

She's not coming back and I don't know y either.

DAT-prep.com

Question 15　B
See: QR 2.4.3 C., 4.10
This is a Quantitative Comparison (QC) question with graph analysis (*a pie chart*).

According to the pie chart, S3 is 20% and S6 is 14%, thus the difference is 6%. Since the question is asking for the annual snowfall in cm, we must take 6% of the total 800 cm (of course, 6% = 6/100 = 0.06).

$0.06(800) = 6(8) = 48$ cm which is a quantity that is less than 52. Thus, 52 is the greater quantity.

Side notes: (1) Notice that the key on the left of the pie chart has labels to colors that are continuous in the pie chart (i.e. the order is *not* random), which is quite standard; (2) The ADA's DAT QR 2022 practice exam has 2 questions with pie charts (one in color, one black/white/gray).

Question 16　B
See: QR 4.1.4
First evaluate f(1) and f(2):

$f(1) = 2(1)^3 - .25(1)^2 - (1/1)$
$= 2 - .25 - 1$
$= .75$

$f(2) = 2(2)^3 - .25(2)^2 - (1/2)$
$= 16 - 1 - .5$
$= 14.5$

Then $f(1) - f(2) = .75 - 14.5 = -13.75$.

Question 17　B
See: QR 4.9.1A
Isolate all terms on the left side of the equation:

$2y^2 - 12 = 2y$
$2y^2 - 2y - 12 = 0$

Now divide through by 2 to obtain a coefficient of 1 in the y^2 term and solve:

$y^2 - y - 6 = 0$
$(y + 2)(y - 3) = 0$
$y = -2$ or 3.

Question 18   D

See: QR 4.4.2, 4.5.4

Begin with the generic slope-intercept equation $y = mx + b$. Plug in the given data points and solve the resulting system of 2 equations to find the value of b, which represents the y-intercept:

$1 = m(-1) + b$

$+4 = m(1) + b$

$5 = 2b$

$b = 2.5$.

Question 19   C

See: QR 4.4.2

First isolate x and y on the left side in the second equation:

$2x + 2y = 4y - x + 1$

$3x - 2y = 1$

Next subtract the equations to eliminate the y term and solve for x:

$$\begin{array}{r} 5x - 2y = 3 \\ -3x - 2y = 1 \\ \hline 2x - 0 = 2 \\ x = 1 \end{array}$$

Now substitute the value of x into one of the equations and solve for y:

$5(1) - 2y = 3$

$2 = 2y$

$y = 1$.

Question 20   E

See: QR 4.2.2B

To get rid of the absolute value without losing any information we must split this into two separate inequalities:

$2 - 3x > 4$ or $2 - 3x < -4$

$-3x > 2$ $-3x < 6$

$x < -2/3$ $x > 2$

So x = 1 is the only choice that does not meet one of these two criteria.

Question 21   A

See: QR 4.9.1B

To find x-intercepts, set y = 0 and solve for x. In this case, factoring directly is difficult so we can complete the square:

$3x^2 - 3x - 5 = 0$

$3x^2 - 3x = 5$

$x^2 - x = 5/3$

$x^2 - x + \frac{1}{4} = 5/3 + \frac{1}{4}$

$(x - \frac{1}{2})^2 = 23/12$

$x - \frac{1}{2} = \pm \sqrt{(23/12)}$

$x = \frac{1}{2} \pm \sqrt{(23/12)}$.

Question 22   D

See: QR 4.1.3, 4.9.1

To solve a quadratic equation like this first move all the terms to one side, setting the equation equal to 0. Then factor if possible:

$x^2 - 3x + 5 = 3$

$x^2 - 3x + 2 = 0$

$(x - 1)(x - 2) = 0$

$x = 1$ or $x = 2$

So the solution is D. 2.

Question 23   A

See: QR 2.2.3, 4.1.1

We must solve the equation for x. Begin by squaring both sides to eliminate the square root:

$\sqrt{[(1/x^2) + 3]} = 5$

$(1/x^2) + 3 = 25$

$1/x^2 = 22$

$x^2 = 1/22$

$x = 1/\sqrt{22}$.

Question 24   D

See: QR 4.1.1

The goal is to manipulate the equation so that we are left with y on one side and some function of x on the other.

$x = (2y - 1)/(y + 3)$

$(y + 3)x = 2y - 1$

$yx + 3x = 2y - 1$

Now move all the y terms to the left and non-y terms to the right:

$yx - 2y = -3x - 1$

$y(x - 2) = -(3x + 1)$

$y = -(3x + 1)/(x - 2)$.

Question 25   B

See: QR 4.1.4

Plug in $y = -2$ to the function given, and evaluate. Remember, the square of a negative number is positive!

$f(-2) = (-2)^3/2 + 2(-2)^2 + 3(-2)$

$= -8/2 + 2(4) - 6$

$= -4 + 8 - 6$

$= -2$.

Question 26   D

See: QR 4.1.3, 4.9.1

When raising a polynomial to a power, treat everything inside the parentheses as if it were a single value. So $(x - y + 3)^2$ is really $(x - y + 3)(x - y + 3)$, NOT $(x^2 - y^2 + 3^2)$. Now let's multiply and expand:

$(x - y + 3)(x - y + 3)$

$= x^2 - xy + 3x - xy + y^2 - 3y + 3x - 3y + 9$

$= x^2 + y^2 - 2xy + 6x - 6y + 9$.

Question 27   A

See: QR 4.2.2, 4.3.2

Before we worry about the different options given, let's isolate the x terms on one side and the constants on the other:

$(2/x) + 3 > 5 - (1/x) = (3/x) > 2 = (1/x) > (2/3)$

Now be careful. It is tempting to multiply through by x to try and clear the denominator, but we don't know whether x is negative or positive. If it is negative, the direction of the inequality will change. We cannot tell whether answer choice C or D is the correct inequality. Therefore, we can only say that answer choice A must be true.

Question 28   B

See: QR 4.1.3, 4.9.1

Notice that there are a lot of binomials hanging around this equation. First look for ways to cancel whole bino-

mials because that would simplify the equation quickly. Before we do that, though, we need to factor $(x^2 - x - 6)$. We need two numbers whose sum is -1 and whose product is -6: -3 and 2 work. So:

$(x^2 - x - 6) = (x - 3)(x + 2)$

Multiplying the equation through by this factorization we get:

$2(x - 3)/3 + 3(x + 2) = (5x - 1)$

Distribute the coefficients and combine like terms, then solve for x:

$(2x - 6)/3 + 3x + 6 = 5x - 1$

$(2x - 6)/3 = 2x - 7$

$2x - 6 = 6x - 21$

$15 = 4x$

$x = 15/4$.

Question 29   E

See: QR 4.4, 4.5

To define a line we only need 2 points in a plane, so the problem gives more information than is necessary. We can pick 2 of the 3 points to use. To make calculations easier, choose any point with 0's or 1's first, then opt for points with integers closest to 0. In this case let's use (1, 0) and (−1, 3) to find an equation for the line in slope-intercept form:

$y = (slope)x + (y\text{-intercept})$

Remember, slope = rise/run:

$slope = (0 - 3)/(1 - (-1)) = -(3/2)$

$y = -(3/2)x + b$

To find b, plug a point into this equation (the point (1, 0) will be easiest to use):

$0 = -(3/2)1 + b$

$3/2 = b$

So the final equation is:

$y = -(3/2)x + (3/2)$

But this doesn't appear as a solution option, so we need to try putting answer choices C, D and E in slope-intercept form. It makes sense to start with answer choice E since there are 2's and 3's as coefficients in it. When we rearrange, we see that answer choice E is in fact correct.

High-level Importance

Question 30   A

See: QR 4.8

This is a Quantitative Comparison question with graph analysis (*a nomogram*). A nomogram is a graph showing the relations between three or more variables using a number of scales arranged so that the value of one variable can be found by, for example, drawing a line or following a curve intersecting the other scales.

First, let's try a 'test' run: Try a fork length of 61 inches and then a dorsal girth of 30 inches and note that it intersects the curvilinear line consistent with a weight of approximately 80 pounds (*see green lines and circles in the graph below*). If it is clear to you now, go back and try to answer the question.

The preceding example brings attention to the curved lines, how they are continuous and numbered every 10 pounds with varying intervals. In particular, notice the curved line that says '80' has 3 segments: a middle segment that intersects the data points that we evaluated, and the curved line extends to the bottom right and to the top left of the graph.

Now when we assess the weight of 210 pounds (*see purple lines in the graph*), we must follow that curve upwards until it intersects the vertical line from 83 inches (fork length) and then we can read the dorsal girth, which is 42 inches, which is a quantity greater than 40.

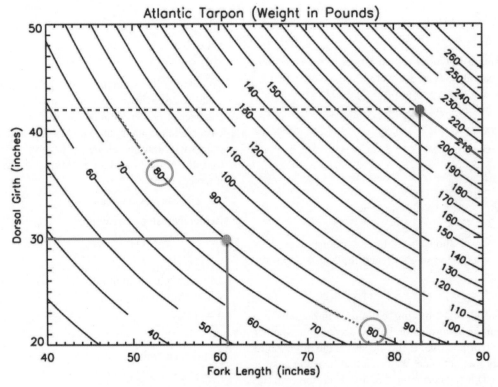

Image from Jerald S Ault, PhD; University of Miami.

If you have any questions or concerns regarding your DAT practice questions, or the solutions, access the free Gold Standard Masters Series Forum for clarification: www.dat-prep.com/forum.

SPOILER ALERT ⚠

Gold Standard has cross-referenced the content in this chapter to examples from the ADA's official DAT practice materials. It is for you to decide when you want to explore these questions since you may want to preserve DAT practice tests for timed mock-exam practice.

We suggest that you acquire the free 2007 DAT practice test from ada.org (digital document format), as well as the 2009 exam or, even better, the most recent online practice test. The online DAT Quantitative Reasoning practice test from the ADA is available through prometric.com and includes content from 2007 (35%), 2009 (10%), and newly added questions (55%). Note below that "Q" is followed by the question number, and cross-references to this chapter are in parentheses.

Examples –

2007 and 2022: Identify the correct equation of a straight line given a point and the equation for a perpendicular line (QR 4.4): 2007 Q12 and 2022 Q27 (*one answer choice is deleted in the 2022 version*); solve a first order inequality (QR 4.2): 2007 Q15 and 2022 Q29 (*one answer choice is deleted in the 2022 version*); determination of f(z) for a second order equation (QR 4.1, 4.1.4): 2007 Q20; rearrange a first order polynomial with two variables (QR 4.1): 2007 Q32; solve a first order polynomial with one variable (QR 4.1): 2007 Q40.

2009 and 2022: Determine the correct equation to describe a set of given numbers (*first order polynomial*, QR 4.1.1): 2009 Q1; solve for *x* in a basic algebraic equation (*first order polynomial*, QR 4.1.1 C.): 2009 Q2; calculate the distance between two points on a standard coordinate plane (QR 4.5.2): 2009 Q11; solve for *x* in a basic algebraic equation involving fractions (*first order polynomial*, QR 2.2.3, 2.4, 4.1.1 C.): 2009 Q17; solve a layered second order polynomial (QR 4.1, 4.6.1): 2009 Q24; determination of f(*x*) (QR 4.1, 4.1.4): 2009 Q39 and 2022 Q6.

2022: Multiply a polynomial by itself (i.e. *square it!*; QR 4.1.3): 2022 Q9; solve a first order polynomial with 2 unknowns and 2 equations (QR 4.4.2): 2022 Q12; understanding equations for lines and the x-y axes (QR 4.4, 4.5): 2022 Q13; basic first order polynomial rearrangement (QR 4.4.2): 2022 Q17; identifying linear equations (QR 4.4, 4.5): 2022 Q18; multiple-line graph analysis (QR 4.5): 2022 Q35; pie chart graph analysis with quantitative comparison (QR 4.5, 4.10): 2022 Q36; histogram graph analysis with quantitative comparison (QR 4.5, 4.10): 2022 Q37; pie chart graph analysis (QR 4.5, 4.10): 2022 Q40.

Note: **The ADA practice tests are composed of questions which have previously appeared on real, past DATs, but have been retired.** Also, note that most of the 2022 ADA DAT practice test questions have had one answer choice removed. In other words, most questions have 4 answer choices instead of 5, which was standard in 2007 and 2009.

Chapter Checklist

☐ Sign up or access your free online account at www.dat-prep.com for discussion boards for any content from this chapter including chapter-ending practice questions.

☐ Reassess your 'learning objectives' for this chapter: Go back to the first page of this chapter and re-evaluate the top 3 boxes and the Introduction.

☐ Complete 1-2 pages of notes using symbols/abbreviations to represent the entire chapter based on your learning objectives. These are your Gold Notes.

☐ Consider your multimedia options based on your optimal way of learning:

    ☐ Download the free Gold Standard DAT app for your Android device or iPhone. Create your own, tangible study cards or try the free app: Anki.

    ☐ Record your voice reading your Gold Notes onto your smartphone (MP3s) and listen during exercise, transportation, etc.

    ☐ Try some online math videos on YouTube like Khan Academy or Leah4sciMCAT playlist for Math Without a Calculator (the latter was produced for MCAT preparation but it remains helpful for DAT QR basics).

☐ Schedule your full-length DAT practice tests: ADA and/or GS exams and/or other free or paid third-party resources. Schedule one full day to complete a practice test and 1-2 days for a thorough assessment of answers and explanations while adding to your abbreviated Gold Notes.

☐ Schedule and/or evaluate stress reduction techniques such as regular exercise (sports), yoga, meditation and/or mindfulness exercises (*see* YouTube for suggestions).

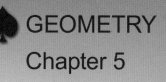

<table>
<tr><td>

Memorize

- The Pythagorean Theorem
- Perimeter, Area, and Volume Formulas
- Properties of Triangles

</td><td>

Understand

* Points in Cartesian Coordinates
* Parallel and Perpendicular Lines
* Similar Polygons
* Types of Triangles and Angles
* Problems with Figures and Solids

</td><td>

Importance

Medium level: 5 of 40
DAT Quantitative Reasoning questions
are based on content in this chapter
(avg. based on past testing patterns).
* Note that approx. **70% of the questions**
in DAT QR are from just
3 of 8 chapters: 2, 4 and 8.

</td></tr>
</table>

DAT-Prep.com

Introduction

Geometry is a very visual branch of mathematics dealing with lines and shapes and relations in space, so drawing and labeling pictures can be extremely helpful when you are confronted with geometric problems. But don't forget about algebra! More often than not, these problems are simply algebraic equations in disguise.

Multimedia Resources at DAT-Prep.com

Free Online Forum

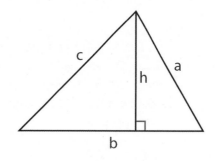

Special Guest

5.0 DAT Has a *Need for Speed*!

Section	DAT Quantitative Reasoning *Need for Speed* Exercises
5.1.1	Add the points (2, 3) and (1, −5):
	Find the distance between the points (5, 0) and (2, −4):
5.1.2 A	The line segment QT of length $4x + 6$ is shown in the figure that follows. Point S is the midpoint of QT and segment RS has length $x − 1$. What is the length of line segment QR? 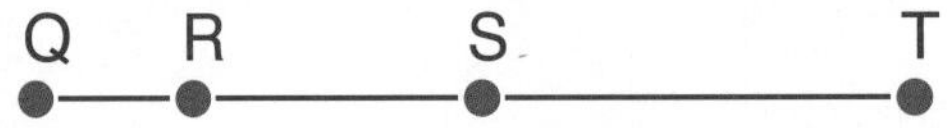
5.1.3 A	Consider the line defined by $y = 2x + 3$. Circle the correct response below. • The line $y = 2x + 2$ must be: perpendicular / parallel / unrelated / identical • The line $y = -\dfrac{1}{2}x + z$ must be: perpendicular / parallel / unrelated / identical
	Consider the line $y = -4x + 10$. What is the slope of the perpendicular line?
	In the following diagram of two parallel lines that are cut by a transversal, there are 8 labeled angles. How many different values can there be? (2 / 4 / 6 / 8 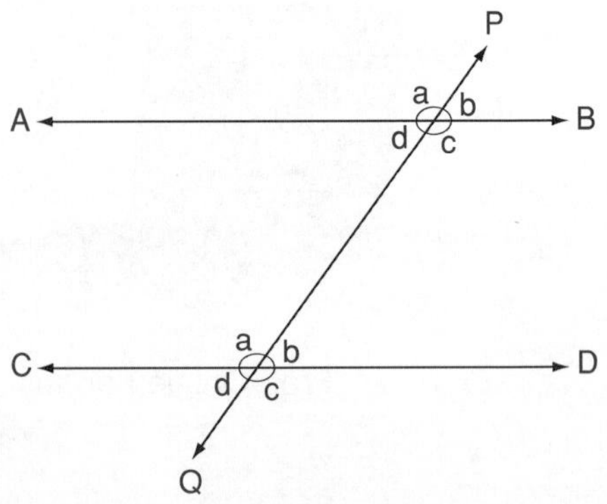)

Medium-level Importance

5.1.3 A	In the diagram below angle *a* is 35°, what is the value of angle *b*? _____

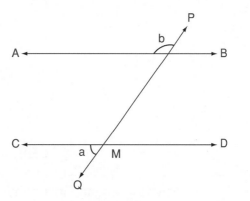

5.1.3C	If a polygon has *x* sides, the sum, S, of the total of all interior angles for that polygon can be calculated by the following formula:

- S = _____

Indicate the interior angles for the 4 common polygons below.

Name	Equilateral Triangle	Square	Pentagon	Hexagon
Shape				
Interior Angle				

5.2.1	Consider the following rectangle.

- What is its perimeter? _____

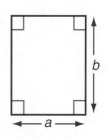

- What is its area? _____

Medium-level Importance

5.2.2

Consider the following triangle. What is the value of *x*?

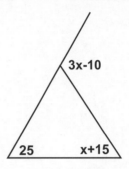

3x-10

25   x+15

Consider the following triangle. What are the possible values for *x*?

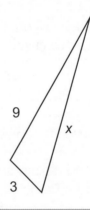

9

x

3

5.2.2A

Consider the following triangle.

- Pythagorean Theorem:

_____

- The area of the triangle, Area =

_____

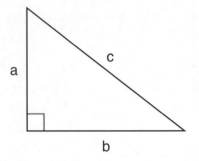

a

c

b

- The sides of a 30°–60°–90°–triangle have the ratio _____ : _____ : _____

- The sides of a 45°–45°–90°–triangle have the ratio _____ : _____ : _____

5.2.3	<ul><li>Circumference of a circle with diameter d: _____</li><li>Circumference of a circle with radius r: _____</li><li>Area of a circle: _____</li></ul>
5.3.1	Consider the following regular, symmetric box. <ul><li>Perimeter: _____</li><li>Surface area: _____</li><li>Volume: _____</li></ul>
5.3.2	<ul><li>Surface area of a sphere: _____</li><li>Volume of a sphere: _____</li></ul>
5.3.3	Consider the following cylinder. <ul><li>Surface area: _____</li><li>Volume: _____</li></ul>
5.3.4	Consider the following cone. <ul><li>Surface area: _____</li><li>Volume: _____</li></ul>

Medium-level Importance

5.1 Points, Lines and Angles

5.1.1 Points and Distance

Knowing your way around the Cartesian coordinate systems begins with understanding the relationships between simple points. As discussed in QR 4.5, points on a graph are represented as an ordered pair of an x and y coordinate, (x, y).

A. Addition and Subtraction of Points

To add or subtract two points, simply add or subtract the two x values to obtain the new x value and add or subtract the two y values to obtain the new y value.

EXAMPLE

Add the points (2, 3) and (1, −5).

$$(2, 3) + (1, -5)$$
$$= (2 + 1, 3 - 5)$$
$$= (3, -2)$$

Graphically, addition of points is easy to visualize. All you are doing when you add two points is treating the first point as the new origin. You then plot the second point in terms of this new origin to find the sum of the two points.

You can add more than two points in the same way. Just add all of the x values together, and then add all of the y values together.

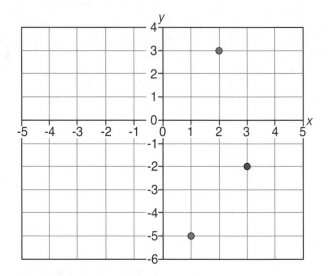

B. Distance between Points

Finding the distance between two points requires the use of the Pythagorean Theorem. This theorem is probably the most important tool you have for solving geometric problems.

> **Pythagorean Theorem:** $x^2 + y^2 = z^2$

This theorem describes the relationship between the lengths of the sides of a right triangle. The lengths x and y correspond to the two legs of the triangle adjacent to the right angle, and the length z corresponds to the hypotenuse of the triangle. For a further discussion of the Pythagorean Theorem and right triangles, *see* QR 5.2.2.

In order to find the distance between two points (x_1, y_1) and (x_2, y_2), consider there to be a line segment connecting them. This line segment (with length z equivalent to the distance between the points) can be thought of as the hypotenuse of a right triangle. The other two sides extend from the points: One is parallel to the x-axis; the other, to the y-axis (with lengths x and y, respectively).

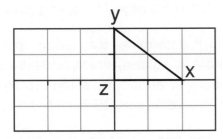

To find the distance between the two points, simply apply the Pythagorean Theorem.

$$x = (x_2 - x_1)$$
$$y = (y_2 - y_1)$$
$$z = \sqrt{(x^2 + y^2)}$$

Plugging in the point coordinates will yield z, the distance between the two points.

EXAMPLE

Find the distance between the points (5, 0) and (2, –4).

$$x = (2 - 5) = -3$$
$$y = (-4 - 0) = -4$$
$$z = \sqrt{(-3^2 + -4^2)}$$
$$= \sqrt{(9 + 16)} = \sqrt{25} = 5$$

So the distance between the points is $z = 5$.

Medium-level Importance

5.1.2 Line Segments

A. Segmentation Problems

These problems are a kind of geometry-algebra hybrid. You are given a line segment that has been subdivided into smaller segments, and some information is provided. You are then asked to deduce some of the missing information.

In a segmentation problem, some of the information you are given may be geometric, and some may be algebraic. There is not, however, a clear algebraic equation to solve. You will need to logically determine the steps needed to reach a solution.

EXAMPLE

The line segment QT of length $4x + 6$ is shown in the figure that follows. Point

S is the midpoint of QT and segment RS has length $x - 1$. What is the length of line segment QR?

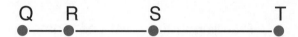

First, determine what information you know. The length of QT and RS are given. Also, since we have a midpoint for QT, the length of QS and ST are simply half of the length of QT.

Now, determine an algebraic relationship regarding the length of QR, which is what we are looking for. We can see that the length of QR is simply QS with the RS segment removed.

$$QR = QS - RS$$

Plugging in our information, we get the following:

$$QR = \frac{(4x + 6)}{2} - (x - 1)$$
$$= 2x + 3 - x + 1$$
$$= x + 4$$

Before you start working out a solution, it can be extremely helpful to list the information you are given. This will help you understand and organize the problem, both in your own mind and on the page.

B. Segments in the Plane

In segmentation problems, you only have to deal with one dimension. However, line segments can also turn up in problems dealing with a two dimensional Cartesian graph.

To determine the length of a line segment in a plane, simply find the distance between its endpoints using the Pythagorean Theorem (*see* QR 5.1.1).

Any line segment in a plane corresponds to a single linear equation. This can be determined as in DAT QR Chapter 4 from any two points on the line segment. Knowing this linear equation can help you find other points on the line segment.

5.1.3 Angles

An **angle** is formed by the intersection of two lines.

In problems that are not trigonometric, angles are almost always measured in degrees. A full circle makes 360°.

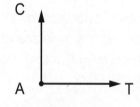

A **right angle** is an angle that is exactly 90°.

An **obtuse angle** is an angle that is greater than 90°.

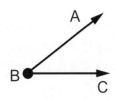

An **acute angle** is an angle that is less than 90°.

A **straight angle** is an angle that is exactly 180°.

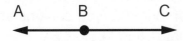

A **vertical angle** is the angle opposite of each other that is formed by two intersecting lines. The two angles across from each other are equal in measure. The following example shows that angles 1 and 3 are vertical angles and equal to each other. Same are angles 2 and 4. At the same time, adjacent vertical angles 1 and 4 or 2 and 3 are also supplementary angles and will form 180°.

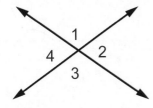

Complementary angles are two angles that add up to 90°. The example that follows shows that angles A and B add up to 90°.

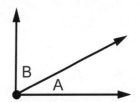

Supplementary angles are two angles that add up to 180°. This example shows that angles A and B add up to 180°.

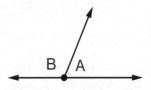

A. Angles and Lines in the Plane

If two lines are **parallel**, they have the same slope. Such lines will never intersect, and so they will never form angles with one another.

If two lines are **perpendicular**, their intersection forms only 90° angles. If the slope of a given line is a/b, then the slope of any perpendicular line is $-b/a$.

EXAMPLE

Consider the line defined by $y = 2x + 3$.

(a) Let us consider an equation for a parallel line:

$$y = 2x + 2.$$

Any line that still has a slope of 2 will suffice. So, in slope-intercept form, any line of the form $y = 2x + a$ will be a parallel line.

Medium-level Importance

Medium-level Importance

(b) Consider an equation for a perpendicular line that intersects both of the preceding two lines.

The solution will be a line with the **negative reciprocal slope** (which, in this instance, is –1/2).

$$y = -\frac{1}{2}x + z$$

Consider the line $y = -4x + 10$. What is the slope of the perpendicular line?

Of course, we take the slope of the line (–4), then take the negative reciprocal: $-(1/-4) = (-1)/(-4) = 1/4$. Thus, the equation of the perpendicular line would have the form $y = x/4 + z$.

The standard kind of angle-line problem deals with a setup of two parallel lines that are cut by a transversal, like the one in the following.

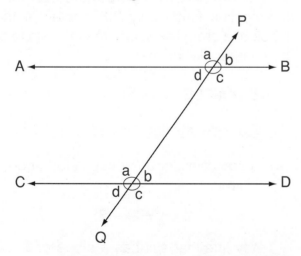

The trick with these problems is to realize that there are only ever **two values** for the angles.

First, think of the two areas of intersection as exact duplicates of each other. The upper left angles are equivalent, as are the upper right, the lower left, and the lower right. Using just this information, you automatically know the value of the twin of any angle that is given to you.

Also, angles that are opposite each other are equivalent. So the lower left angle is the same as the upper right and vice versa.

The other fact you can use to determine unknown angles is that the angle along a straight line is 180°. When you are given an angle a, you can find supplement b by subtracting $180° - a$.

EXAMPLE

In the figure that follows, if angle a is 35°, what is the value of angle b?

Angle b is the twin of the supplement of a, so b is equal to $180° - a$.

$$b = 180° - 35° = 145°$$

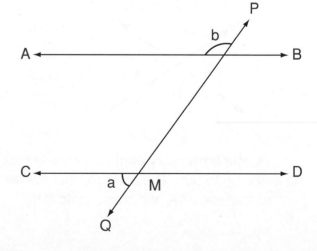

B. Properties of Parallel Line Angles

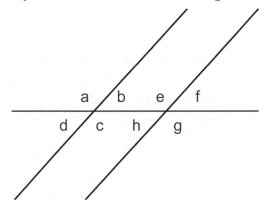

When two parallel lines are cut by a transversal line:

1. both pairs of acute angles as well as obtuse angles are equal: *a* = *e, b* = *f, d* = *h, c* = *g.*

2. alternate interior angles are equal in measure as well: *c* = *e, b* = *h.*

C. Interior Angles of a Polygon

Sometimes you may be dealing with a shape that you are not familiar with and do not know the total of all interior angles. If the polygon has *x* sides, the sum, S, is the total of all interior angles for that polygon. For a polygon with *x* sides, the sum may be calculated by the following formula:

$$S = (x - 2)(180°)$$

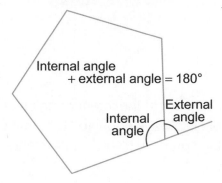

Internal angle + external angle = 180°

External angle

Internal angle

EXAMPLE

A triangle has 3 sides, therefore,

S = (3 – 2) × 180°
S = 180°

A rectangle has 4 sides,

S = (4 – 2) × 180°
S = 360°.

Given the total angles for a polygon, you can determine each interior angle of a polygon by dividing the sum of the polygon by the number of sides.

EXAMPLE

A rectangle has a sum of 360°. Given that x = 4, 360° ÷ 4 = 90°. Therefore, each angle in a rectangle is 90°.

> **NOTE**
>
> The assumption here is that all angles of a given polygon have the same measure, which may not always be the case on the DAT. In order to apply this, be certain that the polygon has equal angles.

Name	Equilateral Triangle	Square	Pentagon	Hexagon
Shape	△	☐	⬠	⬡
Interior Angle	60°	90°	108°	120°

Medium-level Importance

5.2 2D Figures

Make sure you know how to find the area, perimeter, side lengths, and angles of all the figures in this section. There are all kinds of ways to combine different shapes into the same problem; but if you can deal with them all individually, you'll be able to break down any problem thrown your way!

5.2.1 Rectangles and Squares

A **rectangle** is a figure with four straight sides and four right angles. In rectangles, opposite sides always have the same length, as do the two diagonals that can be drawn from corner to corner.

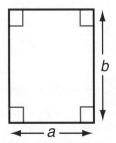

Perimeter: The perimeter of a rectangle is equal to the sum of its sides.

$$\text{Perimeter} = a + b + a + b = 2a + 2b$$

Area: The area of a rectangle is equal to the product of its length and width.

$$\text{Area} = \text{Length} \times \text{Width} = a \times b$$

A **square** is a rectangle with all four sides of the same length, so $a = b$.

The perimeter of a square is

$$P = a + a + a + a = 4a.$$

The area of a square is

$$A = a \times a = a^2.$$

5.2.2 Types of Triangles

While there are a wide variety of types of triangles, every one shares these properties:

(i) The sum of the interior angles of a triangle is always equal to $180°$. In the following figure, a, b, and c are interior angles.

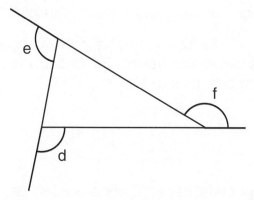

$$3x - 10 = 25 + x + 15$$
$$2x = 10 + 25 + 15$$
$$2x = 50$$
$$\boxed{x = 25}$$

(ii) The sum of the exterior angles of a triangle is always equal to 360°. The following figure shows *d, e,* and *f* to be exterior angles.

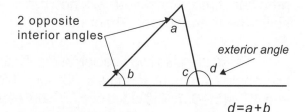

(iii) The value of an exterior angle is equal to the sum of the opposite two interior angles.

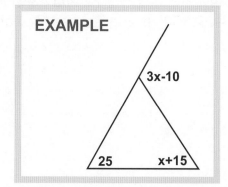

$$d = a + b$$

EXAMPLE

(iv) The perimeter of a triangle is equal to the sum of its sides.

(v) The area of a triangle is always half the product of the base and the height.

$$\text{Area} = \frac{1}{2} \text{ Base} \times \text{Height}$$

You can pick any side of the triangle to function as the base, and the height will be the line perpendicular to that side that runs between it and the opposite vertex.

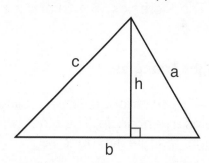

(vi) The sum of any two sides of a triangle is always greater than or equal to the third side. So if *a, b,* and *c* are the three sides of a triangle,

$$a + b \geq c.$$

If the sum of two sides is equal to the length of the third side, the triangle is a line segment. This property is known as the **triangle inequality**.

Medium-level Importance

(vii) The difference of any two sides of a triangle is always smaller than the third side. So if a, b and c are three sides of a triangle, a − b < c.

What are the possible values for x?

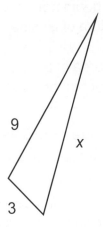

Therefore, x < (9 + 3) and x > (9 - 3), 6 < x < 12.

A. Right Triangles

A **right triangle** is a triangle that contains a right angle. The other two angles in a right triangle add up to 90°.

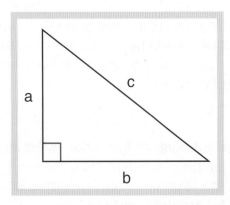

The two short legs of a right triangle (the legs that come together to form the right angle) and the hypotenuse (the side opposite the right angle) are related by the Pythagorean Theorem:

$$a^2 + b^2 = c^2$$

To find a missing side of the triangle, plug the values you have into the Pythagorean Theorem and solve algebraically.

The two legs of a right triangle are its base and height. So to find the area, compute as thus shown.

$$Area = \frac{1}{2}(a \times b)$$

Special Cases: There are a few cases of right triangles you should know. First, the ratios of side lengths 3:4:5 and 5:12:13 are often used. Identifying that a triangle corresponds to one of these cases can save you precious time since you will not have to solve the Pythagorean Theorem.

There are also two special ratios of interior angles for right triangles: 30°–60°–90° and 45°–45°–90°. The sides of a 30°–60°–90° triangle have the ratio 1:$\sqrt{3}$:2 and the sides of a 45°–45°–90° triangle have the ratio 1:1:$\sqrt{2}$.

> **NOTE**
>
> **Pythagorean Theorem**
>
> Knowing any two sides of a right triangle lets you find the third side by using the Pythagorean formula: $a^2 + b^2 = c^2$.
>
> 3-4-5 triangle: if a right triangle has two legs with a ratio of 3:4, or a leg to a hypotenuse ratio of either 3:5 or 4:5, then it is a 3-4-5 triangle.
>
> 5-12-13 triangle: if a right triangle has two legs with a ratio of 5:12, or a leg to a hypotenuse ratio of either 5:13 or 12:13, then it is a 5-12-13 triangle.
>
> 45°-45°-90° triangle: if a right triangle has two angles that are both 45°, then the ratio of the three legs is $1:1:\sqrt{(2)}$.
>
> 30°-60°-90° triangle: if a right triangle has two angles of 30° and 60°, then the ratio of the three legs is $1:\sqrt{(3)}:2$.

B. Isosceles Triangles

An **isosceles triangle** is a triangle that has two equal sides. The angles that sit opposite the equal sides are also equal.

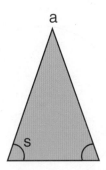

For an isosceles triangle, use the odd side as the base and draw the height line to the odd vertex. This line will bisect the side, so it is simple to determine the height using the Pythagorean Theorem on one of the new right triangles formed.

C. Equilateral Triangles

An **equilateral triangle** is a triangle with all three sides equal. All three interior angles are also equal, so they are all 60°.

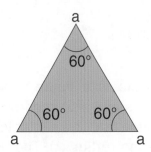

Drawing a height line from any vertex will divide the triangle into two 30°–60°–90° triangles, so you can easily solve for the area.

D. Scalene Triangles

A **scalene triangle** is any triangle that has no equal sides and no equal angles. To find the value for the height of this kind of triangle requires the use of trigonometric functions (*see* DAT QR Chapter 6).

Medium-level Importance

E. Similar Triangles

Two triangles are **similar** if they have the same values for interior angles. This means that ratios of corresponding sides will be equal. Similar triangles are triangles with the same shape that are scaled to different sizes.

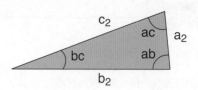

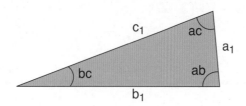

To solve for values in a triangle from information given about a similar triangle, you will need to use ratios. The ratios of corresponding sides are always equal, for example $\frac{a_1}{a_2} = \frac{b_1}{b_2}$. Also, the ratio of two sides in the same triangle is equal to the corresponding ratio in the similar triangle, for example $\frac{a_1}{b_1} = \frac{a_2}{b_2}$.

5.2.3 Circles

A **circle** is a figure in which every point is the same distance from the center. This distance from the center to the edge is known as the **radius** (r). The length of any straight line drawn from a point on the circle, through the center, and out to another point on the circle is known as the **diameter** (d). The diameter is twice the radius.

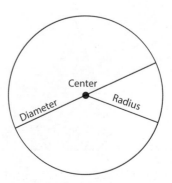

$$d = 2 \times r \quad \text{or} \quad r = \frac{1}{2}d$$

There are no angles in a circle.

Circumference: The circumference of a circle is the total distance around a circle. It is equal to pi times the diameter.

$$\text{Circumference} = \pi \times d = 2\pi \times r$$

Area: The area of a circle is equal to pi times the square of the radius.

$$\text{Area} = \pi \times r^2 = \frac{1}{4}\pi \times d^2$$

Length: Length of an arc is defined as a piece of circumference formed by an angle of n degrees measured as the arc's central angle in a circle of radius r.

$$L = \frac{n°}{360°} \times 2\pi r$$

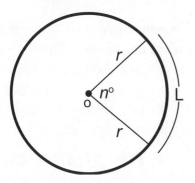

Area of a sector: The area of a sector is a portion of the circle formed by an angle of n degree measured as the sector's central angle in a circle of radius r.

$$\text{Area (sector)} = \frac{1}{2}r^2\theta \text{ (in radians)}$$

$$\text{Area (sector)} = \frac{n°}{360°} \times \pi r^2 \text{ (in degrees)}$$

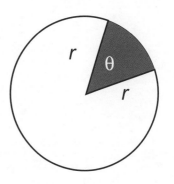

5.2.4 Trapezoids and Parallelograms

A. Trapezoids

A **trapezoid** is a four-sided figure with one pair of parallel sides and one pair of non-parallel sides.

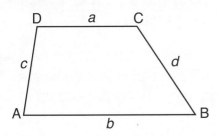

Usually the easiest way to solve trapezoid problems is to drop vertical lines down from the vertices on the smaller of the two parallel lines. This splits the figure into two right triangles on the ends and a rectangle in the middle. Then, to find information about the trapezoid, you can solve for the information (side length, area, angles, etc.) of these other shapes.

Medium-level Importance

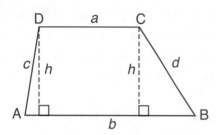

1. The area of a trapezoid is calculated as

$$\frac{a+b}{2}h$$

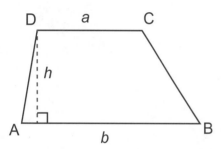

2. The upper and lower base angles are supplementary angles (i.e., they add up to 180°).

Angle A + Angle D = 180°

Angle B + Angle C = 180°

Sometimes it can be useful to draw a line from vertex to vertex and construct a triangle that way, but this usually only makes sense if the resulting triangle is special (i.e. isosceles).

Isosceles Trapezoids: Just like isosceles triangles, **isosceles trapezoids** are trapezoids with two equal sides. The sides that are equal are the parallel sides that form angles with the base of the trapezoid. Similarly, if the left and right sides are of the same lengths, these angles are the same as well.

In this isosceles trapezoid, ABCE means that Angle A = Angle D, Angle B = Angle C, and Diagonal AC = Diagonal BD.

The perimeter = $a + b + 2c$

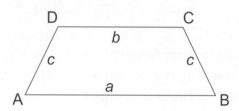

B. Parallelograms

A **parallelogram** is a quadrilateral that has two sets of parallel sides. A square, for example, is a special kind of parallelogram, as is a rhombus (which has four sides of equal length but, unlike a square, has two different pairs of angle values).

Area: The area of a parallelogram is simply the base times the height.

Area = (Base) × (Height)

The height of a parallelogram can be found by dropping a vertical from a vertex to the opposite side and evaluating the resulting right triangle.

The sum of all the angles in a parallelogram is 360°. Opposite angles are equivalent, and adjacent angles add up to 180°.

Medium-level Importance

5.3 3D Solids

In three dimensions, it doesn't always make sense to talk about perimeters. Shapes with defined edges (such as boxes and pyramids) still have them, but rounded shapes (such as spheres) do not. Instead, we are generally concerned with the values of surface area and volume.

5.3.1 Boxes

Boxes are the three-dimensional extension of rectangles. Every angle in a box is 90°, and every box has six rectangular faces, twelve edges, and eight vertices. Opposite (and parallel) faces are always of the same length, height, and width, as are opposite (and parallel) edges.

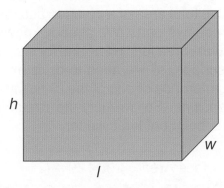

Perimeter: The perimeter of a box is the sum of its edges. There are, however, only three different lengths and four edges corresponding to each one. So to find the perimeter, we can simply take the sum of four times each the width, length, and height.

$$\text{Perimeter} = 4l + 4w + 4h = 4(l + w + h)$$

Surface Area: The surface area of a box is the sum of the area of each of its faces. Since there is one duplicate of each unique face, we only need to find three products, double them, and add them together.

$$\text{Surface Area} = 2lw + 2wh + 2lh$$
$$= 2(lw + wh + lh)$$

Volume: Calculating the volume of a box can be visualized as taking the surface of any of its rectangular faces and dragging it through space, like you were blowing a box-shaped bubble. So you start with the product of a width times a height, and then you multiply that by a length.

$$\text{Volume} = l \times w \times h$$

5.3.2 Spheres

The definition of a sphere is basically identical to that of a circle, except that it is applied in three dimensions rather than two: It is a collection of points in three dimensions that are all of the same distance from a particular center point. Again, we call this distance the radius, and twice the radius is the diameter. A sphere has no vertices or edges, so it has no circumference.

Surface Area:

$$\text{Surface Area} = 4\pi \times r^2$$

Volume:

$$\text{Volume} = (4/3)\pi \times r^3$$

5.3.3 Cylinders

Spheres may be the 3D equivalent of circles, but if you start with a circle and extend it into the third dimension, you obtain the tube shape known as a cylinder. Cylinders have two parallel circular faces, and their edges are connected by a smooth, edgeless surface.

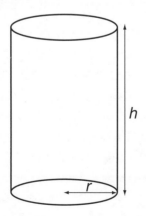

Surface Area: The surface area of a cylinder is composed of three parts: The two circular faces and the connecting portion. To find the total area of a cylinder, add the areas of these two parts. We already know how to calculate area for circles; and for the connecting surface, all we need to do is extend the circumference of one of the circles into three dimensions. So, multiply the circumference by the height of the cylinder.

$$\text{Surface Area} = 2(\pi \times r^2) + (2\pi \times r) \times h$$

Volume: The volume of a cylinder is equal to the area of one of its bases (circle) multiplied by the height.

$$\text{Volume} = (\pi \times r^2) \times h$$

5.3.4 Cones

A cone is like a cylinder, except that instead of having a circle on either end; it has a circle on one and a single point on the other. The height of the cone is the distance from the center of the circle to the single vertex, and the slant length is the distance from the edge of the circle to the vertex.

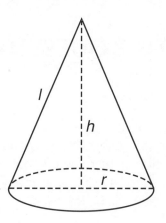

Surface Area: To find the surface area of a cone, we use the same strategy as we did with a cylinder. We find the surface area of the circle and add it to the surface area of the smooth lateral portion. The area of the circle can be found from the radius as usual, and the area of the lateral portion is ½ the circumference of the circle times the slant length.

$$\text{Surface Area} = (\pi \times r^2) + \frac{1}{2}c \times l$$
$$= (\pi \times r^2) + \frac{1}{2}(2\pi \times r) \times l$$

Volume: To find the volume of a cone, we need the radius of the circle and the cone's height.

$$\text{Volume} = (1/3)\pi \times r^2 \times h$$

5.3.5 Other Solids

There are all kinds of different solids that can be constructed out of basic 2D figures and the solids we've already discussed. If you are able to deal with all of these individually though, you will be able to break down and tackle any wacky solid that might be thrown at you.

5.3.6 Vertices

You have now heard the word "vertex" used in different instances with similar meanings. Just for clarification, we may define the vertex as: **(1)** the point at which the sides of an angle intersect; **(2)** the points on a triangle or pyramid opposite to and farthest away from its base; and finally, **(3)** a point on a polyhedron (a solid bounded by faces/polygons) common to three or more sides.

GOLD STANDARD DAT QR PRACTICE QUESTIONS

CHAPTER 5: Geometry

1) The area of a circle is 144π. What is its circumference?

A. 6π
B. 24π
C. 72π
D. 12π
E. 36π

2) How many cubes with edges of length 6 inches will fit inside a cubical box with an edge of length 1 yard?

A. 216
B. 36
C. 18
D. 108
E. 72

3) The points $(2,-3)$ and $(2,5)$ are the end-points of a diameter of a circle. What is the radius of the circle?

A. 64
B. 4π
C. 16
D. 8
E. 4

4) A cylinder of radius 1 foot and height 1 foot is full of water. The water is poured into a cyclinder of radius 1 foot and height 6 inches until it is full. How many cubic feet of the water will be left over?

A. 0.6π
B. 0.4π
C. 0.64π
D. 0.5π
E. 0.75π

5) A and B are similar 45°-45°-90° triangles. If B has an area of 12 square feet, and A has three times the area of B, what is the length of A's hypotenuse?

A. $\sqrt{72}$ feet
B. 36 feet
C. 72 feet
D. 12 feet
E. 6 feet

6) Leslie drives from Highway 1 to the parallel Highway 2 using the road that crosses them, as in the given figure below. Leslie misses the turn onto Highway 1 at point Q and drives 2 km further, to point P. Driving in a straight line from point P to get back to Highway 1, how much further will Leslie travel?

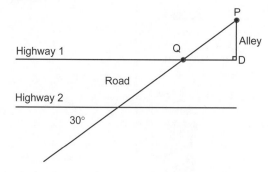

A. 1/2 km
B. $\sqrt{3}$ km
C. 1 km
D. 2 km
E. $2\sqrt{3}$ km

7) A circle is inscribed in a square with a diagonal of length 5. What is the area of the circle?

A. $\dfrac{25}{8}\pi$

B. $\dfrac{25}{2}\pi$

C. $\dfrac{25}{16}\pi$

D. $\dfrac{25}{4}\pi$

E. 50π

8) A circle is drawn inside a larger circle so that they have the same center. If the smaller circle has 25% the area of the larger circle, which of the following is the ratio of the radius of the small circle to that of the larger circle?

A. $\dfrac{1}{8}$

B. $\dfrac{3}{4}$

C. $\dfrac{1}{4}$

D. $\dfrac{1}{25}$

E. $\dfrac{1}{2}$

9) A circle passes through the point (0,0) and the point (10,0). Which of the following could NOT be a third point on the circle?

A (1, –3)
B (2, 4)
C (7, 4)
D (5, 0)
E (2, –4)

10) A rectangular picture 4½ feet wide and 3½ feet long is enclosed by a border 3 inches wide. What is the total area, in square feet, of the picture and border?

A. 12
B. 15
C. 15¾
D. 17¹³⁄₁₆
E. 20

11) Mary wants to wallpaper a room. It has one bay window that measures 3 feet by 4 feet, and a door that measures 3 feet by 7 feet. The room is 12 feet by 12 feet, and is 10 feet tall. If only the walls are to be covered, and rolls of wallpaper are 100 square feet, what is the minimum number of rolls that she will need?

A. 4 rolls

B. 5 rolls

C. 6 rolls

D. 7 rolls

E. 8 rolls

12) In order to protect her new car, Stacey needs to build a new garage. The concrete floor needs to be 64.125 square feet and is 9.5 feet long. How wide does it need to be?

A. 7.25 feet

B. 8.25 feet

C. 6.75 feet

D. 6.25 feet

E. 7.50 feet

13) What is the measure of the missing length?

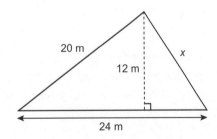

A. 7 m   C. 14 m

B. 10 m   D. 17 m

14) How high is the height h as measured along the wall from the ground to the end of the ladder against the building?

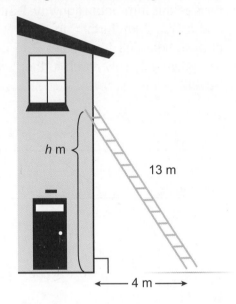

A. $4^2 + h^2 = 13^2$; 12.4 m

B. $4^2 + 13^2 = h^2$; 12.7 m

C. $4^2 + h^2 = 13^2$; 10.6 m

D. $4^2 + h^2 = 13^2$; 14.4 m

15) A square is connected to a triangle below. What is the measure of the hypotenuse of the triangle?

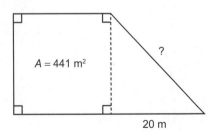

A. 21 m   C. 35 m

B. 29 m   D. 40 m

16) An equilateral triangle with sides of length 4 is inscribed in a circle. What is the radius of the circle?

   A. $1/\sqrt{3}$
   B. 2
   C. $4/\sqrt{3}$
   D. $2/\sqrt{3}$
   E. 4

17) What is the area of a right triangle with legs of length 3 and 4?

   A. 4
   B. 5
   C. 6
   D. 7
   E. 8

18) A cone of height 3 in has a volume of 12π in^3. What is the radius of base of the cone in inches?

   A. $\sqrt{3}$
   B. $2\sqrt{3}$
   C. π
   D. $\pi\sqrt{3}$
   E. 2π

19) What is the measure of the acute angle between the x-axis and the line $y = x - 3$?

   A. 10°
   B. 25°
   C. 30°
   D. 45°
   E. 60°

20) What is the area of the triangle formed by the points A = (5,2), B = (1,2), and C = (1, 4)?

   A. 1
   B. 2
   C. 3
   D. 4
   E. 5

21) On a Euclidean plane, what is the distance between (−5, 9) and (4, 3)?

   A. $\sqrt{131}$
   B. $\sqrt{117}$
   C. 13
   D. 11
   E. 10

22) A right triangle has a hypotenuse of length 13 and a longer leg of length 12. What is the area of a circle with a radius of the same length as the shorter side of the given triangle?

   A. 12π
   B. 20π
   C. 25π
   D. 100π
   E. 156π

23) Which of the following represents the length of the side of a square that has an area of 8?

   A. 1.5
   B. $\sqrt{2}$
   C. 2
   D. $2\sqrt{2}$
   E. 4

24) On a Euclidean plane, what is the distance between $(-3, 5)$ and $(4, 1)$?

A. $\sqrt{65}$

B. $\sqrt{85}$

C. 11

D. 13

E. 14

25) A cylinder has a height of 10 cm and a base diameter of 6 cm. Which of the following is the best approximation of the total surface area, in cm²?

A. 245

B. 220

C. 180

D. 120

E. 60

CHAPTER REVIEW SOLUTIONS: CHAPTER 5

Question 1   B

See: QR 5.2, 5.2.3

Using the given information to write an equation, we have:

$$\pi r^2 = 144\pi$$

We need the value of the radius to find the circumference, so we solve for r:

$$r^2 = \frac{144\pi}{\pi}$$
$$r = \sqrt{144}$$
$$r = 12$$

The formula for the circumference of a circle gives us:

$$2\pi r = 2\pi(12) = 24\pi$$

Question 2   A

See: QR 5.3, 5.3.1

We need to divide the volume of the box by the volume of one of the smaller cubes. One edge of the large box is 1 yard, or 36 inches, so its volume is $(36 \text{ in})^3 = 46656$ in. The volume of the cube is $(6 \text{ in})^3 = 216 \text{ in}^3$

$$\frac{46656 \text{ in}^3}{216 \text{ in}^3} = 216$$

Question 3   E

See: QR 5.2, 5.2.3

The length of the radius is half of the length of the diameter, which is $d = \sqrt{(2-2)^2 + (-3-5)^2} = \sqrt{0 + 64} = 8$ units long. The radius is therefore equal to 4.

Question 4   D

See: QR 5.3, 5.3.3

The difference in volume of the cylinders will give us the difference in the amount of water they can hold. The larger cylinder has volume $\pi(1)^2(1)^2 = \pi \text{ ft}^3$ and the smaller cylinder has volume $\pi(1)^2(0.5) = 0.5\pi \text{ ft}^3$. The difference is $\pi \text{ ft}^3 - 0.5\pi \text{ ft}^3 = 0.5\pi \text{ ft}^3$.

Question 5   D

See: QR 5.2, 5.2.2

Triangle A has an area of $\frac{bh}{2} = 3(12 \text{ ft}^2) = 36\text{ft}^2$, which means that its base times its height is equal to 72 square feet. The base and height of all $45°-45°-90°$ triangles are the same, so

$(b \times h)/2 = (b \times b)/2 = 36$. Solving for b gives us $b = \sqrt{72}$. Using the Pythagorean Theorem, we can solve for the hypotenuse. $h^2 = (\sqrt{72})^2 + (\sqrt{72})^2 = 144$, therefore $h = \sqrt{144} = 12$.

Question 6   C

See: QR 5.1, 5.1.3

The angle PQD has a measure equal to that of the given angle, 30 degrees, because the highways are parallel and the road forms a transversal across them. The hypotenuse of the right triangle PQD is 2 km long, and the alley, which forms the leg of the triangle that is opposite angle PQD, has a length of

$$(2 \text{ km}) \sin(30°) = 1 \text{ km}$$

Question 7   A

See: QR 5.2, 5.2.1, 5.2.3

The relationship between the length of a side s and the length of the diagonal d of a square is

$$d = s\sqrt{2}$$

The length of a side of the given square is therefore

$$s = \frac{d}{\sqrt{2}} = \frac{5}{\sqrt{2}}$$

This is always the length of the diagonal of the inscribed circle, which has a radius of length $\frac{5}{\sqrt{2}} \div 2 = \frac{5}{2\sqrt{2}}$. The area of the circle is therefore

$$\pi\left(\frac{5}{2\sqrt{2}}\right)^2 = \frac{25\pi}{8}$$

Question 8   E

See: QR 5.2, 5.2.3

Represent the areas of the large and small circle by πr_L^2 and πr_S^2, respectively. 25% is equivalent to $\frac{1}{4}$, so

$$\pi r_S^2 = \frac{1}{4}(\pi r_L^2)$$

$$r_S^2 = \frac{1}{4}r_L^2$$

$$\sqrt{r_S^2} = \sqrt{\frac{1}{4}r_L^2}$$

$$r_S = \frac{1}{2}r_L$$

and the ratio of the radii is $\dfrac{r_S}{r_L} = \dfrac{\frac{1}{2}r_L}{r_L} = \dfrac{1}{2}$.

Question 9   D

See: QR 5.1, 5.1.1, 5.2.3

(0, 0), (10, 0), and any given point except (5, 0) can be connected by an arc, which can form part of a circle. (0, 0), (10, 0), and (5, 0) can only be connected by a line, which can never form part of a circle.

Question 10   E

See: QR 5.2, 5.2.1

The 3-inch border at each end of both dimensions adds 6 in., or 0.5 ft. to both the length and the width of the picture. The total area of both picture and border is therefore: (5) (4) = 20 sq. ft.

Question 11   B

See: QR 5.3, 5.3.1

The four walls have a total area of 4(10)(12) = 480 sq. ft. The total area of the door and bay window are (3)(7) + (3) (4) = 21 + 12 = 33 sq. ft. The total surface area that needs to be covered with wallpaper is therefore 480 − 33 = 447 sq. ft. The number of wallpaper rolls needed is $\frac{447}{100} = 4.47$, which rounds up to 5.

Question 12   C

See: QR 5.3, 5.3.1

The surface area of the floor is given by its length times its width, so its width is given by the surface area divided by the length:

$$\frac{64.125}{9.5} = 6.75 \text{ feet}$$

Question 13   C

See: QR 5.1.1, 5.2.2

There are several triangles! At the far right, we have the hypotenuse x of a little triangle. We know its height (12 m) but we do not yet know the length of its small base. But, we have the hypotenuse (20 m) of the triangle to the left and its height (12 m). Let's use Pythagoras to calculate the base of the triangle on the left:

$$20^2 = 12^2 + b^2$$

Medium-level Importance

$400 = 144 + b^2$

$400 - 144 = b^2$

$256 = b^2$

$16 = b$

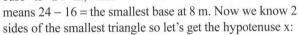

and since the biggest base is 24 m, that means $24 - 16 =$ the smallest base at 8 m. Now we know 2 sides of the smallest triangle so let's get the hypotenuse x:

$x^2 = 8^2 + 12^2 = 64 + 144 = 208$

The square root of 196 is 14, and the square root of 225 is 15 (QR 2.5.6), so the answer must be just over 14, answer choice C.

Question 14   A

See: QR 5.1.1, 5.2.2
The image is that of a right angle triangle where we know the hypotenuse (the side opposite the right angle, 13) and one side (4) so it is easy to calculate:

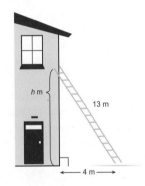

$x^2 + y^2 = z^2$ (QR 5.1.1)

$4^2 + h^2 = 13^2$

$16 + h^2 = 169$ (QR 2.5.6)

$h^2 = 169 - 16 = 153$

So we need the square root of 153 which must be a number between 12 (squared is 144) and 13 (squared is 169), and so the answer is A. Note that you should know the squares of numbers from 1 to 15 (QR 2.5.6).

Question 15   B

See: QR 5.1.1, 5.1.2

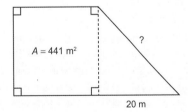

We want the hypotenuse but we only have one side of the triangle (20 m). We can get the height of the triangle by

changing the area of the square into length. Area is one side times the other, so we can take the square root of 441 to get length in m. $20 \times 20 = 400$, let's try $21 \times 21 =$ bingo, 441.

So, we have a triangle with 20 m and 21 m as sides and we need the hypotenuse.

$c^2 = 20^2 + 21^2 = 400 + 441 = 841$

c is equal to a number just below 30 (since $30 \times 30 = 900$), and the closest number is 29 (of course you can double check that 29 x 29 is indeed 841).

Question 16   C

See: QR 5.2.2C, 6.1.2
If you place a point at the center of the triangle and draw a line to one of its vertices, that is the radius of the circle. To find the length of this line, consider the right triangle for which it is the hypotenuse, and the two legs are formed by dropping a perpendicular line from the midpoint to one of the sides of the right triangle. We know the longer leg has length 2 (half of the right triangle side, 4) and the interior angle measures 30° (half of one angle of the right triangle, all of which are 60°). So using basic trigonometry we can find the hypotenuse, r:

$r \cos(30°) = 2$

$r = 2/\cos(30°)$

$r = 2/(\sqrt{3}/2)$

$r = 4/\sqrt{3}$.

Question 17   C

See: QR 5.2.2A
Remember A = 1/2 (a x b), and you are given a = 3, b = 4.

A = 1/2 (3 x 4)

A = 6.

Question 18   B

See: QR 5.3.4
Remember $A = (1/3)\pi(r^2)h$. You are given $A = 12\pi$ in³, and h = 3 in. Plug these into the equation and solve for r:

$12\pi = (1/3)\pi(r^2)(3)$

$12\pi = \pi r^2$

$12 = r^2$

$r = 2\sqrt{3}$ in.

Question 19   D

See: QR 4.5.4, 5.2.2A

This is an equation in slope-intercept form, so the slope of the line is 1. Therefore the ratio of rise to run (or triangle leg a to leg b, in the case of a triangle drawn with the x-axis) is 1:1. Therefore both interior angles of the triangle are 45°.

Question 20   D

See: QR 5.1.1, 5.2.2A

The angle ABC is a right angle, so the line segments AB and BC are the legs of the right triangle. Therefore the area of the triangle is 1/2 (AB x BC).

$$AB = \sqrt{[(5-1)^2 + (2-2)^2]} = \sqrt{(4^2)} = 4$$

$$AB = \sqrt{[(1-1)^2 + (4-2)^2]} = \sqrt{(2^2)} = 2$$

So:

Area = 1/2 (4 x 2) = 4.

Question 21   B

See: QR 5.1.1

To find the distance between two points on a plane, use the Pythagorean theorem. The distance you are looking for is the hypotenuse of the right triangle formed using the two points. The other two sides have lengths $|x_1 - x_2|$ and $|y_1 - y_2|$, or in this case $|-5 - 4| = 9$ and $|9 - 3| = 6$. So:

$$x^2 = 9^2 + 6^2 = 81 + 36 = 117$$

$$x = \sqrt{117}$$

Question 22   C

See: QR 5.2.2 A.

This is a 5-12-13 triangle, so the shorter leg has length 5. A circle with radius 5 has an area of:

$$A = \pi(5^2)$$
$$= 25\pi.$$

Question 23   D

See: QR 5.2.1

The area of a square with side length x is: Area = x^2, so in this case:

$$8 = x^2$$

$$x = \sqrt{8} = 2\sqrt{2} \,.$$

Question 24   A

See: QR 5.1.1

To find the distance between two points on a plane, use the Pythagorean theorem. The distance you are looking for is the hypotenuse of the right triangle formed using the two points. The other two sides have lengths $|x_1 - x_2|$ and $|y_1 - y_2|$, or in this case $|-3 - 4| = 7$ and $|5 - 1| = 4$. So:

$$x^2 = 7^2 + 4^2 = 49 + 16 = 65$$

$$x = \sqrt{65}.$$

Question 25   A

See: QR 5.3.3

The surface area of a cylinder is:

A = (circumference of its base) x (height) + 2(area of base)

$$A = (2\pi r)(h) + 2(\pi r^2)$$

The radius of the base r = diameter x ½ = 3.

$$A = (6\pi \text{ cm})(10 \text{ cm}) + 18\pi \text{ cm}^2 = 78\pi \text{ cm}^2$$

To approximate this value, let $\pi = 3.14$ (*we do not need more precision because the answer choices are not extremely close to each other*)

$$A = 78 \times 3.14 \text{ cm}^2 \approx 245.$$

Medium-level Importance

If you have any questions or concerns regarding your DAT practice questions, or the solutions, access the free Gold Standard Masters Series Forum for clarification: www.dat-prep.com/forum.

⟨SPOILER ALERT ⚠⟩

Gold Standard has cross-referenced the content in this chapter to examples from the ADA's official DAT practice materials. It is for you to decide when you want to explore these questions since you may want to preserve DAT practice tests for timed mock-exam practice.

We suggest that you acquire the free 2007 DAT practice test from ada.org (digital document format), as well as the 2009 exam or, even better, the most recent online practice test. The online DAT Quantitative Reasoning practice test from the ADA is available through prometric.com and includes content from 2007 (35%), 2009 (10%), and newly added questions (55%). Note below that "Q" is followed by the question number, and cross-references to this chapter are in parentheses.

Examples –

2007 and 2022: Determine the area of a square given the perimeter (QR 5.2.1): 2007 Q2; a box and a triangle, find the hypotenuse (QR 5.2.2, 5.3.1): 2007 Q9 and 2022 Q11 (*one answer choice is deleted in the 2022 version*); calculate the distance between two points on a graph (QR 5.1): 2007 Q22 and 2022 Q31 (*one answer choice is deleted in the 2022 version*); solve for length in a right angle triangle (QR 5.1.1, 5.2.2): 2007 Q23 and 2022 Q20 (*one answer choice is deleted in the 2022 version*); solve for length in a right angle triangle (QR 5.1.1, 5.2.2): 2007 Q28; three circles, areas and diagram given, determine the perimeter of the triangle made by their radii (QR 5.1.1, 5.2.2, 5.2.3): 2007 Q36.

2009 and 2022: Determine the length of a square's side where area and perimeter are the same value (QR 5.2.1): 2009 Q10 and 2022 Q1; calculate the length of a right triangle's side given the angle and the hypotenuse (QR 5.2.2): 2009 Q12 and 2022 Q2 (*one answer choice is deleted in the 2022 version*); determine the area of a circle given the radius (QR 5.2.3): 2009 Q30; calculate the length of a side of a regular hexagon inscribed in a circle with a given diameter (QR 5.2.2, 5.2.3; *note: we will explore this question type in Chapter 8*): 2009 Q31; surface area of part of a cylinder (*label on a soup can!* QR 5.3.3): 2009 Q32; determine the length of the short side of an isosceles triangle given area and the length of the longer sides (QR 5.2.2): 2009 Q40.

Note: **The ADA practice tests are composed of questions which have previously appeared on real, past DATs, but have been retired.** Also, note that most of the 2022 ADA DAT practice test questions have had one answer choice removed. In other words, most questions have 4 answer choices instead of 5, which was standard in 2007 and 2009.

Chapter Checklist

☐ Sign up or access your free online account at www.dat-prep.com for discussion boards for any content from this chapter including chapter-ending practice questions.

☐ Reassess your 'learning objectives' for this chapter: Go back to the first page of this chapter and re-evaluate the top 3 boxes and the Introduction.

☐ Complete 1-2 pages of notes using symbols/abbreviations to represent the entire chapter based on your learning objectives. These are your Gold Notes.

☐ Consider your multimedia options based on your optimal way of learning:

   ☐ Download the free Gold Standard DAT app for your Android device or iPhone. Create your own, tangible study cards or try the free app: Anki.

   ☐ Record your voice reading your Gold Notes onto your smartphone (MP3s) and listen during exercise, transportation, etc.

   ☐ Try some online math videos on YouTube like Khan Academy or Leah4sciMCAT playlist for Math Without a Calculator (the latter was produced for MCAT preparation but it remains helpful for DAT QR basics).

☐ Schedule your full-length DAT practice tests: ADA and/or GS exams and/or other free or paid third-party resources. Schedule one full day to complete a practice test and 1-2 days for a thorough assessment of answers and explanations while adding to your abbreviated Gold Notes.

☐ Schedule and/or evaluate stress reduction techniques such as regular exercise (sports), yoga, meditation and/or mindfulness exercises (*see* YouTube for suggestions).

Medium-level Importance

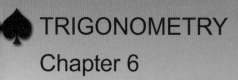

TRIGONOMETRY
Chapter 6

Memorize (*DAT-30*)	Understand (*DAT-30*)	Importance
* Formulas for Sine, Cosine, and Tangent * Important Values of Sine and Cosine * Important Identities * Polar Coordinate Conversions	* Graphing Sine, Cosine, and Tangent * Secant, Cosecant, and Cotangent * The Unit Circle * Degrees vs. Radians * Inverse Trigonometric Functions * Graphing in Polar Coordinates * Distance and Midpoint Formulas	**Low level: 0 of 40** DAT Quantitative Reasoning questions are based on content in this chapter (avg. based on past testing patterns). * Note that approx. **70%** of the questions in DAT QR are from just 3 of 8 chapters: 2, 4 and 8.

DAT-Prep.com

Introduction

Trigonometry once represented, on average, 4 of 40 DAT QR exam questions. Trigonometry has been removed from the official ADA syllabus since 2017. When asked about this in an online ADA DAT information session, the head of DAT testing would not say: "Do not study any trigonometry for DAT QR." However, it is telling that there are no traditional trigonometry questions in the ADA's 2022 DAT QR practice test (*no trig functions, no unit circle, no identities, no polar coordinates*).

This chapter is for students aiming for a perfect DAT score. There may be rare instances where the logic, reasoning or just working with right angle triangles may be of help for geometry. Naturally, there are no *Need for Speed* exercises and only 10 practice questions at the end of this chapter (*the fewest of any chapter*).

Multimedia Resources at DAT-Prep.com

Free Online Forum

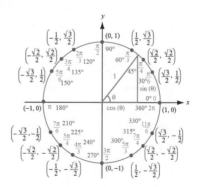

Special Guest

6.1 Basic Trigonometric Functions

The trigonometric functions describe the relationship between the angles and sides of right triangles. The angle in question is generally denoted by θ, the Greek letter theta, but you will never see the right angle used as θ.

We call the leg connecting to the vertex of θ the *adjacent side* ("b" in the diagram), and the leg that does not touch the *opposite side* ("a" in the diagram). The edge across from the right angle is called the *hypotenuse*.

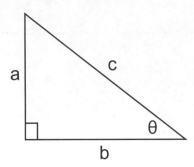

6.1.1 Sine

A lot of people like to use the mnemonic device "SOH-CAH-TOA" to remember how to evaluate the three basic trigonometric functions: Sine, cosine, and tangent. The first three letters, "SOH," refer to the first letter of each word in the following equation.

$$\text{Sine} = \frac{\text{Opposite}}{\text{Hypotenuse}}$$

Sine of an angle θ is written sin(θ). So to calculate this value, simply divide the length of the opposite side by the length of the hypotenuse.

EXAMPLE

What is sin(θ) in the following triangle?

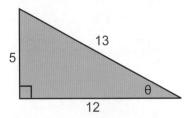

The opposite side has length 5, and the hypotenuse has length 13, so:

$$\sin(\theta) = \frac{5}{13}$$

Low-level Importance

6.1.2 Cosine

The second set of three letters in SOH-CAH-TOA refers to the equation for the cosine of an angle.

$$\text{Cosine} = \frac{\text{Adjacent}}{\text{Hypotenuse}}$$

The abbreviation for the cosine of an angle is $\cos(\theta)$.

EXAMPLE

In the 5–12–13 triangle in Section 6.1.1, what is $\cos(\theta)$?

Dividing the adjacent side by the hypotenuse, we obtain the following solution:

$$\cos(\theta) = \frac{12}{13}$$

6.1.3 Tangent

The final three letters in SOH-CAH-TOA refer to the equation for finding the tangent of an angle.

$$\text{Tangent} = \frac{\text{Opposite}}{\text{Adjacent}}$$

You can also find the tangent of an angle if you know the value for sine and cosine. Notice that the hypotenuse cancels out if you divide sine and cosine.

$$\text{Tangent} = \frac{\text{Sine}}{\text{Cosine}}$$

You can also manipulate this equation to express sine or cosine in terms of the tangent.

EXAMPLE

In the 5–12–13 triangle in Section 6.1.1, what is $\tan(\theta)$?

Dividing the opposite side by the adjacent side, we obtain:

$$\tan(\theta) = \frac{5}{12}$$

Low-level Importance

6.1.4 Secant, Cosecant, and Cotangent

These three functions are far less commonly used than sine, cosine, and tangent, but you should still be familiar with them. They are not very hard to remember because they are just the reciprocals of the main three functions.

$$\text{Cosecant} = \frac{1}{\text{Sine}}$$

$$= \frac{\text{Hypotenuse}}{\text{Opposite}}$$

$$\text{Secant} = \frac{1}{\text{Cosine}}$$

$$= \frac{\text{Hypotenuse}}{\text{Adjacent}}$$

$$\text{Cotangent} = \frac{1}{\text{Tangent}}$$

$$= \frac{\text{Adjacent}}{\text{Opposite}}$$

The abbreviations for these functions are sec, csc, and cot, respectively.

6.2 The Unit Circle

6.2.1 Trig Functions on a Circle

As you can see from the equations in QR 6.1, the trigonometric functions are ratios of side lengths. This means that every angle has a value for each of the functions that *does not* depend on the scale of the triangle.

In QR 6.1, we looked at examples with a 5–12–13 triangle. Our solutions were as follows:

$$\sin(\theta) = \frac{5}{13}$$

$$\cos(\theta) = \frac{12}{13}$$

$$\tan(\theta) = \frac{5}{12}$$

Let's compare these results with the trigonometric functions for the similar triangle 10, 24, 26, which clearly has longer sides but the same angle θ:

Low-level Importance

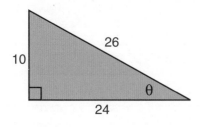

$$\sin(\theta) = \frac{10}{26} = \frac{5}{13}$$

$$\cos(\theta) = \frac{24}{26} = \frac{12}{13}$$

$$\tan(\theta) = \frac{10}{24} = \frac{5}{12}$$

As you can see, the trigonometric values for the angle remain the same.

Also, the absolute value of sine and cosine is never greater than 1 for any angle. This makes perfect sense because the hypotenuse of a triangle is always its longest side, and for sine and cosine, the hypotenuse is in the denominator.

If we plot the graph of sine and cosine for θ from 0° to 360° in Cartesian Coordinates with $x = \cos(\theta)$ and $y = \sin(\theta)$, we obtain a circle of radius 1. This is known as the **unit circle**, as shown in the succeeding picture. The angle formed at the vertex of the x-axis is equal to θ.

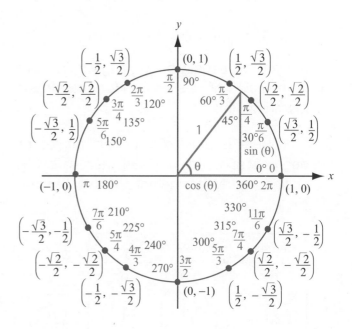

When simply dealing with right triangle figures, we never use negative numbers because negative length does not make sense. With the unit circle, though, legs of the triangle can be in negative space on the Cartesian plane. This can result in negative values for sine and cosine.

6.2.2 Degrees and Radians

Up until this point, we have measured angles using degrees. When dealing with trigonometric functions, however, it is often more convenient to use the unit-less measurement of **radians**. There are 2π radians in 360°, so one trip around the unit circle is an increase in θ by 2π radians.

$$2\pi \text{ radians} = 360°$$

This translates to 1 radian $= \dfrac{360}{2\pi}$, but you will usually be working with radians in multiples of π, so it is not necessary to memorize this.

Here is a list of important angles (in degrees and radians) and their sine and cosine values to memorize from the unit circle:

Degrees	Radians	Sine	Cosine
0°	0	0	1
30°	$\dfrac{\pi}{6}$	$\dfrac{1}{2}$	$\dfrac{(\sqrt{3})}{2}$
45°	$\dfrac{\pi}{4}$	$\dfrac{1}{\sqrt{2}}$	$\dfrac{1}{\sqrt{2}}$
60°	$\dfrac{\pi}{3}$	$\dfrac{(\sqrt{3})}{2}$	$\dfrac{1}{2}$
90°	$\dfrac{\pi}{2}$	1	0

Note that $\dfrac{1}{\sqrt{2}}$ is the same as $\dfrac{\sqrt{2}}{2}$.

These major angles repeat for each quadrant of the unit circle, but the signs of the sine and cosine values change. Moving counterclockwise around the circle and beginning with the upper right, the quadrants are labeled I, II, III, and IV.

Quadrant	Sine	Cosine
I	+	+
II	+	−
III	−	−
IV	−	+

NOTE

How many degrees are there in $\dfrac{3(\pi)}{4}$ radians?

Because 2π radians = 360°, this makes 1(π) radian = 180°.

Solution:

1π radian = 180°

$$\dfrac{3\pi}{4} = \dfrac{3\pi}{4} \times \dfrac{180°}{\pi}$$
$$= 135°$$

How many radians are there in 270°?

Solution:

1π radian = 180°

$$270° \times \dfrac{\pi}{180°} = \dfrac{3\pi}{2}$$

6.2.3 Graphing Trig Functions

Looking at the unit circle, it is very apparent that the trigonometric functions are **periodic**. This means that they continue to repeat the same cycle infinitely. After you go once around the circle, a full 360°, you end up right back at the beginning and begin to cycle through again.

A. Sine

As you can see from the table in 6.2.2, the sine function increases for the first 90°. For the next 90° it decreases while staying positive, then it continues to decrease into the negatives, and finally for the last 90°, it increases from −1 back to 0. From this information, we can picture the general shape of the graph, and we know that the period of the function is a full 360° or 2π radians.

The graph itself looks like this:

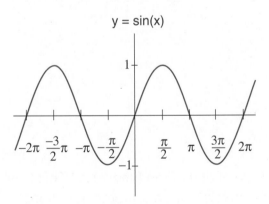

As you can see in the graph, the sine function reaches a maximum at $\frac{\pi}{2} + 2\pi \times n$, has an x-intercept at $\pi \times n$, and a minimum at $\frac{3\pi}{2} + 2\pi \times n$ where n is any integer.

B. Cosine

The cosine function is identical to the sine function, except that it is shifted along the x-axis by half a period. So rather than starting at 0 and increasing, it starts at one and decreases. The period is still 2π radians.

The graph looks like this:

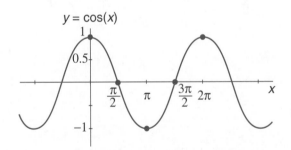

Just like with the sine function, you can see where the maxima, minima, and intercepts of the cosine function are from the graph. It reaches a maximum at $2\pi \times n$, an x-intercept at $\frac{\pi}{2} + \pi \times n$, and a minimum at $2\pi \times n + \pi \times n$ where n is any integer.

Low-level Importance

C. Tangent

The graph of the tangent function differs from sine and cosine graphs in a few important ways. First of all, the tangent function repeats itself every π radian instead of every 2π. So it is π-periodic rather than 2π-periodic. Also, it has vertical **asymptotes**, vertical lines that the function approaches but never crosses, at $(n)\left(\dfrac{\pi}{2}\right)$ for every odd integer *n*. The value of the tangent

goes infinity as it approaches an asymptote from left to right; and negative infinity as it approaches from right to left.

Remember, the tangent function is the ratio of the sine function to the cosine function, so the asymptotes occur when the cosine of an angle is equal to zero, where cos(x) = 0, because division by zero is undefined. 0/0 is never possible for the tangent function, so it is irrelevant.

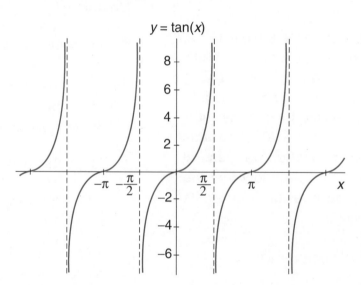

6.3 Trigonometric Problems

6.3.1 Inverse Trig Functions

We have discussed the formulas for finding the value of trigonometric functions for different angles, but how can you find the value of an angle if all you know is the

value of one of the functions? This is where the inverse trigonometric functions come into play.

The **inverse** of a trigonometric function takes an input value x and outputs an angle. The value of the inverse trigonometric function of x is equal to the angle. To represent an inverse function, we write -1 in superscript like we would an exponent. But remember, this is not actually an exponent.

Inverse sine is represented as $\sin^{-1}$ and it is defined as such:

$$\sin(\sin^{-1}(x)) = x$$

So, $\sin(\theta) = x$ and $\sin^{-1}(x) = \theta$.

Now that we have inverse functions in our toolbox, we can begin to solve algebraic problems that contain trigonometric functions.

Solve the following equation for x.

$$\pi - \tan 2x = \left(\frac{4}{3}\right)\pi$$

$$\Rightarrow -\tan 2x = \left(\frac{1}{3}\right)\pi$$

$$\Rightarrow \tan 2x = \frac{-\pi}{3}$$

$$\Rightarrow 2x = \tan^{-1}\left(\frac{-\pi}{3}\right)$$

$$\Rightarrow x = \left(\frac{1}{2}\right)\tan^{-1}\left(\frac{-\pi}{3}\right)$$

6.3.2 Trigonometric Identities

There are a few other identities that can be extremely useful in the manipulation of equations involving trigonometric functions. If you encounter such an equation and it seems like it would be difficult to solve using only inverses, you should try to apply these identities. You may have to do some algebraic work, though, before you can apply them.

(i) $\sin^2\theta + \cos^2\theta = 1$

This identity follows directly from the Pythagorean Theorem. Since the sine and cosine compose the legs of a right triangle and the hypotenuse has length 1, this identity always holds.

Low-level Importance

(ii) $\quad \tan^2\theta + 1 = \sec^2\theta$

(iii) $\quad \cot^2\theta + 1 = \csc^2\theta$

(iv) $\quad \sin(2\theta) = 2\sin\theta\cos\theta$

(v) $\quad \cos(2\theta) = 1 - 2\sin^2\theta$

(vi) $\quad \tan(2\theta) = \dfrac{2\tan\theta}{1-\tan^2\theta}$

EXAMPLE

Simplify the following equation:

$$\sin^2(x) + \sin^2(x) \times \cos^2(x) = \sec^2(x)$$

Since the only functions on the left side at this point are sines and cosines, let's factor out a $\sin^2(x)$ and then try to use identity (i).

$$\sin^2(x)[\sin^2(x) + \cos^2(x)] = \sec^2(x)$$
$$\sin^2(x) \times 1 = \sec^2(x)$$

Now let's replace $\sec^2(x)$ using identity (ii).

$$\sin^2(x) = \tan^2(x) + 1$$

We can even simplify this further using the equation for tangent (= sin/cos) and then multiply each side by $\cos^2(x)$.

$$\sin^2(x) = \frac{\sin^2(x)}{\cos^2(x)} + 1$$

$$\sin^2(x)\cos^2(x) = \left(\frac{\sin^2(x)}{\cos^2(x)} + 1\right)\cos^2(x)$$

$$\sin^2(x)\cos^2(x) = \cos^2(x) + \sin^2(x)$$

By using identity (i) again, we have

$$\sin^2(x)\cos^2(x) = 1$$

6.3.3 The Pythagorean Theorem

The Pythagorean Theorem is fundamental to trigonometry.

If a problem requires you to set up an equation involving trigonometric functions, whether it is from an arbitrary right triangle or the unit circle, you will most likely need to use the Pythagorean Theorem. Remember, it is the primary relationship we have in relating the lengths of sides in a right triangle, so now we can relate side length to trigonometric functions.

Low-level Importance

6.4 Polar Coordinates

So far, we have only discussed graphs using Cartesian coordinates. As we have seen, the Cartesian system makes it easy to work with straight lines, but this does not hold true for all types of curves.

There is another important two-dimensional system that uses what are known as **polar coordinates**. Instead of plotting a point using the two legs of a right triangle (the x and y coordinates in the Cartesian system), polar coordinates use the hypotenuse of the triangle (r) and the angle from the x-axis (θ). Instead of two distance components, polar coordinates use one radial distance component (the distance from the origin) and an angle component. A point is written as the ordered pair (r, θ).

Conversions: Sometimes, it is necessary to convert points between polar and Cartesian coordinates. Here are the identities to use:

(i) $r^2 = x^2 + y^2$

(ii) $x = r \times \cos(\theta)$

(iii) $y = r \times \sin(\theta)$

EXAMPLE

Convert the Cartesian point (3,4) to polar coordinates.

Before we can find θ we need to find the value for r using (i).

$$r^2 = 3^2 + 4^2$$
$$\Rightarrow r^2 = 25$$
$$\Rightarrow r = 5$$

Now we can find θ using either (ii) or (iii).

$$3 = 5 \times \cos(\theta)$$
$$\Rightarrow 3/5 = \cos(\theta)$$
$$\Rightarrow \theta = \cos^{-1}(3/5)$$
$$\Rightarrow \theta \approx 53°$$

Combining this information, we see that the Cartesian point (3,4) is the point (5, 53°) in polar coordinates.

EXAMPLE

Convert $x^2 + y^2 = 4$ to polar coordinates and graph.

This conversion happens to be extremely simple. All we need to do is apply (i) directly.

$$\Rightarrow r^2 = 4$$
$$\Rightarrow r = 2$$

Notice that in this equation, r does not depend on θ. It contains simply all points that are 2 units away from the origin.

Low-level Importance

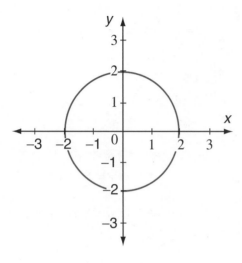

In polar coordinates, a circle of radius x centered at the origin results when $r = x$ for any constant x.

6.5 Additional Helpful Formulas

Sum or Difference of Two Angles

For angles α and β, the following sum and difference identities may be applied:

1. $\sin(\alpha + \beta) = \sin\alpha\cos\beta + \cos\alpha\sin\beta$

2. $\sin(\alpha - \beta) = \sin\alpha\cos\beta - \cos\alpha\sin\beta$

3. $\cos(\alpha + \beta) = \cos\alpha\cos\beta - \sin\alpha\sin\beta$

4. $\cos(\alpha - \beta) = \cos\alpha\cos\beta + \sin\alpha\sin\beta$

5. $\tan(\alpha + \beta) = \dfrac{\tan\alpha + \tan\beta}{1 - \tan\alpha\tan\beta}$

6. $\tan(\alpha - \beta) = \dfrac{\tan\alpha - \tan\beta}{1 + \tan\alpha\tan\beta}$

Low-level Importance

Cofunction Identities

$$\sin\left(\frac{\pi}{2} - \theta\right) = \cos\theta \qquad \cos\left(\frac{\pi}{2} - \theta\right) = \sin\theta$$

$$\tan\left(\frac{\pi}{2} - \theta\right) = \cot\theta \qquad \cot\left(\frac{\pi}{2} - \theta\right) = \tan\theta$$

$$\sec\left(\frac{\pi}{2} - \theta\right) = \csc\theta \qquad \csc\left(\frac{\pi}{2} - \theta\right) = \sec\theta$$

Odd-Even Identities

For angle θ at which the functions are defined:

1. $\sin(-\theta) = -\sin(\theta)$
2. $\cos(-\theta) = \cos(\theta)$
3. $\tan(-\theta) = -\tan(\theta)$
4. $\cot(-\theta) = -\cot(\theta)$
5. $\sec(-\theta) = \sec(\theta)$
6. $\csc(-\theta) = -\csc(\theta)$

Low-level Importance

GOLD STANDARD DAT QR PRACTICE QUESTIONS

CHAPTER 6: Trigonometry

1) In a right triangle ABC with right angle at C, hypotenuse AB = 7 cm and side AC = 2 cm, approximately what is the measure of the angle at A?

   A. 17°
   B. 1°
   C. 0.5°
   D. 73°
   E. 16°

2) What percentage of the unit circle is represented by the angle 8π/5?

   A. 1.6%
   B. 80%
   C. 0.25%
   D. 160%
   E. 502%

3) Which of the following is the value of -cos(π/2)?

   A. 0
   B. −1
   C. 1
   D. $1/\sqrt{2}$
   E. $\sqrt{2}$

4) The tangent of one of the acute angles in a right triangle is 3/2. If the leg opposite this angle has a length of 12, what is the length of the hypotenuse?

   A. 8
   B. $6\sqrt{13}$
   C. $4\sqrt{13}$
   D. 18
   E. $3\sqrt{13}$

5) $\cos(x) - \sin(x) = 0$, $x = ?$

   A. 45°
   B. 30°
   C. 180°
   D. 60°
   E. 270°

6) If the secant of an angle is 5/4, what is the tangent of the angle?

   A. 9/16
   B. 1/2
   C. 4/5
   D. 3/4
   E. $\sqrt{41}/25$

Low-level Importance

7) The value of $\cos(\pi/6)$ equals the value of:

   A. $\sin(\pi/2)$
   B. $\sin(\pi/4)$
   C. $\sin(\pi)$
   D. $\sin(\pi/6)$
   E. $\sin(\pi/3)$

8) The sine of an angle is negative, and the tangent of the same angle is positive. In which quadrant does the angle lie?

   A. First
   B. Second
   C. Third
   D. Fourth
   E. Any

9) A line segment in the Cartesian plane extends from the origin to point (x,y) and has a length of 5. If θ is the angle between the x-axis and the line, and cos (θ) = 1/2, what is the value of y?

   A. $\sqrt{3}/2$
   B. 2
   C. $2\sqrt{3}$
   D. 5/2
   E. $5\sqrt{3}/2$

10) A right triangle has an area of $\sqrt{3}/2$. For interior angle θ, tan (θ) = $\sqrt{3}$. What is the length of the hypotenuse?

   A. 1
   B. 2
   C. 3
   D. $2\sqrt{3}$
   E. $3\sqrt{3}$

Low-level Importance

CHAPTER REVIEW SOLUTIONS: CHAPTER 6

Question 1   D
See: QR 6.3, 6.3.1
The lengths of the hypotenuse and the side adjacent to angle A are given, so we can use the inverse cosine of the ratio of these sides to fnd the angle:

$$\cos^{-1}\left(\frac{2}{7}\right) \approx 73°$$

Question 2   B
See: QR 6.2, 6.2.1
A circle covers a total of 2π radians, and

$$\frac{\frac{8\pi}{5}}{2\pi} = \frac{4}{5}$$

which is equivalent to 80%.

Question 3   A
See: QR 6.5

$$-\cos\left(\frac{\pi}{2}\right) = \cos\left(\frac{\pi}{2}\right) = 0$$

Question 4   C
See: QR 6.1, 6.1.3, 6.3, 6.3.3
In a right triangle, the tangent of an angle represents the ratio of sides $\frac{opposite}{adjacent}$, so the given values form the proportion $\frac{3}{2} = \frac{12}{x}$, where x is the side adjacent the angle in Question. Cross-multiplication gives us $3x = 24$, or $x = 8$, and we can fnd the length of the hypotenuse using the Pythagorean Theorem:

$$12^2 + 8^2 = c^2$$
$$144 + 64 = c^2$$
$$\sqrt{208} = c$$
$$\sqrt{4 \times 4 \times 13} = c$$
$$4\sqrt{13} = c$$

Question 5   A
See: QR 6.3, 6.3.2
Simplifying the expression, we get: Cos $(x) = $ sin(x). The only angle for which the sine and cosine are equal is

45°. This can be inferred from the fact that the legs of a 45°-45°-90° triangle are of equal lengths.

Question 6   D
See: QR 6.3, 6.3.2
Using the identity $\tan^2(x) + 1 = \sec^2(x)$,

$$\tan^2(x) + 1 = \left(\frac{5}{4}\right)^2$$
$$\tan^2(x) = \frac{25}{16} - \frac{16}{16}$$
$$\tan(x) = \sqrt{\frac{9}{16}}$$
$$\tan(x) = \frac{3}{4}$$

Question 7   E
See: QR 6.2, 6.2.3
The cosine of an angle is equal to the sine of its complement. $\frac{\pi}{6}$, or $\left(\frac{\pi}{6}\right)\left(\frac{180°}{\pi}\right) = 30°$, is the complement of $\frac{\pi}{3} = 60°$.

Question 8   C
See: QR 6.2, 6.2.1
On the unit circle, the sine of an angle is equivalent to the y-coordinate of the terminal side of the angle, so the angle must lie in one of the quadrants in which y is negative: The third or fourth. The tangent of an angle is represented by the quotient of the y-coordinate and x-coordinate of the angle's terminal side, so it is positive in quadrants in which x and y have the same sign: The third and first. Therefore, the angle must be located where the two possible regions overlap: The third quadrant.

Question 9   E
See: QR 6.1.1, 6.2.2
Notice that the values x and y describe the length of the sides a right triangle with hypotenuse 5 and interior angle θ. The value of y can be described as 5sin (θ). Since cos (θ) = 1/2, sin (θ) = $\sqrt{3}$/2. So:

y = 5sin (θ)
y = 5$\sqrt{3}$/2.

Question 10   B

See: QR 6.1, 6.3.1

Since tan $(\theta) = \sqrt{3}$, $\theta = 60°$. The legs of the triangle have length a = x cos (60°) and b = x sin (60°) where x is the length of the hypotenuse. Plug these values into the equation for area of a right triangle and solve for x:

$$\sqrt{3}/2 = 1/2 \ (a)(b)$$
$$\sqrt{3} = (x \cos (60°))(x \sin (60°))$$
$$\sqrt{3} = x^2 \ (1/2)(\sqrt{3}/2)$$
$$4 = x^2$$
$$2 = x.$$

If you have any questions or concerns regarding your DAT practice questions, or the solutions, access the free Gold Standard Masters Series Forum for clarification: www.dat-prep.com/forum.

⚠ SPOILER ALERT ⚠

Gold Standard has cross-referenced the content in this chapter to examples from the ADA's official DAT practice materials. It is for you to decide when you want to explore these questions since you may want to preserve DAT practice tests for timed mock-exam practice.

We suggest that you acquire the free 2007 DAT practice test from ada.org (digital document format), as well as the 2009 exam or, even better, the most recent online practice test. The online DAT Quantitative Reasoning practice test from the ADA is available through prometric.com and includes content from 2007 (35%), 2009 (10%), and newly added questions (55%). Note below that "Q" is followed by the question number, and cross-references to this chapter are in parentheses.

Examples –

2007: Cosine odd-even identity (QR 6.5): 2007 Q34; cosine and the unit circle (QR 6.2.1): 2007 Q35.

2009: Convert secant to cosine given the range (QR 6.1.2, 6.1.4, 6.2.1): 2009 Q9; given coordinates and an image, find the cosine of an angle (QR 6.1.2, 6.2.1): 2009 Q14; the value of the tangent of an angle (QR 6.1.3, 6.2): 2009 Q15; the value of the tangent or arctan given 2 sides (QR 6.1.3, 6.3.1): 2009 Q34; again, the value of the tangent or arctan given 2 sides (QR 6.1.3, 6.3.1): 2009 Q36.

2022: Nothing.

Note: **The ADA practice tests are composed of questions which have previously appeared on real, past DATs, but have been retired.** Also, note that most of the 2022 ADA DAT practice test questions have had one answer choice removed. In other words, most questions have 4 answer choices instead of 5, which was standard in 2007 and 2009.

Chapter Checklist

☐ Sign up or access your free online account at www.dat-prep.com for discussion boards for any content from this chapter including chapter-ending practice questions.

☐ Reassess your 'learning objectives' for this chapter: Go back to the first page of this chapter and re-evaluate the top 3 boxes and the Introduction.

☐ Complete a maximum of 1 page of notes using symbols/abbreviations to represent the entire chapter based on your learning objectives. These are your Gold Notes.

☐ Consider your multimedia options based on your optimal way of learning:

    ☐ Download the free Gold Standard DAT app for your Android device or iPhone. Create your own, tangible study cards or try the free app: Anki.

    ☐ Record your voice reading your Gold Notes onto your smartphone (MP3s) and listen during exercise, transportation, etc.

    ☐ Try some online math videos on YouTube like Khan Academy or Leah4sciMCAT playlist for Math Without a Calculator (the latter was produced for MCAT preparation but it remains helpful for DAT QR basics).

☐ Schedule your full-length DAT practice tests: ADA and/or GS exams and/or other free or paid third-party resources. Schedule one full day to complete a practice test and 1-2 days for a thorough assessment of answers and explanations while adding to your abbreviated Gold Notes.

☐ Schedule and/or evaluate stress reduction techniques such as regular exercise (sports), yoga, meditation and/or mindfulness exercises (*see* YouTube for suggestions).

PROBABILITY AND STATISTICS
Chapter 7

Memorize	Understand	Importance
Formula for Average Formula for Probability Standard Deviation with Formula, the Normal Curve and Associated Percentages Definitions: Variance, Z scores Probability; Permutations vs Combinations	* Determining Probabilities * Combining Probabilities of Multiple Events * Mode, Median, Variance, Standard Deviation and its Corresponding Graph * Correlation Coefficient * Permutations and Combinations	**Medium level: 4 of 40** **DAT Quantitative Reasoning questions** are based on content in this chapter (avg. based on past testing patterns). * Note that approx. 70% of the questions in DAT QR are from just 3 of 8 chapters: 2, 4 and 8.

DAT-Prep.com

Introduction

Probability and statistics are branches of mathematics concerned with the laws governing random events. This includes the collection, analysis, interpretation, and display of numerical data. This has always been a core DAT QR subject. However, since 2017, it has become somewhat more important.

Sometimes related questions in DAT probability and statistics are types of "word problems," which we will explore in this chapter, or paired with Quantitative Comparison, which we will explore in Chapter 8.

Multimedia Resources at DAT-Prep.com

Free Online Forum

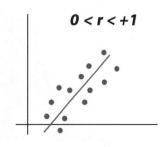

Special Guest

7.0 DAT Has a *Need for Speed*!

Section	DAT Quantitative Reasoning *Need for Speed* Exercises
7.1.1	Probability of rolling a die: Out of 6, how many ways can you roll a number that is not divisible by 3?
7.1.2	If you flip a coin twice, what is the probability that it will come up heads exactly one time?
7.2.1	What is the average of the set {4, 7, 6, 7}?
7.2.2	Find the mode, median, and mean of the following set: {3, 5, 11, 3, 8}. • Mode: _____ • Median: _____ • Mean: _____
7.3.2	Consider the normal distribution curve. Green + Blue + Red = _____% or _____ Standard Deviation(s) Green + Blue = _____% or _____ Standard Deviation(s) Green Area = _____% or _____ Standard Deviation(s)

Medium-level Importance

7.3.3	Consider the following two curves.
	• The yellow curve represents relatively (high / low) variance.
	• The blue curve represents relatively (high / low) variance.
7.3.4	Equation for the standard deviation of a population (*DAT-30*):
	How is variance (v) and standard deviation (s) related? (*circle the correct response*) They are not related. / $v = s$ / $v = s^2$ / $v = s^3$ {*Note that the latter is also described in QR 7.3.3.*}
7.3.6	Suppose you have 7 books and place 3 on a shelf. What are the total number of ways to fill the 3 slots on the shelf?
7.3.7	Suppose you have 7 books and place 3 on a shelf. This time, the order the books appear on the shelf is not relevant. What is the number of different combinations?
Chapter 7, Appendix	*Z* scores are measures of: p-values / standard deviation / null hypothesis / degrees of freedom

Medium-level Importance

7.1 Probability

7.1.1 What is Probability?

Probability is a measure of the likelihood that something will happen.

In mathematics, probability is represented as a ratio of two numbers. The second number - the denominator - corresponds to the total number of possible outcomes the situation can have. The first number - the numerator - corresponds to the number of ways the particular outcome in question can occur.

$$\text{Probability} = \frac{(\text{number of ways the outcome can occur})}{(\text{number of possible outcomes})}$$

Let's look at a simple example.

Let's consider the flipping of a coin. Of course, we know that there are only two possible outcomes of a coin flip, heads or tails. So the total number of outcomes is 2, which will be our denominator.

Say we want to find the probability that a flipped coin will be heads. There is only one way this outcome can come about, so the numerator will be 1. Therefore, the probability of flipping heads is 1 in 2:

$$\text{Probability of Heads} = \frac{1}{2}$$

It is important to note that the quantity in the numerator of a probability ratio is a subset of the quantity in the denominator. The number of ways an outcome can occur is always less than or equal to the total number of outcomes. This means that a probability will never be more than 1, since 1 would mean the outcome is the *only* possibility. Also, the sum of the probabilities of all possible outcomes will always be 1.

Let's look at a slightly more complicated example.

Say you have a typical six-sided die with the sides labeled 1 through 6. If you roll the die once, what is the probability that the number will not be divisible by 3?

Let's begin by finding the total number of outcomes. Be careful here. The only outcomes we wish to determine the probability of are rolls of numbers divisible by 3, but the total number of possible outcomes is not affected by this restriction. There are still 6 in total, one for each number it is possible to roll.

Now we want to know how many ways out of these 6 we can roll a number that is not divisible by 3. Well, the only two numbers that are divisible by 3 that are possibilities are 3 and 6. So 1, 2, 4, and 5 are not. This means that there are 4 ways for the outcome to occur.

$$\text{Probability} = \frac{4}{6}$$

Reducing fractions is usually fine when working with probability; just know that if you do, the numerator and denominator will not necessarily correspond to the number of possibilities anymore.

$$\text{Probability} = \frac{2}{3}$$

The simplest way to complicate a probability problem is to allow for multiple correct outcomes. To find the total probability, simply add the individual probabilities for each correct outcome. For the above example, the total probability is actually the sum of the probabilities of rolling 1, 2, 4, and 5.

7.1.2 Combining Probabilities

What if you are asked to find the probability that multiple events will occur?

The solution to such a problem will still be a ratio in which the numbers represent the same quantities as before. The new difficulty is figuring out how many different outcome possibilities there are. Luckily, there is an easy way to calculate this. All you have to do is find the probability of each individual event and then multiply them together.

Why does this work? Think about it this way: For each possible outcome of the first event, there is still every possible outcome for the second. So the total number of possibilities will be the number of outcomes in the first times the number of outcomes in the second.

EXAMPLE

Let's go back to the flipping coin! If you flip it twice, what is the probability that the first flip will turn up heads and the second tails?

When dealing with multiple events, always focus on one event at a time before combining. So start with the first flip. We know that the probability it will be heads is ½. Now for the second flip, the probability it will be tails is also ½.

Now to find the probability that both of the events will occur, we multiply the individual probabilities:

$$\text{Probability} = \frac{1}{2} \times \frac{1}{2}$$
$$= \frac{1}{4}$$

Medium-level Importance

Medium-level Importance

Probability questions will not always be as clear-cut as this. Let's look at another coin flip example.

EXAMPLE

If you flip a coin twice, what is the probability that it will come up heads exactly one time?

This question seems almost identical to the previous example, but be careful! The difference is that the phrasing of this question does not specify particular outcomes for the individual events.

Let's solve this in two ways:

(i) Let's combine both events into one. To find the total number of possible outcomes, multiply the totals of each event, so there are $2 \times 2 = 4$ possibilities. Now count the number of ways we can flip heads once. Well, we could have heads on the first flip and tails on the second, so that is 1, or we could have tails then heads, so that is 2. Therefore, the probability of flipping heads exactly once is 2 to 4.

$$\text{Probability} = \frac{2}{4}$$
$$= \frac{1}{2}$$

(ii) Now let's treat the events separately. Ask yourself: What are the odds that an outcome of the first event will be compatible with flipping heads once? The answer is

$\frac{2}{2}$ since we can still achieve the overall desired outcome with the second flip no matter what the first flip is.

Now what are the odds that an outcome of the second event will be compatible with flipping heads once? Since you already have a first flip determined, there is only one outcome for the second flip that will give the desired result. If the first flip was heads we need a tails flip, and if the first flip was tails we need a heads flip. So the odds for the second flip are ½ .

$$\text{Probability} = \frac{2}{2} \times \frac{1}{2}$$
$$= \frac{2}{4}$$

There are all kinds of confusing ways probability problems can be written. You have to be extra careful to break them down and determine exactly what is being asked because the test writers love to try and trick you. Double and triple-check that you have the setup right for probability problems because it is so easy to accidentally overlook something.

NOTE

When you want to know the probability of event A or B, the probabilities must be added. If you want to know the probability of events A and B, the probabilities must be multiplied.

7.2 Statistics

7.2.1 Averages

When given a collection of numbers, the **average** is the sum of the numbers divided by the total number of numbers.

$$\text{Average} = \frac{\text{(sum of numbers)}}{\text{(number of numbers)}}$$

EXAMPLE

What is the average of the set {4, 7, 6, 7}?

Add up the numbers and, since there are 4 of them, divide by 4.

$$\text{Average} = \frac{(4+7+6+7)}{4}$$
$$= \frac{24}{4}$$
$$= 6$$

The average may or may not actually appear in the set of numbers, but it is a common way to think of the typical value for the set.

7.2.2 Mode, Median, Mean

Here are a few other statistics terms you should know:

The **mode** of a set of values is the number that appears the most times. Mode can be bimodal or multimodal. Simply stated, bimodal means that two numbers are repeated the most while multimodal indicates two or more numbers are repeated the most.

The **median** of a set of values is the number that appears exactly in the center

of the distribution. This means there are an equal number of values greater than and less than the median.

Arithmetic mean is just another name for the average of a set of numbers. The terms are interchangeable.

EXAMPLE

Find the mode, median, and mean of the following set: {3, 5, 11, 3, 8}.

Medium-level Importance

Let's begin with the mode. All we need to do is see which value or values repeat the most times. In this case, the only one that repeats is 3.

Mode = 3

To find the median we always need to first arrange the set in numerical order.

{3, 3, 5, 8, 11}

Now the median is whichever number lies in the exact center.

Median = 5

Since the mean is the same as the average, we add the values and divide by 5.

$$\text{Mean} = \frac{(3+3+5+8+11)}{5}$$

$$= \frac{30}{5}$$

$$= 6$$

NOTE

If a set has an even number of values, there will be no value exactly in the center. In this case, the median is the average of the two values that straddle the center.

Example

Given: 3, 4, 5, 6, 6, 8, 9, 10, 10, 12

The median is the average of the two middle data: $\frac{(6+8)}{2} = 7$

7.3 More Tools for Probability and Statistics

7.3.1 The Correlation Coefficient

The correlation coefficient r indicates whether two sets of data are associated or *correlated*. The value of r ranges from -1.0 to 1.0. The larger the absolute value of r, the stronger the association. Given two sets of data X and Y, a positive value for r indicates that as X increases, Y increases. A negative value for r indicates that as X increases, Y decreases.

Imagine that the weight (X) and height (Y) of everyone in the entire country was determined. There would be a strong positive correlation between a person's weight and their height. In general, as weight increases, height increases (*in a population*). However, the correlation would not be perfect (i.e. $r < 1.0$). After all, there would be some people who are very tall but very thin, and others who would be very short but overweight. We might find that $r = 0.7$. This would suggest there is a strong positive association between weight and height, but it is not a perfect association.

If two sets of data are correlated, does that mean that one *causes* the other? Not necessarily; simply because weight and height are correlated does not mean that if you gained weight you will necessarily gain height! Thus association does not imply causality.

Note that a correlation greater than 0.8 is generally described as strong, whereas a correlation that is less than 0.5 is generally described as weak. However, the interpretation and use of these values can vary based upon the "type" of data being examined. For example, a study based on chemical or biological data may require a stronger correlation than a study using social science data.

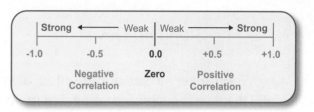

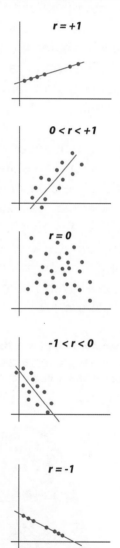

Varying values of the correlation coefficient (r) based on data plotted for two variables (= scatter diagrams). In red is the line of "best fit" (= *regression line;* Appendix A.1.3).

7.3.2 The Standard Deviation

When given a set of data, it is often useful to know the average value, *the mean*, and the *range* of values. As previously discussed, the mean is simply the sum of the data values divided by the number of data values. The range is the numerical difference between the largest value and the smallest value.

Another useful measurement is the *standard deviation*. The standard deviation indicates the dispersion of values around the mean. Given a bell-shaped distribution of data (i.e., the height and weight of a population, the GPA of undergraduate students, etc.), each standard deviation (SD) includes a given percentage of data. For example, the mean +/– 1 SD includes approximately 68% of the data values, the mean +/– 2 SD includes 95% of the data values, and the mean +/– 3 SD includes 99.7% of the data values.

For example, imagine that you read that the mean GPA required for admission to Belcurve University's Dental School is 3.5 with a standard deviation of 0.2 (SD = 0.2). Thus approximately 68% of the students admitted have a GPA of 3.5 +/– 0.2, which means between 3.3 and 3.7. We can also conclude that approximately 95% of the students admitted have a GPA of 3.5 +/– 2(0.2), which means between 3.1 and 3.9. Therefore the standard deviation becomes a useful measure of the dispersion of values around the mean 3.5.

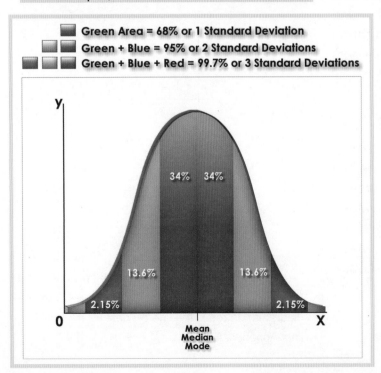

Green Area = 68% or 1 Standard Deviation
Green + Blue = 95% or 2 Standard Deviations
Green + Blue + Red = 99.7% or 3 Standard Deviations

Figure 7.1: The Normal Curve (also referred to as: the Normal Distribution Curve, or Bell Curve).

7.3.3 Variance

Variance is another measure of how far a set of numbers is spread out or, in other words, how far numbers are from the mean. Thus variance is calculated as the average of the squared differences from the mean.

There are three steps to calculate the variance:

1. Determine the mean (the simple average of all the numbers)

2. For each number: subtract the mean and square the result (the squared difference)

3. Determine the average of those squared differences

The variance is also defined as the square of the standard deviation. Thus unlike standard deviation, the variance has units that are the square of the units of the variable itself.

For example, a variable measured in meters will have a variance measured in meters squared. Note: for those of you aiming for a perfect QR score, the equations for standard deviation and variance can be found in the next section, QR 7.3.4.

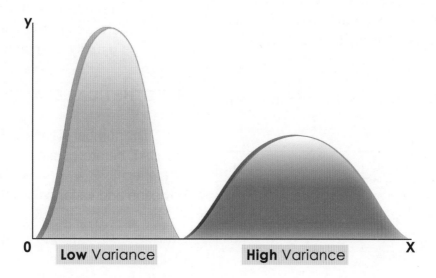

Figure 7.2: Variance.

Medium-level Importance

7.3.4 Equations for Standard Deviation and Variance (*DAT-30*)

Standard deviation and variance problems are common for DAT QR; however, because of time constraints, it is not likely that you would need to calculate the standard deviation or variance using the formulas in this section. However, if you are aiming for a perfect score then it is prudent to have all the tools at your disposal.

First, let's revisit the mean or average of a data set.

In statistics, a sample is a subset of a population. Typically, the population is very large, making an analysis of all the values in the population impractical or impossible. The sample is a subset of manageable size. Samples are collected and statistics are calculated so one can make inferences or extrapolations from the sample to the population.

For any data set, the mean can be calculated:

Sample Mean	Population Mean
$\bar{X} = \dfrac{\sum x}{n}$	$\mu = \dfrac{\sum x}{N}$

$\sum$ = the sum of

$\sum x$ = the sum of all data values

n = the number of data items in the sample

N = the number of data items in the population

The standard deviation (SD) - a measure of the dispersion of a set of data from its mean - is calculated using the following formula:

Sample SD	Population SD
$s = \sqrt{\dfrac{\sum \left(x - \bar{X} \right)^2}{n-1}}$	$\sigma = \sqrt{\dfrac{\sum \left(x - \mu \right)^2}{N}}$

x = each value in the sample or population

$n - 1$ = "degrees of freedom" and is used to compensate for the fact that the more accurate population mean (μ) is usually unknown.

HYPOTHETICAL EXAMPLE

The number of times students completed the DAT before obtaining a QR score of 25 or higher: 3, 2, 4, 1, 4, 4. Find the standard deviation and variance of the data set.

Step 1: Calculate the mean and deviation of this small data set. Note that because $n = 6$, this is very likely a subset of all students who scored 25 or higher in QR, we regard this as a sample size and we use the equations accordingly.

Medium-level Importance

x	$\bar{X}$	$\left(x - \bar{X}\right)$	$\left(x - \bar{X}\right)^2$
3	3	0	0
2	3	-1	1
4	3	1	1
1	3	-2	4
4	3	1	1
4	3	1	1

Step 2: Using the deviation, calculate the standard deviation by squaring both sides of the relevant equation:

$$s^2 = \frac{(0 + 1 + 1 + 4 + 1 + 1)}{(6 - 1)} = \frac{8}{5}$$

$$= 1.6$$

Since s^2 = 1.6, the standard deviation of the sample s = 1.265. And the variance (QR 7.3.3) of the sample (= s^2) = 1.6.

The Coefficient of Variation

A standard deviation of 1.265 with a mean of 3, as we calculated, is much different than a standard deviation of 1.265 with a mean of 20. By calculating how the standard deviation relates to the mean (= coefficient of variation = CV), we can have a standard way of determining the relevance of the standard deviation and what it suggests about the sample. The closer the CV is to 0, the greater the uniformity of the data. The closer the CV is to 1, the greater the variability of the data.

$$CV = \frac{s}{\bar{X}}$$

Using our example of a standard deviation of 1.265 and a mean of 3, you will see that the coefficient of variation is rather large, indicating that the data has a great deal of variability with respect to the mean and there is no general consensus among the sample.

$$CV = \frac{s}{\bar{X}} = \frac{(1.265)}{(3)} = 0.42$$

Using the example of a standard deviation of 1.265 and a mean of 20, we see that the coefficient of variation is rather small, indicating that the data has a greater deal of uniformity with respect to the mean and there is a general consensus among the sample.

$$CV = \frac{s}{\bar{X}} = \frac{(1.265)}{(20)} = 0.06$$

7.3.5 Simple Probability Revisited

Let's apply a formula to simple probability. If a phenomenon or experiment has n equally likely outcomes, s of which are called successes, then the probability P of

Medium-level Importance

success is given by $P = \dfrac{s}{n}$.

EXAMPLE

- if "heads" in a coin toss is considered a success, then

$$P(\text{success}) = \frac{1}{2};$$

- if a card is drawn from a deck and diamonds are considered successes, then

$P(\text{success}) = \dfrac{13}{52}$. It follows that $P(\text{success}) = 1 - P(\text{failure})$.

7.3.6 Permutations

Suppose n is a positive integer. The symbol $n!$, read n-factorial, is defined as follows:

$$n! = (n)(n - 1)(n - 2) \dots (3)(2)(1)$$

By definition $0! = 1$.

A permutation of a set is an *ordered* arrangement of the elements in that set. The number of permutations of n objects is $n!$. For example, using 5 different amino acids, the number of possible permutations creating different outcomes (*oligopeptides*) is: $5! = (5)(4)(3)(2)(1) = 120$.

Suppose you have 7 books and place 3 on a shelf. The first slot can be filled by any of 7 choices, the second slot can be filled by one less or 6 choices, and again there is one less choice for the third slot leaving 5 books from which to choose. The total number of ways to fill the 3 slots on the shelf is thus $(7)(6)(5) = 210$.

The general rule is that the number of permutations of n things taken r at a time is n_r, where $n_r = n!/(n - r)!$. In the preceding example, $n = 7$ and $r = 3$ thus,

$$
\begin{aligned}
n_r &= 7!/(7 - 3)! \\
&= (7)(6)(5)(4)(3)(2)(1)/(4)(3)(2)(1) \\
&= (7)(6)(5)(4!)/(4!) \\
&= (7)(6)(5) = 210
\end{aligned}
$$

NOTE

Permutations may be simplified if it is found in both the numerator and the denominator.

In the given example, $4!$ could be canceled out, leaving you with $(7)(6)(5) = 210$. This will save you time on the DAT and you will not have to waste too much effort expanding a permutation.

For the DAT, it is very important to pay attention to the wording of the problem and identify what is known about the problem. In this example, we know that there are 7 books and as each is placed on the shelf, there is 1 less book to choose from. Since the outcome of the first depends on the outcome of the second, these events are considered dependent. This is called sampling without replacement.

In the case where the object is being put back into your sample after each event, the amount of possible outcomes does not change from one event to another. If the outcome of the first event does not affect the outcome of the second, the two events are independent of each other. This is called sampling with replacement.

7.3.7 Combinations

Permutations are important when the *order* of selection matters (e.g., *simply by changing the order of the amino acids, the activity of the oligopeptide or the* outcome *changes*). Combinations are important when the order of selection does not matter (e.g., *as long as there is a red book, a green book, and a blue book on the shelf, the order does not matter*).

Since the order does not matter, there are fewer combinations than permutations. In fact, the combination C_r is given by:

$$C_r = \frac{n_r}{r!} = \frac{n!}{\left[r!(n-r)!\right]}$$

For example, once again consider a total of 7 books where there are only 3 slots on the shelf. This time you are told that the order the books appear on the shelf is not relevant. The number of different combinations is therefore:

$$C_r = \frac{n_r}{r!} = \frac{n!}{\left[r!(n-r)!\right]} = \frac{7!}{\left[3!(7-3)!\right]}$$

$$= \frac{210}{3!} = \frac{210}{6} = 35$$

Medium-level Importance

7.3.8 Probability Tree

The probability tree may be used as another means to solve probability of independent and dependent events. It is a very useful visual that will show all possible events. Each branch represents a possible outcome and its probability. Depending on what the question is asking for, the probabilities of each event may be added or multiplied to determine the combined probability of events.

Suppose that you were observing the probability of choosing 2 balls from a basket that contained 8 red and 4 white balls. What is the probability of picking 2 red balls without replacement?

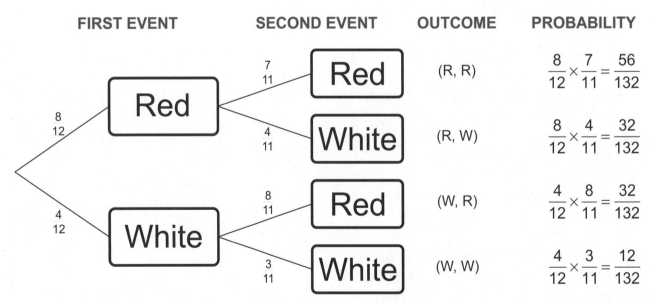

FIRST EVENT	SECOND EVENT	OUTCOME	PROBABILITY

Thus the probability of picking 2 red balls without replacement (R, R) is: $\dfrac{8}{12} \times \dfrac{7}{11} = \dfrac{56}{132} = \dfrac{14}{33}$

If the question had asked the probability of having at least 1 white ball without replacement, the answer would be $\dfrac{8}{12} \times \dfrac{4}{11} + \dfrac{4}{12} \times \dfrac{8}{11} + \dfrac{4}{12} \times \dfrac{3}{11} = \dfrac{76}{132} = \dfrac{19}{33}$. Notice that this answer represents all outcomes NOT given by (R, R) and so it is numerically 1 - P(R, R).

GOLD STANDARD DAT QR PRACTICE QUESTIONS

CHAPTER 7: Probability and Statistics

1. A jar contains 4 red marbles and 6 blue marbles. What is the probability that a marble chosen at random will be red?

   A. 4/6
   B. 4/10
   C. 2/6
   D. 6/10
   E. 2/4

2. In how many different ways can six different objects be arranged in a line?

   A. 120
   B. 30
   C. 720
   D. 36
   E. 6

3. A box contains 6 yellow balls and 4 green balls. Two balls are chosen at random without replacement. What is the probability that the first ball is yellow and the second ball is green?

   A. 5/12
   B. 1/10
   C. 6/25
   D. 1
   E. 4/15

4. An English teacher wants to prepare a class reading list that includes 1 philosophy book, 1 work of historical fiction, and 1 biography. She has 3 philosophy books, 2 works of historical fiction, and 4 biographies to choose from. How many different combinations of books can she put together for her list?

   A. 32
   B. 288
   C. 28
   D. 9
   E. 24

5. An unemployment office's survey shows that the distribution of the local residents' annual income is a bell curve. 2,516 residents are within one standard deviation of the local average annual income. How many residents were in the survey's sample?

   A. 3,700
   B. 2,648
   C. 2,524
   D. 2,523
   E. 7,862

Medium-level Importance

6. The average time it takes 3 students to complete a test is 35 minutes. If 1 student takes 41 minutes to complete the test and another takes 37 minutes, how many minutes does the third student take to complete the test?

   A. 4
   B. 38
   C. 27
   D. 39
   E. 43

7. A small library receives a shipment of gray books, blue books, black books, and brown books. If the librarian decides to shelve all the books of one color on Monday, all of the books of another color on Tuesday, and the rest of the books on Wednesday, in how many different ways can the book shelving be completed?

   A. 3
   B. 4
   C. 8
   D. 12
   E. 24

8. A list of four integers has the following properties: the range is equal to 14, the median is equal to 7, and the mean is equal to 8. One of the numbers is 9. What are the other three numbers?

   A. 1, 7, 15
   B. 2, 5, 16
   C. −11, 3, 7
   D. 0, 0, 23
   E. −12, 2, 7

9. When you roll a die, what is the probability to first get a 3 and then a 1 or a 2?

   A. 1/6
   B. 1/8
   C. 1/32
   D. 1/16
   E. 1/18

10) Consider the sets {-1, 3, -2}, {4, 5, -2}, and {1, 3, 1}. What is the average of their median values?

   A. -1
   B. 0
   C. 1
   D. 2
   E. 3

11) Find the mode of the following set: {0, 2, 1, 7, 3, 3, 7, 2, 4, 7, 11}.

   A. 2
   B. 3
   C. 4
   D. 7
   E. 11

12) A sample of 3 items is selected at random from 10 items, of which 4 are defective. What is the probability that none of the selected items are defective?

   A. 1/8
   B. 1/6
   C. 1/4
   D. 3/10
   E. 2/5

13) A jar contains 2 red balls, 4 green balls, and 6 blue balls. If three balls are drawn at random, what is the likelihood each one will be a different color?

A. 1/5
B. 12/55
C. 23/55
D. 1/2
E. 2/3

14) A group of 5 men and 5 women are asked to form a line, but there can never be two men or two women next to each other. How many unique ways can this be accomplished?

A. 14,400
B. 28,800
C. 57,600
D. 500,000
E. 3,628,800

15) Consider the set {1, 3, 4, 6, 10, 22}. How many different ways can these numbers be arranged if the leading entry must be odd?

A. 72   D. 400
B. 120   E. 720
C. 240

16) A child is stacking 12 blocks in columns. If every block must be used and each column must contain an identical number of blocks, but the ordering of the blocks doesn't matter, how many different ways can they be stacked?

A. 3   D. 24
B. 6   E. 144
C. 12

17) A fair coin is flipped 4 times. What is the probability that the coin turns up both heads and tails twice each?

A. 3/8
B. 1/2
C. 9/16
D. 5/8
E. 3/4

18) Two fair coins are flipped together a total of 3 times. What is the probability that both coins show the same face every time?

A. 1/2
B. 1/4
C. 1/5
D. 1/6
E. 1/8

19) Consider a regular 4 suit, 52 card deck of playing cards. If a random card is flipped, what is the probability that it will be both red and a face card (aces not included)?

A. 1/52
B. 3/52
C. 3/26
D. 3/13
E. None of the above

20) What is the standard deviation of the set {2, 4, 3, 6, 5}?

A. $\sqrt{2}$
B. $\sqrt{3}$
C. 2
D. 3
E. 4

Medium-level Importance

21) Four friends have heights of 1.5 m, 1.7 m, 1.8 m, and 1.8 m. What is the variance of this data set in m²?

    A. .0015   **D.** 1.5

    B. .015   **E.** 15

    C. .15

22) How many different ways is it possible to choose 3 beans from a bowl containing 7 total beans?

    A. 7   **D.** 30

    B. 9   **E.** 35

    C. 21

23) A book has 6 chapters of length 7, 10, 8, 14, 13, and 8 pages, respectively. What is the mean page length for a chapter?

    A. 7   **D.** 10

    B. 8   **E.** 11

    C. 9

24) A weighted coin turns up heads 40% of the time and tails 60% of the time. If this coin is flipped three times, what is the probability it shows heads all three times?

    A. 1/6   **D.** 27/125

    B. 1/9   **E.** 8/125

    C. 1/12

25) What is the coefficient of variation of the set {10, 11, 12, 13, 14}? (*DAT-30*)

    A. $\sqrt{2}$

    B. $\sqrt{2}/2$

    C. $\sqrt{2}/4$

    D. $\sqrt{2}/8$

    E. $\sqrt{2}/12$

26) Find the average of these four numbers which includes mixed numbers: 1 1/3, 3 1/4, 3 1/2, and 4.

    A. 3

    B. 3 1/2

    C. 3 1/3

    D. 3 1/4

    E. 3 1/48

27) The numbers (1, 2, 3, 6) have a mean of 3 and a variance of 3.5. What is the mean and variance of (2, 4, 5, 9)?

    A. 5, 6.5

    B. 5, 5.5

    C. 5, 4.5

    D. 4, 8.5

    E. 4, 7.5

28) If a six-sided die is rolled three times, what is the probability that every roll will turn up an even number?

    A. 3/2

    B. 1/2

    C. 1/6

    D. 1/8

    E. 1/16

29) A jar contains 4 red and 8 blue marbles. What is the probability that two marbles drawn with replacement are both red?

    A. 1/2

    B. 1/3

    C. 1/9

    D. 4/33

    E. 8/33

APPENDIX

CHAPTER 7: Probability and Statistics

Advanced DAT-30 Passage: ANOVA, Scheffe Test and Chi-Square

> **NOTE**
>
> This section is not for all students. This content is "low yield" meaning that it takes a lot of energy to review it properly but the questions pop up on the DAT rarely. If you have the time and the will to aim for a perfect score, this additional statistics review is followed by questions so that the material can be learned in an interactive way. As per usual, explanations are at the end of this chapter. You should decide if you wish to read these sections based on the requirements of the dental program(s) you wish to attend.

Student's *t*-test and ANOVA

The *t*-test (= Student's t-test) and analysis of variance (= ANOVA) are statistical procedures that assume normal distributions (= *parametric*) and make use of the mean and variance to determine the significance of the differences of the means of two or more groups of values.

The *t*-test uses the mean, the variance and a "Table of Critical Values" for the "*t*" distribution. The *t*-test is used to determine the significance of the difference between the means of two groups based on a standard that no more than 5% of the difference is due to chance or sampling error, and that the same difference would occur 95% of the time should the test be repeated. Rarely, a more rigorous standard of 1% (= .01 level) is used and, as a result, the

same difference would occur 99% of the time should the test be repeated.

EXAMPLE

The experiment or treatment group ($\bar{X}$ = 73.30, SD = 3.91) scored significantly higher than the control group ($\bar{X}$ = 67.30, SD = 4.32), $t(75) = 4.90$, $p < .05$. Note that the number in parenthesis (75) after the t value is the number of cases adjusted for the values that are free to vary = "degrees of freedom" = $n - 1$. The p value (= probability value or alpha level) expresses statistical significance.

In the preceding example, p is most important and indicates at what level a statistically significant difference exists (i.e .05 level; this will be discussed further).

Medium-level Importance

There are one sample and two sample *t*-tests:

1. a one sample *t*-test is a hypothesis test for answering questions about the mean where the data are a random sample of independent observations from an underlying normal distribution where the variance is unknown;

2. a two sample *t*-test is a hypothesis test for answering questions about the mean where the data are collected from two random samples of independent observations, each from an underlying normal distribution where the variances of the 2 populations are assumed to be equal.

Analysis of variance (ANOVA) is a parametric statistical measure used for determining whether differences exist among two or more groups. ANOVA uses the mean, the variance and a "Table of Critical Values for the *F* Distribution". Statistical significance is usually based on the .05 level.

ANOVA can be used for several different types of analyses:

- One-way ANOVA - assumes there are two variables with one variable a dependent, interval or ratio variable (numerical data that show quantity and direction), and one variable, an independent, nominal variable or factor such as an ethnicity code or sex code.

- *N*-way ANOVA - assumes there are more than two variables with one variable a dependent, interval or ratio variable and two or more, independent, nominal variables or factors such as ethnicity code or sex code.

- Multiple Regression - assumes there are more than two variables with one variable a dependent, interval or ratio variable and two or more, independent, interval or ratio variables such as test scores, income, GPA, etc.

- Analysis of Covariance - assumes there are more than two variables with one variable a dependent, interval or variable and two or more variables are a combination of independent, nominal, interval or ratio variables.

Scheffe Test

The Scheffe test is used with ANOVA to determine which variable among several independent variables is statistically the most different.

Effect Size

For both *t*-test and one-way ANOVA procedures, a secondary statistical procedure called effect size is sometimes used to determine the level of significance. This could be used in an experimental study comparing the means of two groups, a control group and an experimental group. Effect size is calculated by taking the difference in the means of the two

Medium-level Importance

groups and dividing it by the standard deviation of the control group. In education experiments, an effect size of +.20 (20% of the standard deviation) would be considered a minimum for significance; an effect size above +.50 is considered very strong.

Chi-Square

t-test and analysis of variance are parametric statistical procedures that assume that the distributions are normal or nearly normal and is used when variables are continuous such as test scores and GPAs. Chi-square is a nonparametric statistical procedure used to determine the significance of the difference between groups when data are nominal and placed in categories such as gender or ethnicity. This procedure compares what is observed against what was expected.

Categories of Chi-Square (χ^2):

1. Chi-Squared Goodness of Fit Test is a test for comparing a theoretical distribution, such as a Normal distribution, with the observed data from a sample.

2. Chi-Squared Test of Association allows the comparison of two attributes in a sample of data to determine if there is any relationship between them. If the value of the test statistic for the chi-squared test of association is too large, then there is a poor agreement between the observed and expected frequencies and the null hypothesis of independence or no association is rejected.

3. Chi-Squared Test of Homogeneity is used to determine if a single categorical variable has the same distribution in 2 (or more) distinct populations from 2 (or more) samples.

Null Hypothesis, Alternative Hypothesis

Consider the following two types of statistical hypotheses:

- **Null hypothesis** (= H_0) is usually the hypothesis that sample observations result purely from chance. {Remember: "If p is low, H_0 has to go!"}

- **Alternative hypothesis** (= H_1 or H_a) is the hypothesis that sample observations are influenced by some non-random cause.

For example, suppose we wanted to determine whether a coin was fair and balanced. A null hypothesis might be that half the flips would result in heads and half, in tails. The alternative hypothesis might be that the number of heads and tails would be very different. Symbolically, these hypotheses would be expressed as

H_0: probability = 0.5
H_a: probability < 0.5 or > 0.5

Suppose we flipped the coin 100 times, resulting in 85 heads and 15 tails. Given this result, we would be inclined to reject the null hypothesis. That is, we would conclude that the coin was probably not fair and balanced.

Z Scores and p-values

The *z* score (= standard score = *z* value) is a test of statistical significance that helps you decide whether or not to reject the null hypothesis. The p-value is the probability that you have falsely rejected the null hypothesis. Z scores are measures of standard deviation. For example, a Z score of +3.0 is interpreted as "+3.0 standard deviations away from the mean". P-values are probabilities. Both statistics are associated with the standard normal distribution.

Very high or a very low (negative) *z* scores (i.e. very small p-values) are found in the tails of the normal distribution. The p value associated with a 95% confidence level is 0.05 and the associated *z* values are approximately -2 and +2 (*see* the normal curve in section 7.3.2).

One and Two-sided Tests

A one-sided test (= one-tailed test of significance) is a statistical hypothesis test in which the values for which we can reject the null hypothesis H_0 are located entirely in one tail of the probability distribution. In other words, the critical region for a one-sided test is the set of values less than the critical value of the test, or the set of values greater than the critical value of the test.

A two-sided test (= two-tailed test of significance) is a statistical hypothesis test in which the values for which we can reject the null hypothesis, H_0 are located in both tails of the probability distribution. In other words, the critical region for a two-sided test is the set of values less than a first critical value of the test and the set of values greater than a second critical value of the test.

Errors

Two types of errors can result from a decision rule:

- **Type I error**. A Type I error occurs when the researcher rejects a null hypothesis when it is true. The probability of committing a Type I error is called the significance level or alpha (= α). The confidence level is $1 - \alpha$.

- **Type II error**. A Type II error occurs when the researcher accepts a null hypothesis that is false. The probability of committing a Type II error is called beta (= β). The probability of not committing a Type II error is called the "power of the test" = $1 - \beta$.

30. What is the meaning of $p < .05$?

   A. The probability of obtaining the data if the null hypothesis were true is less than 5%.

   B. There is a 5% chance of making a type I error.

   C. There is a less than a 1 in 20 probability of the result occurring by chance alone if the null hypothesis were true.

   D. All of the above.

31. The ANOVA test is based on which assumption(s)?

    I.   The samples are randomly selected.

    II. The populations are statistically significant.

    III. The populations are normally distributed.

    A. III only
    B. II and III only
    C. I, II, and III only
    D. I, and III only

32. The chi-square goodness of fit test can be used to test for:

    A. credibility.
    B. probability.
    C. differentiability.
    D. normality.

33. The null hypothesis is:

    A. the assumption that a significant result is very unlikely.
    B. the analysis of the pattern between the variables being tested.
    C. the assumption there is no relationship or difference between the variables being tested.
    D. the assumption that there is a relationship or difference between the variables being tested.

34. Which of the following is consistent with the null hypothesis and the alternative hypothesis?

    A. It is possible for neither hypothesis to be true.
    B. Exactly one hypothesis must be true.
    C. Both hypotheses must be true.
    D. It is possible for both hypotheses to be true.

35. In a two-tailed test of significance:

    A. results in either of two directions can lead to the rejection of the null hypothesis.
    B. no results lead to the rejection of the null hypothesis.
    C. results in only one direction can lead to the rejection of the null hypothesis.
    D. a standard deviation leads to the rejection of the null hypothesis.

36. If the Gold Standard was trying to prove that their materials are more effective at getting high DAT scores compared to older methods of preparation, they would conduct a:

    A. one-tailed test.
    B. two-tailed test.
    C. Chi-Squared Test of Homogeneity.
    D. Chi-Squared Test of Association.

Medium-level Importance

37. The alternative hypothesis can be:

- A. one-sided.
- B. two-sided.
- C. one or two-sided.
- D. neither one nor two-sided.

38. A type II error occurs when:

- A. the test is biased.
- B. the sample mean differs from the population mean.
- C. the null hypothesis is incorrectly accepted when it is false.
- D. the null hypothesis is incorrectly rejected when it is true.

39. The value set for α is known as:

- A. the significance level.
- B. the rejection level.
- C. the confidence level.
- D. the acceptance level.

40. When someone asks "how significant" the sample evidence is, they are referring to the:

- A. causality.
- B. value of β.
- C. sample value.
- D. p-value.

CHAPTER REVIEW SOLUTIONS: CHAPTER 7

Question 1   B

See: QR 7.1.1

There are four red marbles, and a total of 4 red + 6 blue = 10 marbles, so the probability is $\dfrac{4}{10}$.

Question 2   C

See: QR 7.3.4

Each ordering of the objects is different, so it is necessary to calculate of the number of permutations in which all 6 objects are used. $6! = 720$

Question 3   E

See: QR 7.1, 7.1.2

With a total of 10 balls and 6 yellow balls, the probability that the first ball is yellow is $\dfrac{6}{10} = \dfrac{3}{5}$. After the first ball is chosen, there are 9 left, of which 4 are green. The probability of choosing a green ball at this point is therefore $\dfrac{4}{9}$.

The total probability is $\left(\dfrac{3}{5}\right)\left(\dfrac{4}{9}\right) = \dfrac{4}{15}$.

Question 4   E

See: QR 7.3, 7.3.5

Multiply all possible choices: $3 \times 2 \times 4 = 24$

Question 5   A

See: QR 7.3.2

The 2516 residents represent 68% of the total number of residents x:

$$2516 = 0.68x$$
$$3700 = x$$

Question 6   C

See: QR 7.2, 7.2.1

If the third student takes x minutes to complete the test:

$$\frac{41 + 37 + x}{3} = 35$$
$$78 + x = 105$$
$$x = 27$$

Question 7   D

See: QR 7.3.5

There are 4 different book colors, so there are 4 different choices for books to shelve on Monday. There are only 3 choices on Tuesday. On Wednesday, the rest of the books will be shelved, so there is only 1 choice. This gives a total of $4 \times 3 \times 1 = 12$ different ways to shelve the books.

Question 8   B

See: QR 7.2

Label the numbers a, b, c, d from smallest to largest. The range is the difference between the largest and smallest:

$$d - a = 14$$

The median is the average of the two middle numbers:

$$\frac{b + c}{2} = 7$$

and so

$$b + c = 14$$

The mean is the average of all of the numbers:

$$\frac{a + b + c + d}{4} = 8$$

Simplifying this equation and substituting 14 for $b + c$:

$$a + b + c + d = 32$$

$$a + 14 + d = 32$$

$$a + d = 18$$

Adding this equation and the equation that represents the range:

$$(a + d) + (d - a) = 18 + 14$$

$$2d = 32$$

$$d = 16$$

Therefore:

$$16 - a = 14$$

$$a = 2$$

Now, we have 3 of the numbers and can use the simplified equation for the mean to find the fourth, which we can call x:

$$2 + 9 + 16 + x = 32$$

$$x = 5$$

Question 9   E

See: QR 7.1, 7.1.2

A die has a total of 6 possible sides. There is only one side that displays a 3, so the probability of rolling a 3 is $\frac{1}{6}$. Similarly, the probability of rolling any other number is also $\frac{1}{6}$. The probability of rolling a 1 or a 2 is the sum of their individual probabilities: $\frac{1}{6} + \frac{1}{6} = \frac{1}{3}$. Because this probability is independent of the probability of first rolling a 3, we multiply the results to get the total probability: $\left(\frac{1}{6}\right)\left(\frac{1}{3}\right) = \frac{1}{18}$.

Question 10   C

See: QR 7.2.2

The median values of these three sets are -2, 4, and 1, respectively. The average of these three numbers is:

(-2 + 4 + 1)/3

= 3/3

= 1.

Question 11   D

See: QR 7.2.2

The number 7 appears three times in this set, more than any other number, so 7 is the mode.

Question 12   B

See: QR 7.1.2

Think of this problem as "what is the probability all three items are effective?" Then the solution is the product of the probability that each item is effective.

P(all 3 effective) = P(1st effective)P(2nd effective)P(3rd effective)

P(all 3 effective) = (6/10)(5/9)(4/8)

P(all 3 effective) = 1/6.

Question 13   B

See: QR 7.3.7

Note that order of the balls does not matter. Probability = (# ways outcome can occur / # possible outcomes). Since we only need one ball of each color, there 2 ways to choose red, 4 ways to choose green, and 6 ways to choose blue, so the numerator is:

$(2)(4)(6) = 48$

The total number of ways to choose 3 balls is (12 choose 3) since there are 12 total balls. So the denominator is:

$12!/[3!(12-3)!]$

$= 12!/[3!(9!)]$

$= (12)(11)(10)/6$

$= 220$

Now:

Probability $= 48/220$

$= 12/55.$

Question 14   B

See: QR 7.3.6

Since no two men and no two women can stand next to each other the line must alternate between men and women. This can be accomplished uniquely with either a man first or a woman first, MWMWMWMWMW or WMWMWM-WMWM. You can think of each case as two lines, one of 5 men and one of 5 women, each with 5! permutations. So:

Total Permutations $= (2)(5!)(5!)$

$= (2)(120)(120) = (2)(14400) = 28,800$

Question 15   C

See: QR 7.3.6

There are two odd numbers, 1 and 3. For each, there are 5! ways to arrange the remaining five numbers after the leading number is chosen. So the total number of permutations is:

$2(5!) = 240.$

Question 16   B

See: QR 7.1.1

12 is divisible by 1, 2, 3, 4, 6, and 12, a total of 6 factors. So the blocks can be stacked into even columns in 6 different ways (1x12, 2x6, 3x4, 4x3, 6x2, and 12x1).

Question 17   A

See: QR 7.1.1, 7.3.7

There are $2^4 = 16$ total possible outcomes for 4 coin flips. There are (4 choose 2) $= 4!/(2!)(2!) = 6$ ways that the coin can turn up heads and tails twice each. So the probability of this outcome is:

$6/16 = 3/8.$

Question 18   E

See: QR 7.1.2

Two coins are flipped three times, making three distinct events. For each event the odds of both coins turning up the same face is $2/4 = ½$. Therefore the odds of this occurring in each of the three events is:

$(½)(½)(½) = 1/8.$

Question 19   C

See: QR 7.1.1

There are 52 total cards in the deck. There are 2 red suits and 3 face cards in each, so there are a total of 6 red face cards in the deck, so the probability of flipping one is:

$6/52 = 3/26.$

Question 20   A

See: QR 7.3.2, 7.3.4

First find the mean of the set:

Mean $= (2 + 4 + 3 + 6 + 5)/5 = 20/5 = 4$

Now find the variance:

Variance $= [(2 - 4)^2 + (4 - 4)^2 + (3 - 4)^2 + (6 - 4)^2 + (5 - 4)^2]/5$

$= (4 + 0 + 1 + 4 + 1)/5$

$= 10/5$

$= 2$

Finally, take the square root to obtain the standard deviation:

Standard Deviation $= \sqrt{2}$.

Question 21   B

See: QR 7.3.3, 7.3.4

First find the mean of the set:

Mean $= (1.5 + 1.7 + 1.8 + 1.8)/4 = 6.8/4 = 1.7$

Now find the variance:

Variance $= [(1.5 - 1.7)^2 + (1.7 - 1.7)^2 + (1.8 - 1.7)^2 + (1.8 - 1.7)^2]/4$

$= (.2^2 + 0^2 + .1^2 + .1^2)/4$

$= (.04 + 0 + .01 + .01)/4$

$= .06/4$

$= .015$.

Question 22   E

See: QR 7.3.6, 7.3.7

This is a grouping problem, where the order of the beans chosen doesn't matter. The same 3 beans can be chosen in any order, but it still only counts as 1 group. If you remember the formula, you can simply plug in the numbers:

(7 choose 3) $= 7!/(3! \times 4!) = (7 \times 6 \times 5) / (3 \times 2 \times 1) = 7 \times 5 = 35$

If you don't remember the formula, you can simply consider the number of ways each bean can be chosen. There are 7 ways the first bean can be chosen, then 6 ways for the second bean (*because the first bean is not replaced*), and 5 ways for the third bean. So, the total number of ways 3 beans can be chosen if order matters is 7 x 6 x 5. Since order does not matter for this problem, we have actually counted every group of 3 beans 3! times because that is how many different ways that we can order them. Therefore, since order doesn't matter, we must divide by 3! and we obtain:

(7 x 6 x 5) / 3! = (7 x 6 x 5) / 6 = 7 x 5 = 35.

Question 23   D

See: QR 7.2.2

Add the total number of pages and divide by the number of chapters:

Mean $= (7 + 10 + 8 + 14 + 13 + 8)/6$

$= 60/6$

$= 10$.

Question 24   E

See: QR 7.1.2

The probability of the coin showing heads is 40%, or 2/5. The probability that this will happen three times in a row is:

(2/5) (2/5) (2/5) = 8/125.

Question 25   E

See: QR 7.3.4

10, 11, 12, 13, 14

First find the mean of the set:

Mean $= (10 + 11 + 12 + 13 + 14)/5 = 60/5 = 12$

Next find the variance:

Variance $= [(10 - 12)^2 + (11 - 12)^2 + (12 - 12)^2 + (13 - 12)^2 + (14 - 12)^2]/5$

$= (4 + 1 + 0 + 1 + 4)/5$

$= 10/5$

$= 2$

Now take the square root to obtain the standard deviation:

Standard Deviation $= \sqrt{2}$.

Finally, the coefficient of variation is obtained by dividing the standard deviation by the mean:

CV $= \sqrt{2}/12$.

Question 26   E

See: QR 7.2.1

To find the average, add the numbers together and divide by how many of them there are (in this case, 4). First, we need to convert the fractions so they all have a common denominator, in this case 12. Adding, we get:

$1\ 1/3 + 3\ \frac{1}{4} + 3\ \frac{1}{2} + 4 = 1\ 4/12 + 3\ 3/12 + 3\ 6/12 + 4$

$$= 11\ 13/12 = 12\ 1/12$$

Now divide by 4:

$(12\ 1/12)\ (1/4) = 3\ 1/48.$

Question 27   A

See: QR 7.2.1, 7.3.2, 7.3.3, 7.3.4

The arithmetic mean is the same as the average. Add the numbers and divide by how many there are:

Mean $= (2 + 4 + 5 + 9)/4 = 5$

To find the variance, subtract each entry from the mean and square it. Then add these together and divide by 4, because that is how many entries there are:

Variance $= [(5-2)^2 + (5-4)^2 + (5-5)^2 + (5-9)^2]/4$

$$= (3^2 + 1^2 + 0^2 + 4^2)/4 = (9+1+16)/4 = 26/4 = 6.5$$

So, the solution is (5, 6.5). Occasionally, there will be "distractors" on the real exam, do not be distracted from the clear steps towards the solution.

Question 28   D

See: QR 7.1

First we need to find the probability that a single roll will turn up an even number. There are three possible even numbers (2, 4, and 6) out of six total possible outcomes. So the probability of rolling an even number once is:

$p = 3/6 = \frac{1}{2}.$

Now to find the odds of rolling three even numbers in a row, multiply:

$(p)(p)(p) = (\frac{1}{2})(\frac{1}{2})(\frac{1}{2}) = 1/8.$

Question 29   C

See: QR 7.1

Notice that the problem specifies that the marbles are drawn "with replacement." This means that after the first one is drawn, it will be placed back into the jar before the second one is drawn. Remember, the probability that multiple events will occur in a row is equal to the product of the probabilities that each individual event will occur. So in this case, the solution is the probability that the first ball is red multiplied by the probability that the second ball is red. Since there is replacement, both of these values will be identical.

P.1 = P2 = (# Red Marbles)/(Total # Marbles) = 4/12 = 1/3

$P = P1 \times P2 = (1/3)^2 = 1/9.$

Question 30   D

See: QR Chap 7 Appendix

The p value (= **p**robability value or alpha level) expresses statistical significance. The probability of committing a Type I error is called the significance level or alpha (= α). All answer choices are accurately describing p<.05.

Question 31   A

See: QR Chap 7 Appendix

The t-test (= Student's t-test) and analysis of variance (= ANOVA) are statistical procedures that assume normal distributions (= *parametric*) and make use of the mean and variance to determine the significance of the differences of the means of two or more groups of values. Whether there is evidence that the samples or data were random or that differences in the populations are significant would be the result of a statistical analysis but not an assumption.

Question 32   D

See: QR Chap 7 Appendix

Chi-Squared Goodness of Fit Test is a test for comparing a theoretical distribution, such as a Normal distribution, with the observed data from a sample.

Question 33   C

See: QR Chap 7 Appendix

Null hypothesis (= H_0) is usually the hypothesis that sample observations result purely from chance. In other words, the null hypothesis says that there is no significant difference between specified populations, any observed difference being due to sampling or experimental error. This is most consistent with answer choice C which states that it is "the assumption that there is no relationship or difference between the variables being tested".

Question 34   B

See: QR Chap 7 Appendix

Either the null hypothesis is true or the alternative hypothesis is true but never both.

Question 35   A

See: QR Chap 7 Appendix

A two-sided test (= two-tailed test of significance) is a statistical hypothesis test in which the values for which we can reject the null hypothesis, H_0 are located in both tails of the probability distribution.

Question 36   A

See: QR Chap 7 Appendix

Test scores follow a normal curve or normal distributions (= *parametric*). Chi-square is a nonparametric statistical procedure. The question is looking at one parameter: are Gold Standard students scoring higher than other students: one-tailed test.

Question 37   C

See: QR Chap 7 Appendix

Again, let's return to flipping a coin.

H_0: probability = 0.5

H_a: probability < 0.5 or > 0.5

Thus the alternative hypothesis could be that heads occur more often, or that heads occur less often as would be predicted by the null hypothesis would suggest that the event is not random.

Question 38   C

See: QR Chap 7 Appendix

A Type II error occurs when the researcher accepts a null hypothesis that is false. Traditionally, a Type I error is considered to be more serious.

Question 39   A

See: QR Chap 7 Appendix

A Type I error occurs when the researcher rejects a null hypothesis when it is true. The probability of committing a Type I error is called the significance level or alpha (= α). The confidence level is $1 - \alpha$.

Question 40   D

See: QR Chap 7 Appendix

The p value (= **p**robability value or alpha level) expresses statistical significance. The probability of committing a Type II error is called beta (= β).

If you have any questions or concerns regarding your DAT practice questions, or the solutions, access the free Gold Standard Masters Series Forum for clarification: www.dat-prep.com/forum.

Medium-level Importance

Medium-level Importance

⚠ **SPOILER ALERT** ⚠

Gold Standard has cross-referenced the content in this chapter to examples from the ADA's official DAT practice materials. It is for you to decide when you want to explore these questions since you may want to preserve DAT practice tests for timed mock-exam practice.

We suggest that you acquire the free 2007 DAT practice test from ada.org (digital document format), as well as the 2009 exam or, even better, the most recent online practice test. The online DAT Quantitative Reasoning practice test from the ADA is available through prometric.com and includes content from 2007 (35%), 2009 (10%), and newly added questions (55%). Note below that "Q" is followed by the question number, and cross-references to this chapter are in parentheses.

Examples –

2007 and 2022: Probability calculation with colored marbles: (QR 7.1, 7.3.6, 7.3.7): 2007 Q30; determine the mean and the variance (QR 7.3.2, 7.3.3): 2007 Q37; calculation of a combination (QR 7.3.7): 2007 Q38 and 2022 Q34 (*one answer choice is deleted in the 2022 version*).

2009: Simple probability calculation: (QR 7.1): 2009 Q22; coin flip probability calculation (QR 7.1, 7.3.6, 7.3.7): 2009 Q37.

2022: Combinations and permutations (QR 7.1, 7.3.6, 7.3.7): 2022 Q5; determine a missing data point when the average is given (QR 7.2.1): 2022 Q10; assess the z-score with quantitative comparison (QR Chapter 7 Appendix, Chapter 8): 2022 Q38; variance and quantitative comparison (QR 7.3.4): 2022 Q39.

Note that the free DAT practice test (GS-Free) and the additional Gold Standard online exams at DAT-prep.com contain specific cross-references to this chapter within the answers and explanations.

Note: **The ADA practice tests are composed of questions which have previously appeared on real, past DATs, but have been retired.** Also, note that most of the 2022 ADA DAT practice test questions have had one answer choice removed. In other words, most questions have 4 answer choices instead of 5, which was standard in 2007 and 2009.

Chapter Checklist

☐ Sign up or access your free online account at www.dat-prep.com for discussion boards for any content from this chapter including chapter-ending practice questions.

☐ Reassess your 'learning objectives' for this chapter: Go back to the first page of this chapter and re-evaluate the top 3 boxes and the Introduction.

☐ Complete 1-2 pages of notes using symbols/abbreviations to represent the entire chapter based on your learning objectives. These are your Gold Notes.

☐ Consider your multimedia options based on your optimal way of learning:

    ☐ Download the free Gold Standard DAT app for your Android device or iPhone. Create your own, tangible study cards or try the free app: Anki.

    ☐ Record your voice reading your Gold Notes onto your smartphone (MP3s) and listen during exercise, transportation, etc.

    ☐ Try some online math videos on YouTube like Khan Academy or Leah4sciMCAT playlist for Math Without a Calculator (the latter was produced for MCAT preparation but it remains helpful for DAT QR basics).

☐ Schedule your full-length DAT practice tests: ADA and/or GS exams and/or other free or paid third-party resources. Schedule one full day to complete a practice test and 1-2 days for a thorough assessment of answers and explanations while adding to your abbreviated Gold Notes.

☐ Schedule and/or evaluate stress reduction techniques such as regular exercise (sports), yoga, meditation and/or mindfulness exercises (*see* YouTube for suggestions).

Medium-level Importance

Memorize	Understand	Importance
Law of Reflection Property of Elliptical Mirrors Equations for Velocity, Combined Work and Interest	* Ellipses * Rates of Change * Velocity Problems, Interest Problems, Work Problems, Age Problems * Strategies for Word Problems * DAT QR content from previous chapters including Quantitative Comparison (QR 4.10)	**High level: 10 of 40** DAT Quantitative Reasoning questions are based on content in this chapter (avg. based on past testing patterns). * Note that approx. **70%** of the questions in DAT QR are from just 3 of 8 chapters: 2, 4 and 8.

DAT-Prep.com

Introduction

Ten of the forty Quantitative Reasoning questions on the DAT are applied mathematics or word problems. There is a huge range of types of word problems that you might encounter on the test. This chapter covers those that require extra explanation, as well as convenient strategies for dealing with any type that gets thrown your way. Of course, this chapter ends with a wide range of word problems that encompass aspects of what you have learnt in previous chapters, as well as the content being presented in this chapter. Let's get started!

Multimedia Resources at DAT-Prep.com

Free Online Forum

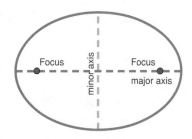

Special Guest

8.0 DAT Has a *Need for Speed*!

Section	DAT Quantitative Reasoning *Need for Speed* Exercises	
8.1.1	Consider the following image. What is the relationship between θ_i and θ_r? Circle the correct response. 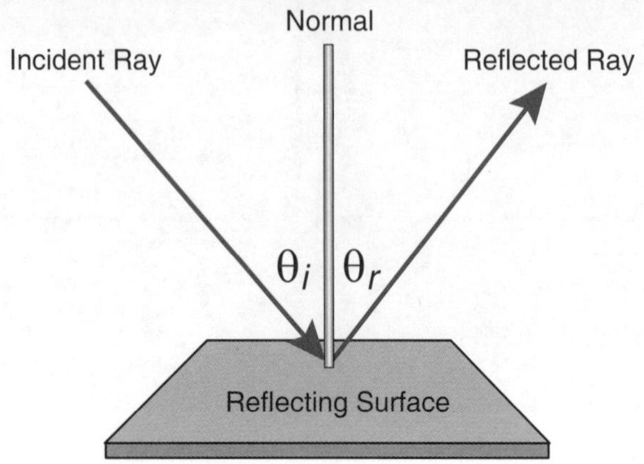 $\theta_i > \theta_r$ / $\theta_i < \theta_r$ / $\theta_i = \theta_r$ / θ_i and θ_r are unrelated	
8.1.2	Regarding an elliptical mirror: The length of the (major / minor / transverse) axis is the same as the distance a light ray will travel between one focus and the other if it is reflected once on the way.	
8.2.1	A glass can hold 10 oz of liquid. Water is being poured in at a rate of 3 oz every 2 seconds. How many seconds will it take for the glass to reach 2/3 full?	
8.2.2	What is the relationship between velocity, distance and time?	
	A jogger runs the first 100 meters of a 5 km race in 24 seconds. If the jogger maintains the same pace until the end of the race, how many minutes will it take her to run the entire race?	
	Two trains, 150 miles apart are traveling towards each other at constant speed with one train at 45 mph and the other at 30 mph. How many hours does it take for both to meet?	

High-level Importance

8.2.3	For simple interest, what is the relationship between I (*the interest earned from the investment*), P (*the principal or the amount of money invested*), R (*the rate of interest, usually a percentage, charged on the principal*), and T (*the time*)?
	Joe borrowed $12,000 from the bank at 10% interest compounded annually. If no payments are made for 3 years without additional penalties, how much does he owe the bank?
8.2.4	Jack takes 5 hours to paint a house while Joan takes 10 hours to do the same task. How long would it take to paint one house if Jack and Joan worked together?
8.2.5	Kim is 20 years older than Joe. In 5 years, Kim will be 5 years older than twice Joe's age. How old is Kim today?
8.2.6	Is $x > 8$? Statement 1: $9x = x^2$ Statement 2: $x^2 = 81$ A. Statement 1 ALONE is sufficient, but Statement 2 ALONE is not. B. Statement 2 ALONE is sufficient, but Statement 1 ALONE is not. C. Both statements TOGETHER are sufficient, but neither statement ALONE is sufficient. D. Each statement ALONE is sufficient. E. Both statements TOGETHER are NOT sufficient.

8.1 Optics

Optics is the branch of physics that deals with light. Problems of this variety show up on the Quantitative Reasoning Test because reflection of light is all about angles.

8.1.1 Reflection, Mirrors

Reflection occurs when light hits a surface and bounces off. An uneven surface reflects light diffusely, scattering it, but an even surface like a mirror reflects light in a very precise way. This is one of the reasons why you can see your image in a mirror but not in, say, a brick wall with reflective paint.

Law of Reflection: This law says that the angle of incidence is always equal to the angle of reflection.

If you draw a line perpendicular to the mirror at the point where the light hits (= the "normal" line), the **angle of incidence** (θ_i) is the angle formed by that line and the incoming light ray. Similarly, the **angle of reflection** (θ_r) is the angle formed by the perpendicular and the reflected light ray.

Using the law of reflection, this must always be true: $\theta_i = \theta_r$. Thus, any plane-mirror problem turns into a simple geometry and/or trigonometry problem involving lines and angles (QR Chapters 5 and 6).

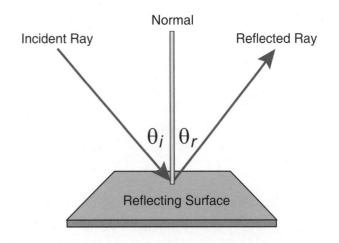

And so, from a technical standpoint, reflection is the process by which light rays (= *imaginary lines drawn perpendicular to the advancing wave fronts*) bounce back into a medium from a surface with another medium (*versus being refracted or absorbed*). The ray that arrives is the *incident* ray while the ray that bounces back is the *reflected* ray. To summarize:

1) the angle of incidence (θ_i) equals the angle of reflection (θ_r) at the normal (*N*, the line perpendicular to the surface)

2) θ_i, θ_r and N all lie in the same plane.

8.1.2 Elliptical Mirrors

The law of reflection still applies to curved mirror surfaces. The only problem is knowing how to draw the perpendicular line at the point of incidence. Dealing with unusually curved mirrors is too complicated for the Quantitative Reasoning Test, but you may still encounter questions about an elliptical mirror.

An **ellipse** is an oval-shaped figure. It has two points in its interior that are equally spaced on either side of the center (called the **foci**) such that, for any point on the perimeter of the ellipse, the sum of the distances to the foci is always the same. The line passing through both foci from one end of the perimeter to the other is known as the **major axis**. The line perpendicular to the major axis passing through the midpoint is the **minor axis**. A circle is a special ellipse for which both foci are the same point.

Property: If a light ray passes through a focus of an elliptical mirror, it will always reflect off the inside of the mirror and pass through the other focus.

> **NOTE**
>
> The length of the major axis is the same as the distance a light ray will travel between one focus and the other if it is reflected once on the way.

8.2 Word Problems

8.2.1 Rates of Change

A rate of change is an amount by which one variable changes in relationship to another variable. Usually, a rate of change specifies how some value changes as time progresses. All rates of change can be written as fractions, so rate of change problems almost always boil down to algebra problems involving fraction manipulation.

EXAMPLE

A glass can hold 10 oz of liquid. Water is being poured in at a rate of 3 oz every 2 seconds. How many seconds will it take for the glass to reach 2/3 full?

The rate in this problem translates to the fraction (3 oz)/(2 sec) [= *dimensional*

analysis; QR 3.2]. We want to find the time "t" it will take for 2/3 of 10 oz to be poured in, so we set up an algebraic equation:

$$\frac{3 \text{ oz}}{2 \text{ sec}} \times t = \frac{2}{3} \times 10 \text{ oz}$$

$$\Rightarrow t = \frac{2 \text{ sec}}{3 \text{ oz}} \times \frac{20 \text{ oz}}{3}$$

$$\Rightarrow t = \frac{40}{9} \text{ sec}$$

8.2.2 Distance, Time and Velocity

A specific type of rate of change with which you should be familiar is **velocity**. Velocity is the distance an object travels in a specific direction per unit of time. Do not get this confused with **speed,** which is a value that is independent of the direction of travel.

$$\text{Velocity} = \frac{\text{Distance}}{\text{Time}}$$

You can use this equation to solve for any one of the three values if you know the other two.

EXAMPLE

A jogger runs the first 100 meters of a 5 km race in 24 seconds. If the jogger maintains the same pace until the end of the race, how long will it take her to run the entire race?

We are given a distance and a time, so we can easily find the velocity of the jogger.

$$v = \frac{100 \text{ m}}{24 \text{ s}}$$

The distance in question is in kilometers, so we could convert this velocity.

$$v = \frac{.1 \text{ km}}{24 \text{ s}}$$

Now we need to apply our velocity formula once more. We have a velocity and a distance, but we ultimately want to find the time.

$$\frac{.1 \text{ km}}{24 \text{ s}} = \frac{5 \text{ km}}{t}$$

$$\Rightarrow 5 \text{ km} \times 24 \text{ s} = .1 \text{ km} \times t$$

$$\Rightarrow \frac{(5 \times 24 \text{ s})}{.1} = \frac{120 \text{ s}}{\left(\frac{1}{10}\right)} = 120(10) \text{ s} = 1200 \text{ s} = t$$

By dimensional analysis (QR 3.2):

$$1200 \text{ s} \times (1 \text{ min.}/60 \text{ s}) = 1200/60 = 120/6 = 20 \text{ min.}$$

Velocity problems can also involve a geometric component if a specific direction (or directions) of travel is included, so be on the lookout! {Vectors are discussed in the QR Appendix (A.6)}

Calculating the average velocity for a trip is sometimes necessary. Given what you have already seen in this section, perhaps you would not be surprised about the following relationship:

$$\text{Average Velocity} = \frac{\text{Total Distance Traveled}}{\text{Total Time}}$$

Some questions aim to see how you rearrange the preceding equations. For example, if you need to isolate time, then you would calculate the distance over the velocity. If you were to have two objects traveling towards each other, then you would need to add the two velocities.

EXAMPLE

Two trains, 150 miles apart are traveling towards each other at constant speed with one train at 45 mph and the other at 30 mph. How many hours does it take for both to meet (*or cross paths or crash*)?

Time = (150 miles)/(45 mph + 30 mph)

= (150 miles)/(75 mph)

= 2 hours

8.2.3 Simple and Compound Interests

Questions dealing with simple and compound interests are very straightforward on the DAT. These questions are essentially plug-and-chug problems. Make sure you differentiate between simple and compound interests.

Simple interest is calculated based on just the initial amount of money invested. Thus the formula for simple interest can be expressed as:

I = PRT

where I is the interest earned from the investment, P is the principal or the amount of money invested, R is the rate of interest (usually in the form of percentage) charged on the principal, and T is the time.

EXAMPLE

Johnny borrowed $15,000 from the bank at 5% simple interest per year. How much does Johnny owe the bank in one year?

I = PRT

= ($15,000)(0.05)(1)

= $750 owed

Compound interest is computed based on the amount of money invested and all interests accumulated during the past periods. Interests may be compounded monthly, semiannually, or annually. The simplest way to approach these questions is to treat each period as a simple interest problem.

EXAMPLE

Joe borrowed $12,000 from the bank at 10% interest compounded annually. If no payments are made for 3 years without additional penalties, how much does he owe the bank?

After the first year:

I = PRT

= ($12,000)(0.1)(1)

= $1,200 in interest for the first year.

After the second year:

I = PRT

= ($12,000 + $1,200)(0.1)(1)

= $1,320 in interest for the second year.

After the third year:

I = PRT

= ($12,000 + $1,200 + $1,320)(0.1)(1)

= $1,452 in interest for the third year.

Total interest:

$1,200 + $1,320 + $1,452 = $3,972 total interest owed after three years.

Thus, after 3 years, Joe owes: $12,000 + $3,972 in interest = $15,972.

Alternatively, for compound interest:

Future Value = $(P)(1 + R)^n$

where n is the number of periods. Thus:

Future Value = $(12,000)(1 + 0.1)^3$

$= 12,000(1.331) = \$15,972$

> **NOTE**
>
> Be comfortable with rearranging the Interest equation. The DAT can ask you to solve for any one of the interest rate, time, or principal.

8.2.4 Work Problems

Work problems are almost guaranteed to show up on the DAT. Fortunately, they are rather simple and can be solved with the following equation:

$$\frac{1}{(t1)} + \frac{1}{(t2)} = \frac{1}{(T)}$$

where $t1$ = time it takes for A to finish the task, $t2$ = time it takes for B to finish the task, and T = total time.

EXAMPLE

Jack takes 5 hours to paint a house while Joan takes 10 hours to do the same task. How long would it take to paint one house if Jack and Joan worked together?

$$\left(\frac{1}{5\ hours}\right) + \left(\frac{1}{10\ hours}\right) = \left(\frac{1}{total\ time}\right)$$

$$\left(\frac{2}{10\ hours}\right) + \left(\frac{1}{10\ hours}\right) = \left(\frac{1}{total\ time}\right)$$

$$\left(\frac{3}{10\ hours}\right) = \left(\frac{1}{total\ time}\right)$$

Cross multiply:

3(total time) = 10 hours

total time = 10/3 or 3 ⅓ hours if Jack and Joan work together.

8.2.5 Age Problems

Age problems are simply algebraic expressions disguised as word problems. There are two methods in approaching these problems.

EXAMPLE

Kim is 20 years older than Joe. In 5 years, Kim will be 5 years older than twice Joe's age. How old is Kim today?

Method 1:

Let K = Kim's age and J = Joe's age

We can set up the first statement as:

K = J + 20

The second statement can be set up as:

(K + 5) − 5 = 2(J + 5)

Let's rearrange the first equation to K − 20 = J since we are solving for Kim's

High-level Importance

age. Then substitute the first equation into the second equation. We get,

$(K + 5) - 5 = 2(K - 20 + 5)$
$K = 2(K - 15)$
$K = 2K - 30$
$K = 30$

Kim is 30 years old while Joe is 10 years old.

Method 2:

Plug and chug the answers provided. Sometimes the quickest way to solving these types of problems are through trial and error.

8.2.6 Data Analysis, Interpretation, and Sufficiency

Data analysis can include a relatively simple table of data followed by a question asking you to identify a basic trend. Sometimes the information is related to probability and statistics, algebra, or graph analysis (*interpretation of data*). The question itself can resemble any other standard DAT QR question but it could be arranged as a "data sufficiency" problem. Although there were no data sufficiency problems in the 2022 ADA DAT QR practice test, the fact that the ADA added this topic to its DAT User Manual suggests that you should at least be familiar with how these questions are presented.

Similar to Quantitative Comparison (QR 4.7), where there is an A vs B scenario, data sufficiency is a statement evaluation question and presents Statement 1 vs Statement 2. Next comes a rather standard format for the answer choices in response to a question (or prompt) related to the two statements:

A. Statement 1 ALONE is sufficient, but Statement 2 ALONE is not.
B. Statement 2 ALONE is sufficient, but Statement 1 ALONE is not.
C. Both statements TOGETHER are sufficient, but neither statement ALONE is sufficient.
D. Each statement ALONE is sufficient.
E. Both statements TOGETHER are NOT sufficient.

EXAMPLE

Is $x > 8$?

Statement 1: $9x = x^2$

Statement 2: $x^2 = 81$

Given the preceding standard multiple choice responses, consider your response (A, B, C, D or E) before continuing.

Statement 1 suggests that x is 9 since that would result in 81 on both sides of the equation. However:

$$9x = x^2$$

$$0 = x^2 - 9x$$

$$0 = (x - 9)x$$

... which has 2 solutions: either x is 9 or x is 0 (*when comfortable with algebra, you would not factor to see the two possible solutions*). Statement 1 is insufficient on its own to decide if the statement x > 8 is correct.

Now let us evaluate Statement 2 which, on the surface, might cause a reflex to confidently say that x must be 9. However, with a few extra seconds to consider the possibilities, you may recall that a negative times a negative is positive, and thus x could be -9. Statement 2 is insufficient on its own to decide if the statement x > 8 is correct.

And finally, if we take both statements TOGETHER, then x can only be 9 and definitely we have sufficient information to say that x > 8; additionally, we proved that either statement ALONE would be insufficient to be certain that x > 8. Thus the correct answer is C.

8.3 Word Problem Strategies

8.3.1 What You Need and What You Know

Identify the Problem Type: The first thing you should do when you encounter a word problem is ask, "What type of problem is it?" If you can identify it as a rate, geometry, probability, or some other kind of problem, you will have an immediate idea of what might need to be done.

What You Need: Next, go through the problem and pick out exactly what information the problem is asking you to find. Are you looking for the distance traveled, the probability of heads, the measure of an angle? Whatever it may be, write it down on the laminated noteboard provided during the test.

What You Know: After you have identified what you are looking for, you should go back and look at what information you are given. The problem will always provide enough information to solve the problem (sometimes even more than enough), but it can often be a little confusing to keep all of it in your mind at once. It may not even be presented in an easy to understand form; for example, ratios and rates are much clearer if you rewrite them as concise fractions. It can be extremely helpful to quickly list out what you know on the noteboard.

8.3.2 Draw a Picture

If a word problem has any kind of geometric component, it can be difficult to keep it straight in your mind. Drawing a simple picture of the situation will solve this problem, but beyond that, a picture can even help you to see connections you would not have otherwise noticed.

Some problems do not lend themselves to pictorial representations. In such cases, you should not spend time worrying about drawing one. If it seems difficult to draw or if you can't even figure out what to draw, then a picture probably would not be helpful.

8.3.3 Set Up the Math

This is the part where you have to bring your math knowledge and skills to the table. You have your lists of what you need and know, you have your picture, and now you have to find a way to solve the problem.

It is up to you to make the connections, but before you start tossing numbers around you should take a moment to set up the math. This means you should write out the equations and relationships you will need before you start evaluating. This way, you can easily keep track of the work you are doing in case you make a mistake, and all you need to do in the end to find the solution is plug in values and crank out some basic algebra and arithmetic.

Naturally, the most important advice is: Practice, practice, practice! Let's get started!

GOLD STANDARD DAT QR PRACTICE QUESTIONS

CHAPTER 8: Applied Mathematics

1. If it takes thirty minutes to walk 1.5 miles, how many miles will be covered in 3 hours?

   A. 12
   B. 4.5
   C. 9
   D. 7.5
   E. 2.25

2. A ray of light passes through one focus of an elliptical mirror with a major axis of length 8. At the point of reflection, it is 6 units away from the other focus. At this point, how far is the ray of light from the first focus?

   A. 2
   B. 4
   C. 6
   D. 8
   E. 10

3. A ray of light passes through the foci of an elliptical mirror at $(\sqrt{5}, 0)$. It is reflected at the endpoint of the minor axis, the point (0, 2). What is the length of the major axis?

   A. $2\sqrt{5}$
   B. 3
   C. 4
   D. 6
   E. $\sqrt{29}$

4. A small pipe allows water to flow at 5 gallons per minute. A larger pipe allows water to flow at 15 gallons per minute. If both pipes are used, how many minutes will it take to fill a 180 gallon tank with water?

   A. 18
   B. 9
   C. 24
   D. 12
   E. 30

5. A beam of light originates at the outer edge of a circular mirror of radius 5 and passes through the center. How far does it travel before being reflected?

   A. 10
   B. 1
   C. 5
   D. 2.5
   E. 15

6. A truck travels 150 miles in 3 hours during the morning, and 180 miles in 3 hours during the afternoon. What is its average speed for the day?

   A. 37 mph
   B. 36 mph
   C. 65 mph
   D. 110 mph
   E. 55 mph

7. The beam from a lighthouse sweeps out $\dfrac{\pi}{4}$ radians every 5 seconds. 500 meters away from the shore, a ship is directly approaching at a rate of 100 meters per minute. If this speed is maintained, how many complete revolutions will the beam make before the ship reaches the shore?

   A. 5
   B. 60
   C. 7.5
   D. 75
   E. 300

8. The bottom of a square basement window with a diagonal length of 1 meter is level with the ground, as shown in the following figure. A ray of light originates at its lower left-hand corner and travels diagonally up to the upper right-hand corner, where it is reflected downwards. How many meters from the corner of the window (point D) is the ray when it reaches the ground again, at point E?

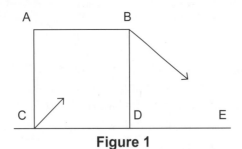

Figure 1

   A. $2/\sqrt{2}$
   B. 1/2
   C. 1
   D. $1/\sqrt{2}$
   E. 2

9. The average age of a wife, her husband and daughter three years ago was 27 years and that of her husband and daughter five years ago was 20 years. What is the wife's present age?

   A. 36
   B. 40
   C. 37
   D. 42
   E. 38

10. Hiking up a mountain took 5 hours, but down only 1½ hours. If the distance each way was 3.3 miles, what is the difference between the two hiking rates in km/s?

    A. 5.63×10^{-4} km/s
    B. 6.84×10^{-4} km/s
    C. 9.03×10^{-4} km/s
    D. 6.16×10^{-4} km/s
    E. 6.43×10^{-4} km/s

11) You are trying to pick one of 2 lines at a grocery store checkout counter. Line A has 4 customers waiting, and they are moving through at a rate of 3 every 5 minutes. Line B has 7 customers waiting. How fast must Line B move in customers per minute for it to be an equal option?

    A. 2
    B. 29/20
    C. 21/20
    D. 1
    E. 4/5

12) An ellipse has foci (-2, 0) and (2, 0), and a major axis of length 6. What is the length of the minor axis?

A. 1

B. $\sqrt{5}/2$

C. $\sqrt{5}$

D. $2\sqrt{5}$

E. 4

13) A light ray strikes a flat mirror at an angle of 60° from the normal line. If there is a second mirror parallel to the first and located 1 meter above it, how far does the light ray travel before hitting the second mirror?

A. 1 m

B. $\sqrt{3}$ m

C. 2 m

D. $2\sqrt{3}$ m

E. 4 m

14) An elliptical mirror has foci (1, 2) and (1, -1), and a major axis of length 4. If a light ray departs from the focus at (1, 2) traveling horizontally, how far does it travel before striking the mirror's surface?

A. 7/8

B. 1

C. 9/8

D. 5/4

E. 3/2

15) A faucet is leaking at a rate of 2 oz every 3 minutes. If the sink is plugged and can hold 60 oz of water, how many hours will it take for the sink to fill halfway?

A. .75

B. .85

C. 1

D. 1.5

E. 45

16) A tree grows at a rate of 5 feet every 3 years. A second tree, 2 years younger than the first tree, grows at a rate of 5 feet every 2 years. How old will the first tree be when both trees are the same height?

A. 6

B. 5

C. 4

D. 3

E. 2

17) Taylor places $8,000 in a certificate of deposit paying 3% simple interest annually. How much interest will Taylor earn over the course of 3 years?

A. $620

B. $720

C. $820

D. $920

E. $1020

18) Lily places $2,000 in a savings account paying 1% interest compounded biannually. How much money will be in the savings account after one year?

A. $2,000.20
B. $2,010.20
C. $2,020.20
D. $2,030.20
E. $2,040.20

19) It takes Aaron 12 minutes to sweep the patio. If Jared can sweep the patio in 9 minutes, how many minutes would it take the two of them working together?

A. 5
B. 36/7
C. 37/7
D. 38/7
E. 39/7

20) Richie and Nick are door-to-door salesmen. Working at the same time, they collectively cover 20 houses in 1 hour. Alone, Nick can cover 20 houses in 1.8 hours. How long would it take Richie to cover 20 houses alone?

A. 3/2 hours
B. 7/4 hours
C. 2 hours
D. 9/4 hours
E. 5/2 hours

21) Two bikers depart from point A at the same time. The first rides 3 miles due North, then 4 miles due West to arrive at point B 28 minutes later. The second rides in a straight line from point A to point B. If both bikers travel at the same constant speed, how much sooner does the second biker arrive at point B?

A. 20 min
B. 16 min
C. 12 min
D. 10 min
E. 8 min

22) A jogger travels at 9 mph for 20 min, 7 mph for 30 min, and 9 mph for the final 10 min. How far does the jogger travel?

A. 7 miles
B. 8 miles
C. 9 miles
D. 10 miles
E. 11 miles

23) A migrating bird flies 100 km in 4 hours, rests for 1 hour, then flies another 60 km in 3 hours. What is the average velocity of the bird?

A. 16 km/hr
B. 18.1 km/hr
C. 20 km/hr
D. 22.9 km/hr
E. 32 km/hr

24) Dave is 12 years older than Jonathan. How old will Jonathan be when his age is 2/3 of Dave's?

A. 12
B. 18
C. 20
D. 24
E. 30

25) Anne is 25 years old. If Tom will be twice her age in three years, how old is Tom now?

A. 49 years
B. 50 years
C. 51 years
D. 52 years
E. 53 years

26) If a jogger goes for a run and takes 6 minutes to travel the first mile, 7 minutes and 13 seconds to travel the second mile, and 1 minute and 47 seconds to travel the final 1056 feet, what was the jogger's average speed in miles per hour?

A. 8.8
B. 9.0
C. 9.4
D. 10.2
E. 10.6

27) Rose buys five items from a clothing store. The first two items each cost $20. The other three items all have the same price. If Rose spent a total of $121, how much did each of the three additional items cost?

A. $23
B. $27
C. $29
D. $31
E. $33

28) It took Andrew 12 minutes to jog 1.5 miles. At this rate, how long will it take him to jog the final half-mile home?

A. 3 minutes
B. 4 minutes
C. 5 minutes
D. 6 minutes
E. 8 minutes

29) A closed rectangular box has a base that is 4 feet wide and 3 feet long. If the box is 5 feet tall, what is the greatest distance between any two corners?

A. $5\sqrt{2}$ feet
B. $2\sqrt{2}$ feet
C. $\sqrt{2}/2$ feet
D. 5 feet
E. 7 feet

30) It takes one pump 30 minutes to drain a tank. A second pump can drain the tank in 45 minutes. If both pumps are operating at once, how long will it take to drain the tank?

A. 25 minutes
B. 21 minutes
C. 20 minutes
D. 18 minutes
E. 15 minutes

31) Consider a box with length l, width w and height h, if the thickness of the cardboard is t, how much empty space is inside this cardboard box?

   A. $l \times w \times h$
   B. $(l - t) \times (w - t) \times (h - t)$
   C. $(l + t) \times (w + t) \times (h + t)$
   D. $(l - 2t) \times (w - 2t) \times (h - 2t)$

32) A 10-year old boy is 1.4 meters tall and preparing for a play in which he wears a top hat that extends the boy's height by 10 cm. What is the vertical length of the smallest mirror that would permit the boy to see his shoes and the top of his hat while standing?

   A. 0.75 m
   B. 1.4 m
   C. 1.5 m
   D. Cannot be determined without knowing how far he is standing from the mirror.

33) What is the value of x?

   Statement 1: x + 17 = 17

   Statement 2: $x^2 = x$

   A. Statement 1 ALONE is sufficient, but Statement 2 ALONE is not.
   B. Statement 2 ALONE is sufficient, but Statement 1 ALONE is not.
   C. Both statements TOGETHER are sufficient, but neither statement ALONE is sufficient.
   D. Each statement ALONE is sufficient.
   E. Both statements TOGETHER are NOT sufficient.

34) A regular hexagon is inscribed in a circle with a radius of 4 cm.

   A: The perimeter of the hexagon in cm
   B: 24

   A. Quantity A is greater.
   B. Quantity B is greater.
   C. The two quantities are equal.
   D. The relationship cannot be determined from the information given.

35) Consider Figure 1 and the Michaelis-Menten equation.

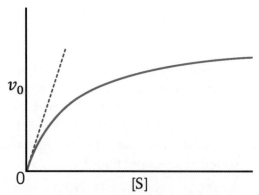

Figure 1: Initial velocity v_0 versus substrate concentration [S] in an enzyme-catalyzed reaction demonstrating Michaelis-Menten kinetics. The dashed line indicates the slope of the curve when [S] << K_m.

The Michaelis-Menten equation:

$$v_0 = \frac{V_{max}[S]}{[S] + K_m}$$

Which of the following corresponds to the slope of the dashed line in Figure 1?

   A. $(1/2)[S]$
   B. V_{max}/K_m
   C. k_{cat}/K_m
   D. $1/V_{max}$

Questions 36–37

Consider the following diagram.

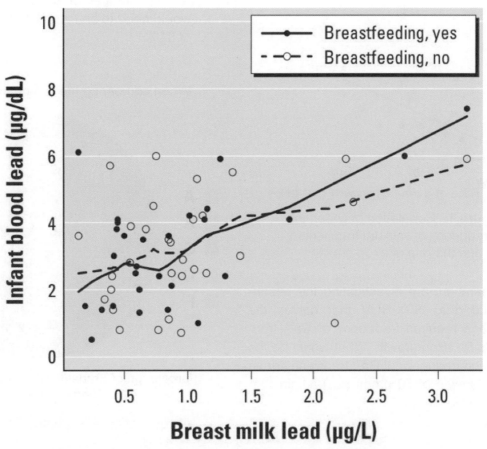

Figure 1: Association between infant blood lead and breast milk lead, separated by infants who were breastfed, and those who were not.

36) According to Figure 1, when breast milk lead is at 1.0 µg/L, as compared to infant blood lead, breast milk lead is approximately:

A. the same concentration.

B. 2.5 times less.

C. 3 times less.

D. 30 times less.

37) According to Figure 1, how much milk breast lead would be projected if the difference in infant blood lead between breastfeeding and non-breastfeeding trials is doubled that present at 2.5 µg/L breast milk lead?

A. 3.0 µg/L

B. 4.0 µg/L

C. 4.5 µg/L

D. 5.0 µg/L

38) Consider Figure 1.

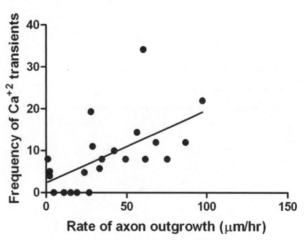

Figure 1: Correlation between the frequency of calcium transients and the rate of axon growth.

Researchers are investigating the experimental drug NSX-RUV that halves the average required frequency of Ca^{2+} transients for axon growth. What would be the average frequency of Ca^{2+} transients for an axon growth of 50 µm/hr post-administration of NSX-RUV?

A. 1
B. 5
C. 10
D. 20

39) A teacher graded the exams of 120 students.

A: The number of students' grades that would need to be increased for a pass rate of 81%.

B: 6

When comparing the two quantities, the

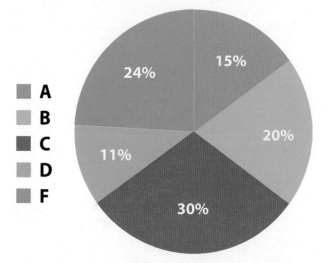

Percentage of Students with Passing and Failing Grades

A. quantity of A is greater than the quantity of B.
B. quantity of B is greater than the quantity of A.
C. relationship cannot be determined from the information given.
D. two quantities are equal.

40) A: The minimum difference in mmHg of pO_2 and pCO_2 during a respiratory cycle

B: 25

When comparing the two quantities, the

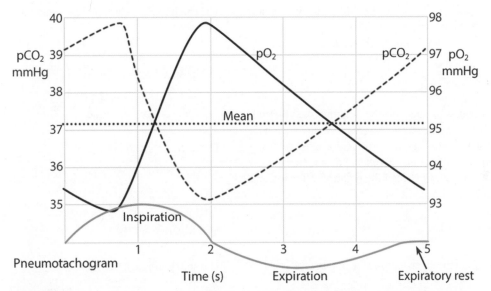

Oscillations in a Respiratory Cycle (pO_2, solid line; pCO_2, dashed line)

A. quantity of A is greater than the quantity of B.

B. quantity of B is greater than the quantity of A.

C. relationship cannot be determined from the information given.

D. two quantities are equal.

CHAPTER REVIEW SOLUTIONS: CHAPTER 8

Question 1   C

See: QR 8.2.2

The walking speed is $\dfrac{1.5\,\text{mi}}{0.5\,\text{hr}} = 3\,\text{mi./hr.}$, and in 3 hours,

$(3\,\text{hr.})\,(3\,\text{mi./hr.}) = 9\,\text{mi.}$ will be covered.

Question 2   A

See: QR 8.1, 8.1.2

Since the ray passes through one focus, it must pass through the other after being reflected. The length of any such path is always equal to the length of the major axis, so if the distance between the point of reflection and the second focus is 6, the distance between the point of reflection and the first focus must be $8 - 6 = 2$.

Question 3   D

See: QR 8.1.2

The distance from the given focus to the point of reflection is

$$\sqrt{(\sqrt{5} - 0)^2 + (0 - 2)^2}$$
$$= \sqrt{(\sqrt{5})^2 + (2)^2}$$
$$= \sqrt{5 + 4}$$
$$= \sqrt{9} = 3$$

The second focus must be located at $(-\sqrt{5}, 0)$. By symmetry, this focus is also 3 units from the point of reflection. The sum of these lengths is the total distance traveled by the ray of light, and is equal to the length of the major axis.

Question 4   B

See: QR 8.2, 8.2.1

Combined, the two pipes fill the tank at a rate of $5 + 15 = 20$ gal./min.. The time t needed to fill the tank is:

$$t = \frac{180\,\text{gal.}}{20\,\text{gal. / min.}} = 9\,\text{min.}$$

Question 5   A

See: QR 8.1, 8.1.1

The beam of light will be reflected on the opposite side of the mirror, and because it passes through the center, its path is a diagonal of the circle, which has length $2r = 2(5) = 10$.

Question 6   E

See: QR 8.2.2

The truck's speed during the morning is

$$\frac{150\,\text{mi}}{3\,\text{hrs}} = 50\,\text{mph}$$

and its speed during the afternoon is

$$\frac{180\,\text{mi}}{3\,\text{hrs}} = 60\,\text{mph}$$

The average speed is

$$\frac{50\,\text{mph} + 60\,\text{mph}}{2} = 55\,\text{mph}$$

Question 7   C

See: QR 8.2, 8.2.2

The ship will reach the shore in

$$\frac{500\,\text{km}}{100\,\text{km / min}} = 5\,\text{min}$$

This is a total of

$$(5\,\text{min.})\,(60\,\text{sec./min.}) = 300\,\text{sec,}$$

which makes up

$$\frac{300\,\text{sec}}{5\,\text{sec}} = 60$$

intervals of 5 seconds each. In this time, the lighthouse beam sweeps out

$$60\left(\frac{\pi}{4}\right) = 15\pi\ \text{radians,}$$

which is equivalent to

$$\frac{15\pi}{2\pi} = 7.5\ \text{revolutions.}$$

Question 8   D

See: QR 8.1, 8.1.1

As the diagonal of a square intercepts the corners of the square at a 45° angle, a ray traveling diagonally across a square must intercept the corner at the same angle. The Law of Reflection tells us that the ray is reflected at 45° as well, so BDC and BED are congruent 45°–45°–90° triangles.

The distance DE, which represents the ray's distance from point D, must be equal to CD. The length of the diagonal of a square is the length of the side times the square root 2, so CD and DE must have length $\dfrac{1}{\sqrt{2}}$.

Question 9   B

See: QR 8.2.1

Let w, h, d represent the current ages of the wife, husband, and daughter, respectively. Three years ago, they were $w - 3$, $h - 3$, $d - 3$ years old. The average of these is:

$$\frac{(w - 3) + (h - 3) + (d - 3)}{3} = 27$$

Five years ago, the husband and daughter were $h - 5, d - 5$ years old, and the average of these ages is:

$$\frac{(h - 5) + (d - 5)}{2} = 20$$

Simplify these fractions to get:

$$w + h + d = 90,$$
$$h + d = 50$$

Now, subtract the second equation from the first:

$$w + h + d - (h + d) = 90 - (50)$$
$$w = 40$$

Question 10   B

See: QR 8.2, 8.2.2

Use the formula $\text{rate} = \dfrac{\text{distance}}{\text{time}}$, where the distance is 3.3 miles. The downhill rate minus the uphill rate is:

$$r_2 - r_1 = \frac{3.3}{1.5} - \frac{3.3}{5}$$
$$= \frac{10(3.3)}{15} - \frac{3(3.3)}{15}$$
$$= \frac{7(3.3)}{15}$$
$$= 1.54 \text{ miles per hour}$$

Given that 1 mile = 1.6 km:

$$\frac{1.54\,\text{mi}}{1\,\text{hr}} \times \frac{1.6\,\text{km}}{1\,\text{mi}} \times \frac{1\,\text{hr}}{3600\,\text{s}}$$
$$= \frac{2.464\,\text{km}}{3600\,\text{s}}$$
$$= 6.84 \times 10^{-4}\ \text{km/s}$$

Question 11   C

See: QR 8.3

Set up an equation using ratios, then cross multiply and solve:

4 (5/3) = 7 (1/x)

20/3 = 7/x

(7)(3) = (20)(x)

21/20 = x

So Line B must travel at a rate of at least 21/20 customers per minute.

Question 12   D

See: QR 8.1.2

Consider a ray of light departing from the focus at (-2, 0) and reaching the edge of the ellipse at point (0, y), the point at which the minor axis meets the ellipse. This ray forms the hypotenuse of a right triangle with vertices at (-2, 0), (0, 0), and (0, y). Notice that the length of the horizontal leg is half of the distance between the two foci, and the vertical leg has length y, which is half the length of the minor axis. So the minor axis has length 2y, the value we seek.

So the horizontal leg has length:

½ (2 – (-2)) = ½ (4) = 2

We can find the length of the hypotenuse using the fact that any ray departing from one focus travels a distance equal to the length of the major axis before reaching the other focus. The hypotenuse, then, is exactly half this distance since its point of reflection is on the minor axis:

½ (6) = 3.

Now find y using the Pythagorean theorem:

$2^2 + y^2 = 3^2$

$4 + y^2 = 9$

$y^2 = 5$

$y = \sqrt{5}$

And the minor axis has length:

$2y = 2\sqrt{5}$.

Question 13   C

See: QR 8.1.1

The light ray reflects off of the first mirror at the same angle from the normal, 60°. Now consider the right triangle formed by the ray, the normal line, and the top mirror. We know the normal line leg has length 1 m. So if the hypotenuse has length x, then:

$x \cos(60°) = 1$ m

$x = 1$ m$/ \cos(60°)$

$x = 1$ m$/ (1/2) = 2$ m.

Question 14   A

See: QR 8.1.1

Consider the right triangle with vertices at each focus and one where the light ray hits the mirror. The length of the side from focus to focus is:

$2 - (-1) = 3$

We can now form a system of two equations using the Pythagorean theorem and the fact that the hypotenuse y and other leg x add to the length of the major axis:

$x + y = 4$ and $x^2 + 3^2 = y^2$

$y = 4 - x$

So:

$x^2 + 9 = (4 - x)^2$

$x^2 + 9 = x^2 - 8x + 16$

$8x = 16 - 9$

$8x = 7$

$x = 7/8$.

Question 15   A

See: QR 8.2.1

For the sink to fill halfway, 60 oz/ 2 = 30 oz of water must leak from the faucet.

$(2$ oz$/3$ min$)$ t = 30 oz

t = 30 oz $(3$ min$/2$ oz$)$

t = 45 min

t = .75 hr.

Question 16   A

See: QR 8.2.1

Let x be the age of the first tree when both trees are the same height. Then:

$(5$ ft$/3$ yr$)$ x = $(5$ ft$/2$ yr$)$ $(x - 2)$

$(2/3)$x = x $- 2$

$(1/3)$x = 2

x = 6.

Question 17   B

See: QR 8.2.3

This is a simple interest problem, so Interest = (Principal)(Rate)(Time):

I = ($8,000)(.03)(3)

I = $720.

Question 18   E

See: QR 8.2.3

This is a compound interest problem, so use the equation Future Value = (Present Value)$(1 + r)^n$ where r is the interest rate and n is the number of periods. In this case, there are 2 periods since interest is compounded biannually.

FV = ($2,000)$(1 + .01)^2$ = ($2,000)(1.0201) = $2,040.20.

Question 19   B

See: QR 8.2.4

This is a combined work problem where $t_1 = 12$, $t_2 = 9$ and we must find $t_{combined}$. So:

$1/12 + 1/9 = 1/t_{combined}$

$t_{combined} = 1/ (7/36)$

$t_{combined} = 36/7$.

Question 20   D

See: QR 8.2.4

This is a combined work problem where $t_1 = 1.8$ hours, $t_{combined} = 1$ hour and we must find t_2. So:

$1/1.8 + 1/t_2 = 1/1$

$1/t_2 = 1 - (1/1.8)$

$1/t_2 = 4/9$

$t_2 = 9/4$ hours.

Question 21　E

See: QR 8.2.2

First construct a right triangle to determine how far the second biker must ride:

$3^2 + 4^2 = c^2$

$9 + 16 = c^2$

$25 = c^2$

$c = 5$

Since the first biker traveled a total of $3 + 4 = 7$ miles, the second biker traveled 5/7 the distance at a pace of 28min/7miles. So it took the second biker:

t = 5miles (28min/7miles)

t = 20 min

So the second biker arrives 28min – 20min = 8 min sooner.

Question 22　B

See: QR 8.2.2

Treat each segment individually and add the distance traveled in each:

(9 mph)(1/3 hour) + (7 mph)(1/2 hour) + (9 mph)(1/6 hour)

= (3 + 7/2 + 3/2) miles

= 8 miles.

Question 23　C

See: QR 8.2.2

The average velocity is given by (total distance)/(total time), so:

v = (100 km + 60 km)/(4 hr + 1 hr + 3 hr)

v = 160 km/8 hr

v = 20 km/hr.

Question 24　D

See: QR 8.2.5

Let J be Jonathan's age and D be Dave's age. We know Dave is 12 years older, so:

D = J + 12

And we want to find Jonathan's age when it is 2/3 of Dave's, or:

J = 2/3 D

Combining, we get:

J = (2/3)(J + 12)

J = (2/3)J + 8

(1/3)J = 8

J = 24.

Question 25　E

See: QR 8.2.5

Let A be Anne's age and T be Tom's age. We are given that A = 25. First find T three years from now:

T = 2(A + 3)

T = 2(25 + 3)

T = 56

Now subtract 3 to obtain Tom's current age:

T = 56 – 3

T = 53.

Question 26　A

See: QR 3.1.1, 3.2.2

First add the time:

6 min + 7 min + 13 sec + 1 min + 47 sec

= 14 min + 60 sec

= 15 min (1 hour/60 min)

= ¼ hour

Now add the distance traveled:

1 mile + 1 mile + 1056 feet

 = 2.2 miles

So the average speed is:

2.2 miles/ ¼ hour

= 8.8 mph.

Question 27　B

See: Deduce

Set up an algebraic equation for the situation. Let the price of each of the three unknown items be represented by the variable X:

$121 = 2 ($20) + 3 (X)

$121 = $40 + 3 (X)

$81 = 3 (X)

$27 = X.

Question 28   B

See: QR 8.2.2

Andrew is traveling at a rate of 1.5 miles/12 minutes = 1 mile/8 minutes. So the time x it takes him to jog a half mile at this rate is:

.5 miles/x minutes = 1 mile/8 minutes

x = (.5 miles)(8 minutes/1 mile) = (.5)(8 minutes)

x = 4 minutes.

Question 29   A

See: QR Chapter 5

To help you visualize this problem, think of any old cardboard box. The corners furthest from each other do not both connect to any single face. In other words, if you want to draw a line between them you have to go through the air within the box, not along a cardboard side. If we think of this line as the hypotenuse of a triangle, what are the other two legs? One is along an edge of the box, so is simply the height (5 ft). The other is the diagonal of the rectangular base, the hypotenuse of a triangle with legs length 3 ft and 4 ft (the length and width). You could use the Pythagorean theorem, or simply recognize that it is a $3 - 4 - 5$ triangle.

So we need to find the hypotenuse of a triangle with legs length 5 ft and 5 ft:

$x^2 = 5^2 + 5^2 = 25 + 25 = 50$

$x = \sqrt{50} = 5\sqrt{2}$ feet.

Question 30   D

See: QR 3.2, 8.2.1

The important thing to recognize in this problem is that you are actually given the rate at which each pump drains water, but the units are tanks per minute. The first has a rate of 1 tank/ 30 minutes and the second 1 tank/45 minutes. To find the rate at which the tank is drained when both pumps are running, add the individual rates together:

1/30 tanks/min + 1/45 tanks/min = 5/90 tanks/min = 1/18 tanks/min

So how many minutes will it take to drain one tank? Here is the resulting equation:

(1/18 tanks/min) x = 1 tank

x = 18 minutes.

Question 31   D

See: QR 5.3.1; deduce

Because it is cube-like, we need to multiply 3 different sides together in order to get the volume. Consider that if you were to just multiply the 3 sides together, you would get a volume which includes the actual cardboard (i.e. calculating the volume that way would get a result which is somewhat greater than the actual volume INSIDE the box). However, if we were to examine the length for example, the space available inside the box would be less than the length of the box because of the thickness at BOTH ends.

Thus, the inside measurements are reduced by the thickness of each side (i.e. *times 2*):

• The inside length will be l - 2t

• The inside width will be w - 2t

• The inside height will be h - 2t

Thus, the space (volume) inside the box = (l - 2t) × (w - 2t) × (h - 2t)

Note: Answer choice A is a reasonable approximation but answer choice D is clearly the best answer among the answer choices provided.

Question 32   A

See: QR 8.1.1, 8.3.2

Half of the total height, from top to bottom, is all that is required of the mirror because of the very important **law of reflection**: the angle of incidence equals the angle of reflection at the normal line (*the line perpendicular to the surface*; note that you can change "Top of head" to "Top of hat" in the image for the same answer: 1.5m/2 = 0.75 m):

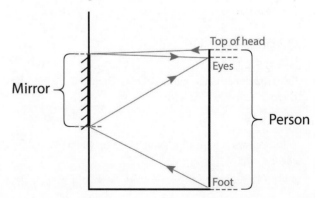

No matter how near, or far away, from the mirror your eyes are, the angles ensure that the size of the image on the mirror remains the same size. Of course, drawing a diagram on your noteboard is helpful for a question like this.

Question 33   A

See: QR 8.2.6

Statement 1 has a unique value of x: 0. Statement 1 alone can answer "What is the value of x?".

Statement 2:

$x^2 = x$

$x^2 - x = 0$

$x(x - 1) = 0$

... which means that Statement 2 has 2 different possible solutions: x = 0 OR x = 1. Statement 2 is thus insufficient to answer the question "What is the value of x?".

Therefore, the answer must be A. Answer choice D is incorrect because Statement 2 has a contradictory possible answer.

Question 34   C

See: QR 4.7, 5.1.3 C., 8.3.2

Draw a picture on your noteboard or scratch paper representing a regular hexagon (6 sides) inscribed in a circle with a radius of 4 cm.

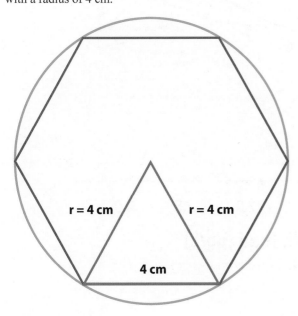

A regular hexagon has 6 equal sides. We can draw the circle's radius to each corner of the hexagon, bisecting the inside angles of a hexagon (which we have seen is 120°, QR 5.1.3 C., thus the angles are 60° each).

A circle is 360°. Since we could draw 6 triangles from the center of the circle: 360°/6 = 60°. Thus all angles of the triangles are the same so all sides must be the same: 4 cm (*equilateral triangles*). Since the hexagon has 6 sides: 6 x 4 cm = 24 cm. The quantity described by A and B are the same so answer choice C is correct.

Question 35   B

See: QR 4.4

This question essentially reduces to a high school math/reasoning problem! Recall the equation for a straight line where m is the slope and b is the y-intercept:

$$y = mx + b$$

We can simplify the right side of the given equation by concluding that if [S] << K_m (*which is information given in the caption to Figure 1*) then [S] + K_m is approximately equal to K_m. Thus, the equation reduces to:

$$v_0 = (V_{max}/K_m) \, [S]$$

which is a graph of v_0 vs [S] (i.e. *y vs. x*) with a y-intercept of 0 (*see* Figure 1 and note that the dashed line intersects y = 0) and therefore the slope must be m = V_{max}/K_m.

Question 36   D

See: QR 3.1, 3.2

According to Figure 1, at a blood milk lead of 1 µg/L, the infant blood lead is approximately 3 µg/dL (*it does not matter if you identified a value a little higher or lower, you will get the same answer*).

Convert infant blood lead to have consistent units: a liter is equal to 10 deciliters (QR Chapter 3).

Thus, the infant blood lead is equivalent to:

$$3 \text{ µg/dL x } 10 \text{ dL/L} = 30 \text{ µg/L}.$$

30 µg/L : 1 µg/L is a 30:1 ratio. Infant blood lead is therefore 30 times greater at a blood milk lead of 1 µg/L, the answer is D.

Question 37   B

See: QR 4.4

First, of course, establish what is the difference in infant blood lead between breastfeeding and non-breastfeeding at 2.5 µg/L breast milk lead. The difference seems to be 1 unit (*see* graph below, blue arrows). So, we want to know: at what point does the difference become 2 units? If you have not considered this, try again to answer the question.

Based on the imperfect regression curves we are given, let's consider the projections and notice visually that the difference increases because the slope is steeper for the breastfeeding cohort. If we had extended graph paper we could see at what point the difference is 2 units, but let's consider another way. If we project backwards, we see that the breastfeeding group seems to come to about where breast milk lead is 1. Similarly, although the non-breastfeeding cohort has more ups and downs, you can see that the future projection intersects breastfeeding at around 1 unit also.

So, it took 1.5 units of breast milk lead (i.e. going from 1.0 to 2.5 along the x-axis) to make a difference of 1 unit in infant blood lead (the blue arrows). Because the relationship continues to be linear, it means that another 1.5 units of breast milk lead for a total of 4 µg/L (2.5 + 1.5 = 4), there will be twice the amount or 2 µg/L difference between the 2 regression lines. The difference in the 2 lines continues on a regular or linear way. Double, double, triple, triple, etc.: The basic concept of linearity.

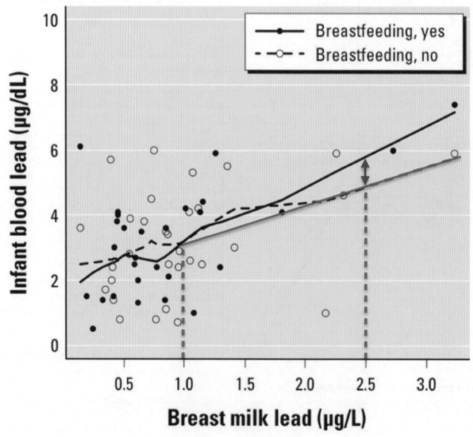

Original image reference: Ettinger, A. et al. *Environ Health Perspect.* 2014; 122(1): 87.

Question 38   B

See: QR 4.4, 7.3.1; Deduce

Looking for 50 μm/hr along the x-axis and checking the regression line (i.e. *the line of best fit*), we get a frequency of 10. However, the question stem stated: "NSX-RUV … halves the average required" so 10 becomes 5.

Original image reference: Hutchins, B., *Dev Neurobiol*. 2011.

Question 39   D

See: QR 2.4.3 C., 4.7, deduce

Assess quantity A: pass of 81% means that 19% failed. However, 24% failed (grade: F) according to the pie chart. We need 5% (24% - 19%) of the students to have their grades increased for the stated pass rate. 5% of 120 students is: $(0.05)(120) = 6$ which is identical to quantity B.

Question 40   A

See: QR 4.7, deduce

To have the minimum difference between the 2 values, the higher value (pO_2) needs to be as low as possible, and the lower value (pCO_2) needs to be as high as possible. Be careful because the left y axis has a different scale as compared to the right y axis. Also, be sure to follow the correct lines as stated below the graph: "**pO_2, solid line; pCO_2, dashed line**"

Thus, the minimum difference can be identified in the graph at approximately 0.75 seconds, approximate values: pO_2 93 – pCO_2 40 = 53 mmHg, which is much more than quantity B. Thus, the correct answer is A.

Going Deeper: Note that at 2 seconds, approximate values: pO_2 98 – pCO_2 35 = 63 mmHg (*the lower value is as low as it can go and the higher value is as high as it can go making the largest difference possible*).

If you have any questions or concerns regarding your DAT practice questions, or the solutions, access the free Gold Standard Masters Series Forum for clarification: www.dat-prep.com/forum.

SPOILER ALERT

Gold Standard has cross-referenced the content in this chapter to examples from the ADA's official DAT practice materials. It is for you to decide when you want to explore these questions since you may want to preserve DAT practice tests for timed mock-exam practice.

We suggest that you acquire the free 2007 DAT practice test from ada.org (digital document format), as well as the 2009 exam or, even better, the most recent online practice test. The online DAT Quantitative Reasoning practice test from the ADA is available through prometric.com and includes content from 2007 (35%), 2009 (10%), and newly added questions (55%). Note below that "Q" is followed by the question number, and cross-references to this chapter are in parentheses.

Examples –

2007 and 2022: Word problem which converts to a simple first order equation to solve (QR 8.2): 2007 Q5 and 2022 Q24 (*one answer choice is deleted in the 2022 version*); average speed for a trip (QR 8.2.2): 2007 Q10 and 2022 Q26 (*one answer choice is deleted in the 2022 version*); word problem with percentages (QR 2.4.3, 8.2): 2007 Q14; word problem with time (QR 8.2): 2007 Q17; word problem with a weighted average (QR 8.2): 2007 Q19 and 2022 Q30 (*one answer choice is deleted in the 2022 version*); word problem with distance and time (QR 8.2.2): 2007 Q21; solve for the length of a side of a square related to area (QR 5.2.1): 2007 Q24 and 2022 Q21; word problem involving age (QR 8.2.5): 2007 Q25; determine the percent area of a rectangle within a rectangle (QR 2.4.3 C., 5.2.1): 2007 Q29; squares within squares (QR 5.2.1): 2007 Q35; calculation of average speed (*velocity*; QR 8.2.2) with simple conversion (QR 3.1.1): 2007 Q39.

2009: Circular mirror calculation given a tangent identity (QR 8.1.2): 2009 Q4; elliptical mirror calculation (QR 8.1.2): 2009 Q5; reflection in a mirrored box (QR 8.1.1): 2009 Q6; distance comparisons in circles vs. ellipses (QR 8.1.2): 2009 Q8; interest calculation (QR 8.2.3): 2009 Q19; word problem involving money (QR 8.2): 2009 Q35.

2022: Word problem with time, distance and velocity (QR 8.2.2, 8.2): 2022 Q7; word problem with work and payment (QR 8.2, 8.2.4): 2022 Q14; reason consecutive odd numbers to add to a specific number (QR 8.2): 2022 Q15; pens, pencils and cost (QR 8.2): 2022 Q16; word problem (*optometry school!*) with percent and ratio (QR 8.2): 2022 Q19; word problem solved by creating 2 simple equations (QR 8.2): 2022 Q22.

Note: **The ADA practice tests are composed of questions which have previously appeared on real, past DATs, but have been retired.** Also, note that most of the 2022 ADA DAT practice test questions have had one answer choice removed. In other words, most questions have 4 answer choices instead of 5, which was standard in 2007 and 2009.

Chapter Checklist

☐ Sign up or access your free online account at www.dat-prep.com for discussion boards for any content from this chapter including chapter-ending practice questions.

☐ Reassess your 'learning objectives' for this chapter: Go back to the first page of this chapter and re-evaluate the top 3 boxes and the Introduction.

☐ Complete 1-2 pages of notes using symbols/abbreviations to represent the entire chapter based on your learning objectives. These are your Gold Notes.

☐ Consider your multimedia options based on your optimal way of learning:

  ☐ Download the free Gold Standard DAT app for your Android device or iPhone. Create your own, tangible study cards or try the free app: Anki.

  ☐ Record your voice reading your Gold Notes onto your smartphone (MP3s) and listen during exercise, transportation, etc.

  ☐ Try some online math videos on YouTube like Khan Academy or Leah4sciMCAT playlist for Math Without a Calculator (the latter was produced for MCAT preparation but it remains helpful for DAT QR basics).

☐ Schedule your full-length DAT practice tests: ADA and/or GS exams and/or other free or paid third-party resources. Schedule one full day to complete a practice test and 1-2 days for a thorough assessment of answers and explanations while adding to your abbreviated Gold Notes.

☐ Schedule and/or evaluate stress reduction techniques such as regular exercise (sports), yoga, meditation and/or mindfulness exercises (*see* YouTube for suggestions).

High-level Importance

Appendix A

DAT MATH REVIEW

In the preceding DAT Masters Series Natural Sciences review and QR sections, several mathematical concepts were presented (i.e. trigonometry, rules of logarithms, the quadratic equation, statistics, etc.). The purpose of this section is to review the DAT mathematical concepts *not* presented elsewhere, though there may be some overlap for emphasis.

A.1 Basic Graphs

A.1.1 The Graph of a Linear Equation

Equations of the type $y = ax + b$ are known as *linear equations* since the graph of y (= *the ordinate*) versus x (= *the abscissa*) is a straight line. The value of y where the line intersects the y axis is called the *intercept b*. The constant a is the *slope* of the line. Given any two points (x_1, y_1) and (x_2, y_2) on the line, we have:

$$y_1 = ax_1 + b$$

and

$$y_2 = ax_2 + b.$$

Subtracting the upper equation from the lower one and dividing through by $x_2 - x_1$ gives the value of the slope,

$$a = (y_2 - y_1)/(x_2 - x_1).$$

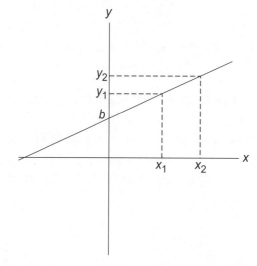

A.1.2 Reciprocal Curve

For any real number x, there exists a unique real number called the multiplicative inverse or *reciprocal* of x denoted $1/x$ or x^{-1} such that $x\,(1/x) = 1$. The graph of the reciprocal $1/x$ for any x is:

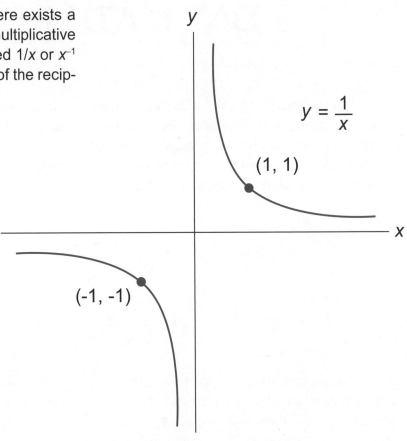

$$y = \frac{1}{x}$$

$(1, 1)$

$(-1, -1)$

A.1.3 Miscellaneous Graphs

There are classical curves which are represented or approximated in the science text as follows: Sigmoidal curve (CHM 6.9.1, BIO 7.5.1), sinusoidal curve (QR 6.2.3), and hyperbolic curves (CHM 9.7 Fig III.A.9.3, BIO 1.1.2).

If you were to plot a set of experimental data, often one can draw a line (A.1.1) or curve (A.1.2/3, A.2.2) which can "best fit" the data. The preceding defines a *regression* line or curve. The main purpose of the regression graph is to predict what would likely occur outside of the experimental data.

A.2 Exponents and Logarithms

A.2.1 Rules of Exponents

$$a^0 = 1 \qquad\qquad a^1 = a$$

$$a^n\, a^m = a^{n+m} \qquad\qquad a^n/a^m = a^{n-m}$$

$$(a^n)^m = a^{nm} \qquad\qquad a^{\frac{1}{n}} = \sqrt[n]{a}$$

A.2.2 Log Rules and Logarithmic Scales

A logarithm (i.e. log) is simply the opposite of expressing exponents (QR 2.5). Using a logarithm answers the question: "How many of one number do we multiply to get another number?"

For example: How many 5s must we multiply to get 125? Answer: $5 \times 5 \times 5 = 125$ (QR 2.5.6), so we had to multiply 3 of the 5s to get 125. Now we can say that the log of 125 with base 5 is 3: $\log_5(125) = 3$.

Just as we have already reviewed various rules for exponents (QR 2.5.1-2.5.5), we will shortly learn basic log rules which will permit manipulations for more complex logs, and we will see that the rules can also be applied to the preceding example thus: $\log_5(125) = \log_5(5)^3 = 3\log_5(5) = 3$.

Like many aspects of math, riding a bike is a good analogy: familiarity will have you applying log rules effortlessly. Logarithmic and exponential scales are found widely in dental and medical research as well as, of course, the basic sciences that we are studying for the DAT.

The rules of logarithms are also discussed in context, for example, Acids and Bases in General Chemistry (CHM 6.5.1). These basic log rules also apply to the "natural logarithm" which is the logarithm to the base e, where "e" is an irrational constant approximately equal to 2.71... (QR 2.1.2). The natural logarithm is usually written as $\ln x$ or $\log_e x$.

In general, the power of logarithms is to reduce wide-ranging numbers to quanti-

Table 1: Common values for the log base 10 (note the trends)

x	Exponential form	$\log_{10}(x)$
0.0001	10^{-4}	-4
0.001	10^{-3}	-3
0.01	10^{-2}	-2
0.1	10^{-1}	-1
1	10^{0}	0
10	10^{1}	1
100	10^{2}	2
1000	10^{3}	3
10000	10^{4}	4

ties with a far smaller range. For example, the graphs commonly seen in this text, are drawn to a unit or *arithmetic scale*. In other words, each unit on the x and y-axes represents exactly *one* unit. This scale can be adjusted to accommodate rapidly changing curves. For example, in a unit scale the numbers 1 (= 10^0), 10 (= 10^1), 100 (= 10^2), and 1000 (= 10^3), are all far apart with varying intervals. Using a logarithmic scale, the sparse values suddenly become separated by one unit: Log 10^0 = 0, log 10^1 = 1, log 10^2 = 2, log 10^3 = 3, and so on.

In practice, logarithmic scales are often used to convert a rapidly changing curve (e.g. an exponential curve) into a straight line. It is called a *semi-log* scale when either the x-axis *or* the y-axis is logarithmic. It is called a *log-log* scale when both the x-axis *and* the y-axis are logarithmic. Note: if not specified otherwise, when you just see "log" with no base, then it is considered to be the "common log" which means log base 10.

Here are the rules you must know:

1) $\log_a a = 1$
2) $\log_a M^k = k \log_a M$
3) $\log_a(MN) = \log_a M + \log_a N$
4) $\log_a(M/N) = \log_a M - \log_a N$
5) $10^{\log_{10} M} = M$
6) $\log_a(1) = 0$, given "a" is greater than zero.

EXAMPLE 1

Given:

$$pH = -\log_{10}[H^+]$$

Let us calculate the pH of 0.001 H^+ (for now, ignore the chemistry, focus only on the math):

$[H^+]$ = 0.001
using the #1 Rule of Algebra (QR 4.1.1):
-log$[H^+]$ = -log (0.001)
pH = -log(10^{-3})
pH = 3 log 10   (log rule #2)
pH = 3   (rule #1, a = 10)

EXAMPLE 2

What is log (1 000 000)?
log (1 000 000) = log 10^6 = 6

EXAMPLE 3

What is log (1/100)?
log (1/100) = log 10^{-2} = -2

EXAMPLE 4

Given that ln2 = 0.69, what is $ln2e^3$?

Try to solve the problem while keeping in mind: **(1)** ln is the natural logarithm, meaning that it is log to the base e; **(2)** our 3rd rule of logarithms permits you separate factors.

$ln2e^3$ = ln2 + lne^3 = 0.69 + 3 = 3.69

Notice that if you have the base of the log and the base of the number with the exponent the same, then the answer is simply the exponent. Thus

Log(1000) = $log10^3$ = lne^3 = 3.

> **NOTE**
>
> DAT log problems come in the form of pH, pKa, pKb, rate law, Nernst equation (BIO 5 Appendix), Gibbs free energy (CHM 9.10), just to name a few! Basically, the 'science' reduces to a basic math problem.

EXAMPLE 5

Approximate log(200).

Because the number 200 is between 100 and 1000 (but clearly closer to 100), and since log(100) = 2 and log(1000) = 3, log(200) must be a number between 2 and 3 but closer to the number 2. Such an approximation is sufficient for a multiple choice exam. {Incidentally, log(200) happens to be approximately 2.3.}

A.2.3 Exponential and Logarithmic Curves

The exponential and logarithmic functions are *inverse functions*. That is, their graphs can be reflected about the $y = x$ line which you can see in Figure IV.3.3.

Let's revisit one of the key reasons for using logarithms: when the data points vary from low numbers to very high numbers, sometimes a log helps to better demonstrate all the data points on one graph.

Consider Figure IV.3.4: two growth curves that both represent the same data of bacteria doubling over time (2^n = 2, 2^2, 2^3, 2^4, 2^5, 2^6, 2^7, 2^8, 2^9, 2^{10} which is 1024; BIO 2.2).

Notice that in the first graph, the y-axis increases in a linear fashion: the difference between each major marking is 250 cells and it starts at zero. The problem however

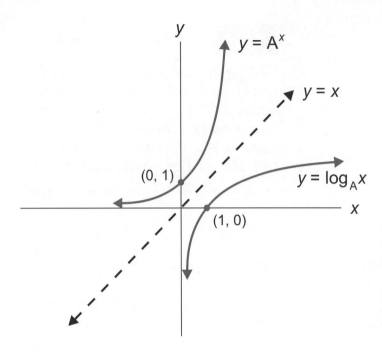

Figure IV.3.3: Exponential and Logarithmic Graphs, A > 1. Notice that when a positive number is raised to the power of 0, then the result is 1 [i.e. the point (0, 1); *see* also QR 2.5.4, 2.5.5 for rules of exponents]. Also note that log(1) = ln (1) = 0 [i.e. the point (1, 0) on the generic logarithmic curve].

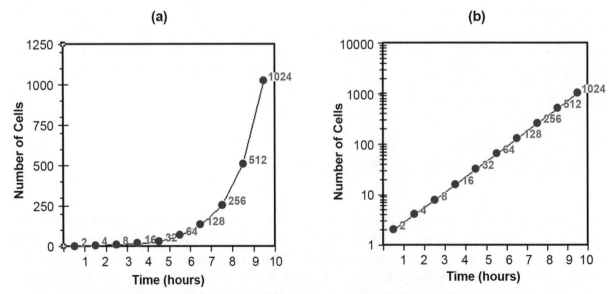

Figure IV.3.4: Growth curves of cells dividing mitotically. (a) An exponential curve with a linear scale for the x and y-axis. (b) A logarithmic scale on the y-axis converts the data rising exponentially into a linear graph. This is referred to as a semi-log graph or semi-log plot. Notice that it is observation or analysis that leads to the conclusion as to what type of graph is being assessed as neither graph is labeled "exponential" nor "logarithm" anywhere. Also, carefully count the notches along the y-axis of the log scale (b), and notice that halfway between 1 and 10, is a number between 3 and 4, halfway between 10 and 100 is 30-40, halfway between 100 and 1000 is 300-400, and so on.

is that the first 4 or 5 points on the exponential curve are not really distinguishable. They are all such small relative numbers making the first ½ of the curve quite flat before it increases rapidly. It is that rapid rise that we recognize visually as an exponential increase (even though, of course, it is the entire curve which is exponential, being 2 to the power of n).

On the other hand, the second graph uses a logarithmic scale on the y-axis (i.e. each number is 10 times the preceding number and equally spaced; the 4th number does not represent 4 times some number, rather, it represents 10 to the power of 4 times which is 10 000 times larger); suddenly the exponential curve is converted to a manageable, more clear, linear relationship where small and large data points are easily visible on one graph. Notice that if you took the log of the 5 numbers along the y-axis, you would get the quite regular result of 0, 1, 2, 3 and 4 (recall that log 10 000 = $\log 10^4$ = 4). Incidentally, because the x-axis increases in a linear fashion, the preceding is a semi-log graph.

Thus a graph that has a scale that is logarithmic on one axis but is linear on the other axis is semi-log. The term for the graph is unimportant for the DAT but recognizing that you are dealing with such a graph is often critical to answering the questions properly. We will now explore another semi-log graph (Figure IV.3.5). Spend a few moments considering Figure IV.3.5.

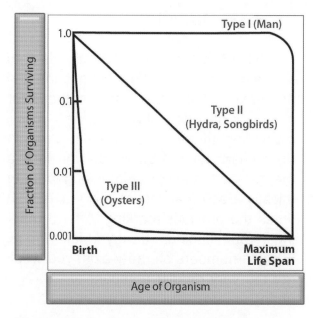

Figure IV.3.5: Type I, II and III survivorship curves scaled to a maximum life span for each species.

QUESTION 1

Based on the diagram provided, is it true that approximately ½ of songbirds would be expected to survive ½ of their maximum lifespan? {Please consider your answer before turning the page.}

QUESTION 2

One perspective regarding the biological success of a species would be to equate success with the absolute number of individual organisms belonging to the species in question. Given this perspective, if oysters, songbirds and humans are all equally successful, based on the diagram, which of the three likely produces the least number of organisms (i.e. the least number of offspring per organism)?

EXPLANATION 1

NO! Not even close!! First, let's get a sense of the scales. We must assume that the x-axis is linear because no other information is provided. However, the y-axis is clearly logarithmic. It looks like it is regular (in a linear sense) but when you look at the numbers, they are increasing logarithmically. Each marking on the y-axis is 10 times the previous marking. After 3 markings, 1000 times or 10^3. If you take the log of the 4 numbers on the y-axis, you would get the very regular numbers of -3, -2, -1 and 0.

Now let's look at ½ of the maximum life span (so ½ of the length of the x-axis). When you look at the Type II line at that point (signifying songbirds and hydra; it's not important that you know what hydra means) and look across to the y-axis, you get a point ½ way between 0.01 and 0.1. Even if we imagine the higher of the 2 numbers, 0.1, that is only 1/10th of the surviving organisms (0.1 = 1/10 = 10%). And because the lower number is 1/100th (= 1%) of the surviving organisms, the actual result is between the two which is far lower than ½ of surviving organisms (i.e. 50%). If you do not understand the scale, you will get the wrong answer.

EXPLANATION 2

Presumably, for the next generation to exist, the current generation must survive long enough to reproduce. The survivorship curve with the most extreme change between birth and a presumed age of reproductive ability would be the Type III survivorship curve. Let's see what we can infer from the shapes of that curve.

Most individuals in populations with Type III survivorship must produce many thousands of individuals, most of whom, according to the diagram, die right away. Once this initial period is over, survivorship is relatively constant. Examples of this would likely include fish, marine larvae, and of course oysters. Relatively little effort or parental care is likely invested in each individual.

> **NOTE**
>
> Notice that neither Figure IV.3.4 (b) nor Figure IV.3.5 had a clear origin of (0, 0). Though not important here, sometimes questions are designed to test whether you observed that the origin was other than (0, 0) and that you took it into account when necessary. We will see some questions like that in Biology.

Type I survivorship includes humans, likely, we could reason, in developed countries. As a result of environment and the resources invested in each individual, there is a high survivorship throughout the life cycle. Most individuals, according to the graph, die of old age. If Type III must produce a lot of individuals to survive the 'die off' and still be successful, then Type I requires relatively few offspring to be successful because the survivorship is better than the other two groups. Thus the answer is: humans.

A.3 Simplifying Algebraic Expressions

Algebraic expressions can be factored or simplified using standard formulae:

$$a(b + c) = ab + ac$$
$$(a + b)(a - b) = a^2 - b^2$$
$$(a + b)(a + b) = (a + b)^2 = a^2 + 2ab + b^2$$
$$(a - b)(a - b) = (a - b)^2 = a^2 - 2ab + b^2$$
$$(a + b)(c + d) = ac + ad + bc + bd$$

A.4 Significant Digits, Experimental Error

If we divide 2 by 3 on a calculator, the answer on the display would be 0.6666666667. The leftmost digit is the *most significant digit* and the rightmost digit is the *least significant digit*. The number of digits which are really significant depends on the accuracy with which the values 2 and 3 are known.

For example, suppose we wish to find the sum of two numbers *a* and *b* with <u>experimental errors</u> (or *uncertainties*) Δa and Δb, respectively. The uncertainty of the sum *c* can be determined as follows:

$$c \pm \Delta c = (a \pm \Delta a) + (b \pm \Delta b)$$

$$= a + b \pm (\Delta a + \Delta b)$$

thus:

$$\Delta c = \Delta a + \Delta b.$$

The sign of the uncertainties are not correlated, so the same rule applies to subtraction. Therefore, *the uncertainty of either the sum or difference is the sum of the uncertainties*.

Now we will apply the preceding to significant digits. A measurement or calculation of 3.7 has an implicit uncertainty. Any number between 3.65000... and 3.74999... rounds off to 3.7, thus 3.7 really means 3.7 $\pm$ 0.05. Similarly, 68.21 really means 68.21 $\pm$ 0.005. Adding the two values and their uncertainties we get: $(3.7 \pm 0.05) + (68.21 \pm 0.005) = 71.91 \pm 0.055$. The error is large enough to affect the first digit to the right of the decimal point; therefore, the last digit to the right is not significant. The answer is thus 71.9.

The rule for significant digits states that *the sum or difference of two numbers carries the same number of significant digits to the right of the decimal as the number with the least significant digits to the right of the decimal.* For example, 105.64 − 3.092 = 102.55.

Multiplication and division is somewhat different. Through algebraic manipulation, the uncertainty or experimental error can be determined:

$$c \pm \Delta c = (a \pm \Delta a)(b \pm \Delta b)$$

After some manipulation we get:

$$\Delta c/c = \Delta a/a + \Delta b/b.$$

The preceding result also holds true for division. Thus for $(10 \pm 0.5)/(20 \pm 1)$, the fractional error in the quotient is:

$$\Delta c/c = \Delta a/a + \Delta b/b = 0.5/10 + 1/20$$
$$= 0.1 \ (10\% \ \text{error})$$

Thus the quotient including its absolute error is $c \pm \Delta c = 0.5(1 \pm 0.1) = 0.5 \pm 0.05$.

The rule for significant digits can be derived from the preceding and it states that *the product or quotient of two numbers has the same number of significant digits as the number with the least number of significant digits.*

A.5 Properties of Negative and Positive Integers

Positive + Positive = Positive

$$5 + 4 = 9$$

Negative + Negative = Negative

$$(-6) + (-2) = -8$$

Positive + Negative = Sign of the highest number and then subtract

$$(-5) + 4 = -1$$
$$(-8) + 10 = 2$$

Negative – Positive = Negative

$$(-7) - 10 = -17$$

Positive – Negative = Positive + Positive
= Positive

$$6 - (-4) = 6 + 4 = 10$$

Negative – Negative = Negative + Positive
= Sign of the highest
number and then
subtract

$$(-8) - (-7) = (-8) + 7 = -1$$

Negative × Negative = Positive

$$(-2) \times (-5) = 10$$

Positive/Positive = Positive

$$8/2 = 4$$

Negative × Positive = Negative

$$(-9) \times 3 = -27$$

Positive/Negative = Negative

$$64/(-8) = -8$$

A.6 Scalars and Vectors

NOTE

Translational motion is the movement of an object (or particle) through space without turning (rotation). Displacement, velocity and acceleration are key vectors - specified by magnitude and direction - often used to describe translational motion. Being able to manipulate and resolve vectors is helpful for some DAT problems. For example, vectors are useful to determine if a molecule has a dipole based on bond polarity (i.e. CHM, ORG). They also help resolve a boat's velocity while it is moving across a river with a downstream current (QR). Because of its rarity on the DAT, we consider acceleration to be an Advanced *DAT-30* Topic.

Scalars, such as speed, have magnitude only and are specified by a number with a unit (55 miles/hour). Scalars obey the rules of ordinary algebra. Vectors, like velocity, have both magnitude and direction (100 km/hour, west). Vectors are represented by arrows where:

(i) the length of the arrow indicates the magnitude of the vector, and;

(ii) the arrowhead indicates the direction of the vector. Vectors obey the special rules of vector algebra. Thus vectors can be moved in space but their orientation must be kept the same.

Addition of Vectors: Two vectors a and b can be added geometrically by drawing them to a common scale and placing them head to tail. The vector connecting the tail of a to the head of b is the sum or resultant vector r.

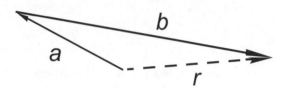

Figure III.B.1.1: The vector sum $a + b = r$.

Subtraction of Vectors: To subtract the vector b from a, reverse the direction of b then add to a.

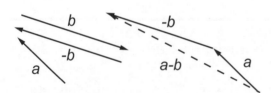

Figure III.B.1.2: The vector difference $a - b = a + (-b)$.

Resolution of Vectors: Perpendicular projections of a vector can be made on a coordinate axis. Thus the vector a can be resolved into its x–component (a_x) and its y–component (a_y).

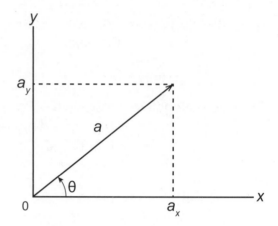

Figure III.B.1.3: The resolution of a vector into its scalar components in a coordinate system.

Analytically, the resolution of vector a is as follows:

$$a_x = a \cos \theta \text{ and } a_y = a \sin \theta$$

Conversely, given the components, we can reconstruct vector a:

$$a = \sqrt{a_x^2 + a_y^2} \text{ and } \tan \theta = a_y / a_x$$

A.7 Common Values of Trigonometric Functions

There are special angles which produce standard values of the trigonometric functions. These values should be memorized. Several of the values are derived from the following triangles:

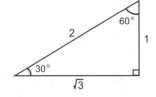

θ	sin θ	cos θ	tan θ
0°	0	1	0
30°	1/2	$\sqrt{3}/2$	$1/\sqrt{3}$
45°	$1/\sqrt{2}$	$1/\sqrt{2}$	1
60°	$\sqrt{3}/2$	1/2	$\sqrt{3}$
90°	1	0	∞
180°	0	-1	0

Table III.B.1.1: Common values of trigonometric functions. The angle θ may be given in radians (R) where $2\pi^R = 360° = 1$ revolution. Recall $\sqrt{3} \approx 1.7$, $\sqrt{2} \approx 1.4$.

Note that 1° = 60 arcminutes, 1 arcminute = 60 arcseconds

Each trigonometric function (i.e. sine) contains an inverse function (i.e. $\sin^{-1}$), where if sin θ = x, θ = $\sin^{-1}x$. Thus cos 60° = 1/2, and 60° = $\cos^{-1}$ (1/2). Some texts denote the inverse function with "arc" as a prefix. Thus arcsec (2) = $\sec^{-1}$ (2).

A.8 Distance and Displacement

Distance is the amount of separation between two points in space. It has a magnitude but no direction. It is a scalar quantity and is always positive.

Displacement of an object between two points is the difference between the final position and the initial position of the object in a given referential system. Thus, a displacement has an origin, a direction and a magnitude. It is a vector.

The sign of the coordinates of the vector displacement depends on the system under study and the chosen referential system. The sign will be positive (+) if the system is moving towards the positive axis of the referential system and negative (–) if not.

The units of distance and displacement are expressed in length units such as feet (ft), meters (m), miles and kilometers (km).

A.9 Speed and Velocity

Speed is the rate of change of distance with respect to time. It is a scalar quantity, it has a magnitude but no direction, like distance, and it is always positive.

Velocity is the rate of change of displacement with respect to time. It is a vector, and like the displacement, it has a direction and a magnitude. Its value depends on the position of the object. The sign of the coordinates of the vector velocity is the same as that of the displacement.

The **instantaneous velocity** of a system at a given time is the slope of the graph of the displacement of that system vs. time at that time. The magnitude of the velocity decreases if the vector velocity and the vector acceleration have opposite directions.

The units of speed and velocity are expressed in length divided by time such as feet/sec., meters/sec. (m/s) and miles/hour.

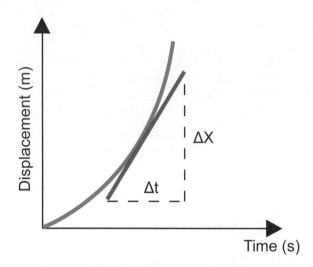

Figure III.B.1.4: Displacement vs. time.

Dimensional Analysis: remember from High School math that a slope is "rise over run" meaning it is the <u>change in the *y*-axis divided by the change in the *x*-axis</u> (*see* Appendix A.1.1). This means when we pay attention to the units, we get, for example, m/s which is velocity.

A.10 Acceleration: Advanced *DAT-30* Content from A.10 to A.12

Acceleration (*a*) is the rate of change of the velocity (*v*) with respect to time (*t*):

$$a = v/t$$

Like the velocity, it is a vector and it has a direction and a magnitude.

The sign of the vector acceleration depends on the net force applied to the system and the chosen referential system. The units of acceleration are expressed as velocity divided by time such as meters/$\sec^2$. The term for negative acceleration is **deceleration**.

A.10.1 Average and Instantaneous Acceleration

The average acceleration *av* between two instants t and $t' = t + \Delta t$, measures the result of the increase in the speed divided by the time difference,

$$a_v = \frac{v' - v}{\Delta t}$$

The instantaneous acceleration can be determined either by calculating the **slope** (*see* Appendix A.1.1) of a velocity vs. time graph at any time, or by taking the limit when Δt approaches zero of the preceding expression.

$$av = \lim_{\Delta t \to 0} \frac{v' - v}{\Delta t}$$

Math involving "limits" does not exist on the DAT. So let's discuss what this definition is describing in informal terms. The limit is the value of the change in velocity over the change in time as the time approaches 0. It's like saying that the change in velocity is happening in an instant. This allows us to talk about the acceleration in that incredibly fast moment: the instantaneous acceleration which can be determined graphically.

Consider the following events illustrated in the graph (Fig. III.B.1.4): your car starts at rest (0 velocity and time = 0); you steadily accelerate out of the parking lot (the change in velocity increases over time = acceleration); you are driving down the

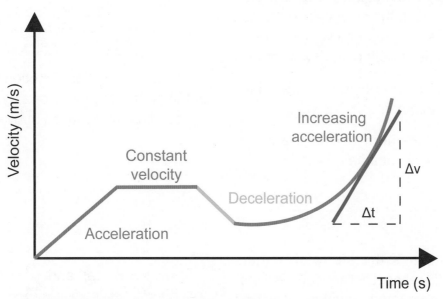

Figure III.B.1.4: Velocity vs. time. Note that at constant velocity, the slope and thus the acceleration are both equal to zero.

street at constant velocity (change in velocity = 0 and thus acceleration is 0 divided by the change in time which means: a = 0); you see a cat dart across the street safely which made you slow down temporarily (change in velocity is negative thus negative acceleration which, by definition, is deceleration); you now enter the on-ramp for the highway so your velocity is now increasing at a faster and faster rate (increasing acceleration). You can examine the instantaneous acceleration at any one point (or instant) during the period that your acceleration is increasing.

To determine the displacement (*not* distance), take the area under the graph or curve. To calculate area: a rectangle is base (*b*) times height (*h*); a triangle is ½*b* × *h*; and for a curve, they can use graph paper and expect you would count the boxes under the curve to estimate the area.

A.11 Uniformly Accelerated Motion

The magnitude and direction of the acceleration of a system are solely determined by the exterior forces acting upon the system. If the magnitude of these forces is constant, the magnitude of the acceleration will be constant and the resulting motion is a **uniformly accelerated motion**. The initial displacement, the velocity and the acceleration at any given time contribute to the overall displacement of the system:

$x = x_0$ – displacement due to the initial displacement x_0.

$x = v_0t$ – displacement due to the initial velocity v_0 at time t.

$x = \frac{1}{2}at^2$ – displacement due the acceleration at time t.

The total displacement of the uniformly-accelerated motion is given by the following formula:

$$x = x_0 + v_0t + \tfrac{1}{2}at^2$$

The translational motion is the motion of the center of gravity of a system through space, illustrated by the above equation.

A.12 Equations of Kinematics

Kinematics is the study of objects in motion with respect to space and time. There are three related equations. The first is above, the others are:

$$v = v_0 + at \text{ and } v^2 = v_0^2 + 2ax$$

where v is the final velocity.